Grade 8

Glencoe

Georgia Math

Volume ①

Mc
Graw
Hill
Education

Bothell, WA • Chicago, IL • Columbus, OH • New York, NY

Cover: (tl) Sun shining behind a bridge in Savannah, Georgia, (tr) Close-up of a Corinthian style cornice with decorative acanthus leaves in Savannah, Georgia, (b) The Atlanta skyline, Georgia.

connectED.mcgraw-hill.com

STEM McGraw-Hill is committed to providing instructional materials in Science, Technology, Engineering, and Mathematics (STEM) that give all students a solid foundation, one that prepares them for college and careers in the 21st century.

Send all inquiries to:
McGraw-Hill Education
STEM Learning Solutions Center
8787 Orion Place
Columbus, OH 43240

ISBN: 978-0-07-665487-1 (*Volume 1*)
MHID: 0-07-665487-7

Printed in the United States of America.

6 7 8 9 QVS 18 17 16 15

Our mission is to provide educational resources that enable students to become the problem solvers of the 21st century and inspire them to explore careers within Science, Technology, Engineering, and Mathematics (STEM) related fields.

CONTENTS IN BRIEF

 Units organized by the Georgia Grade 8 Curriculum Map

GO digital

it's all at connectED.mcgraw-hill.com

Go to the Student Center for your eBook, Resources, Homework, and Messages.

Write your Username _____ Password _____

Get your resources online to help you in class and at home.

Vocab

Find activities for building vocabulary.

Watch

Watch animations and videos.

Tutor

See a teacher illustrate examples and problems.

Tools

Explore concepts with virtual manipulatives.

Check

Self-assess your progress.

eHelp

Get targeted homework help.

Masters

Provides practice worksheets.

GO mobile

Scan this QR code with your smart phone* or visit mheonline.com/apps.

*May require quick response code reader app.

Available on the App Store

Chapter 1
Transformations

Online Transition Lessons
- Classify Angles
- Complementary and Supplementary Angles

Essential Question

HOW can we best show or describe the change in position of a figure?

Chapter 2
Congruence
and Similarity

 Essential Question

HOW can you determine congruence and similarity?

Chapter 3
Real Numbers

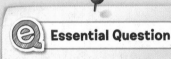

Essential Question

WHY is it helpful to write
numbers in different ways?

Paul & Lindamarie Ambrose/Taxi/Getty Images (t); C Squared Studios/Getty Images (c); Image Source/Getty Images (b)

Copyright © The McGraw-Hill Companies, Inc.

Chapter 4
Equations in One Variable

Online Transition Lessons

- **Inquiry Lab:** Solve Inequalities
- Solve Inequalities by Addition or Subtraction
- Solve Inequalities by Multiplication or Division

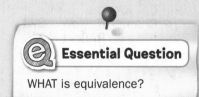

Essential Question

WHAT is equivalence?

UNIT 3 Geometric Applications of Exponents

Chapter 5
Triangles and the Pythagorean Theorem

Essential Question

HOW can algebraic concepts be applied to geometry?

Chapter 6
Volume and Surface Area

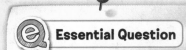

Essential Question

WHY are formulas important in math and science?

Chapter 7
Functions

Essential Question

HOW can we model relationships between quantities?

Chapter 8
Scatter Plots and Data Analysis

Essential Question

HOW are patterns used when comparing two quantities?

the McGraw-Hill Companies, Inc.   Royalty-Free/CORBIS (t); Karl Weatherly/Getty Images (c); Thinkstock/Comstock Images/Getty Images (b)

UNIT 7 Solving Systems of Equations

Chapter 9
Equations in Two Variables

Online Transition Lessons
- Probability of Simple Events
- **Inquiry Lab:** Relative Frequency
- Theoretical and Experimental Probability
- **Inquiry Lab:** Fair and Unfair Games
- Probability of Compound Events

Essential Question

WHY are graphs helpful?

Stocktrek Images/The Agency Collection/Getty Images (t); George Doyle/Stockbyte/Getty Images, Steven P. Lynch (b)　Copyright © The McGraw-Hill Companies, Inc.

Georgia Grade 8 Curriculum Map

Georgia Math, Grade 8, focuses on teaching the CCGPS standards in the order of the Georgia Grade 8 Curriculum map.

Unit 1: Transformations, Congruence and Similarity

MCCS addressed in Unit 1:

MCC8.G.1 Verify experimentally the properties of rotations, reflections, and translations:

  a. Lines are taken to lines, and line segments to line segments of the same length.

  b. Angles are taken to angles of the same measure.

  c. Parallel lines are taken to parallel lines.

MCC8.G.2 Understand that a two dimensional figure is congruent to another if the second can be obtained from the first by a sequence of rotations, reflections, and translations; given two congruent figures, describe a sequence that exhibits the congruence between them.

MCC8.G.3 Describe the effect of dilations, translations, rotations and reflections on two dimensional figures using coordinates.

MCC8.G.4 Understand that a two dimensional figure is similar to another if the second can be obtained from the first by a sequence of rotations, reflections, translations, and dilations; given two similar two dimensional figures, describe a sequence that exhibits the similarity between them.

MCC8.G.5 Use informal arguments to establish facts about the angle sum and exterior angle of triangles, about the angles created when parallel lines are cut by a transversal, and the angle angle criterion for similarity of triangles.

Transition Standard to be addressed:

MCC7.G.5 Use facts about supplementary, complementary, vertical, and adjacent angles in a multi step problem to write and solve simple equations for an unknown angle in a figure.

Unit 2: Exponents

MCCS addressed in Unit 2:

MCC8.EE.1 Know and apply the properties of integer exponents to generate equivalent numerical expressions.

MCC8.EE.2 Use square root and cube root symbols to represent solutions to equations of the form $x^2 = p$ and $x^3 = p$, where p is a positive rational number. Evaluate square roots of small perfect squares and cube roots of small perfect cubes. Know that $\sqrt{2}$ is irrational.

MCC8.EE.3 Use numbers expressed in the form of a single digit times an integer power of 10 to estimate very large or very small quantities, and to express how many times as much one is than the other.

MCC8.EE.4 Perform operations with numbers expressed in scientific notation, including problems where both decimal and scientific notation are used. Use scientific notation and choose units of appropriate size for measurements of very large or very small quantities (e.g., use millimeters per year for seafloor spreading). Interpret scientific notation that has been generated by technology.

MCC8.EE.7 Solve linear equations in one variable.

  MCC8.EE.7a Give examples of linear equations in one variable with one solution, infinitely many solutions, or no solutions. Show which of these possibilities is the case by successively transforming the given equation into simpler forms, until an equivalent equation of the form $x = a$, $a = a$, or $a = b$ results (where a and b are different numbers).

MCC8.EE.7b Solve linear equations with rational number coefficients, including equations whose solutions require expanding expressions using the distributive property and collecting like terms.

MCC8.NS.1 Know that numbers that are not rational are called irrational. Understand informally that every number has a decimal expansion; for rational numbers show that the decimal expansion repeats eventually, and convert a decimal expansion which repeats eventually into a rational number.

MCC8.NS.2 Use rational approximations of irrational numbers to compare the size of irrational numbers, locate them approximately on a number line diagram, and estimate the value of expressions (e.g., π^2).

Transition Standards to be addressed:
MCC7.EE.4b Solve word problems leading to inequalities of the form $px + q > r$ or $px + q < r$, where p, q, and r are specific rational numbers. Graph the solution set of the inequality and interpret it in the context of the problem.

Unit 3: Geometric Applications of Exponents

MCCS addressed in Unit 3:
MCC8.G.6 Explain a proof of the Pythagorean Theorem and its converse.

MCC8.G.7 Apply the Pythagorean Theorem to determine unknown side lengths in right triangles in real world and mathematical problems in two and three dimensions.

MCC8.G.8 Apply the Pythagorean Theorem to find the distance between two points in a coordinate system.

MCC8.G.9 Know the formulas for the volume of cones, cylinders, and spheres and use them to solve real-world and mathematical problems.

MCC8.EE.2 Use square root and cube root symbols to represent solutions to equations of the form $x^2 = p$ and $x^3 = p$, where p is a positive rational number. Evaluate square roots of small perfect squares and cube roots of small perfect cubes. Know that $\sqrt{2}$ is irrational.

Additional MCCS incorporated in Unit 3:
MCC8.EE.7 Solve linear equations in one variable.

> *MCC8.EE.7a Give examples of linear equations in one variable with one solution, infinitely many solutions, or no solutions. Show which of these possibilities is the case by successively transforming the given equation into simpler forms, until an equivalent equation of the form $x = a$, $a = a$, or $a = b$ results (where a and b are different numbers).*

> *MCC8.EE.7b Solve linear equations with rational number coefficients, including equations whose solutions require expanding expressions using the distributive property and collecting like terms.*

Unit 4: Functions

MCCS addressed in Unit 4:
MCC8.F.1 Understand that a function is a rule that assigns to each input exactly one output. The graph of a function is the set of ordered pairs consisting of an input and the corresponding output.

MCC8.F.2 Compare properties of two functions each represented in a different way (algebraically, graphically, numerically in tables, or by verbal descriptions).

Additional MCCS incorporated in Unit 4:
Graphing of functions from MCC8.F.4 (Unit 6) is included in this unit.

Unit 5: Linear Functions

MCCS addressed in Unit 5:

MCC8.EE.5 Graph proportional relationships, interpreting the unit rate as the slope of the graph. Compare two different proportional relationships represented in different ways.

MCC8.EE.6 Use similar triangles to explain why the slope m is the same between any two distinct points on a non vertical line in the coordinate plane; derive the equation $y = mx$ for a line through the origin and the equation $y = mx + b$ for a line intercepting the vertical axis at b. Analyze and solve linear equations and pairs of simultaneous linear equations.

MCC8.F.3 Interpret the equation $y = mx + b$ as defining a linear function, whose graph is a straight line; give examples of functions that are not linear.

Additional MCCS incorporated in Unit 5:

*Graphing of functions from **MCC8.F.4 (Unit 6)** is included in these chapters.*

MCC8.EE.7 *Solve linear equations in one variable.*

> ***MCC8.EE.7a*** *Give examples of linear equations in one variable with one solution, infinitely many solutions, or no solutions. Show which of these possibilities is the case by successively transforming the given equation into simpler forms, until an equivalent equation of the form $x = a$, $a = a$, or $a = b$ results (where a and b are different numbers).*

> ***MCC8.EE.7b*** *Solve linear equations with rational number coefficients, including equations whose solutions require expanding expressions using the distributive property and collecting like terms.*

Unit 6: Linear Models and Tables

MCCS addressed in Unit 6:

MCC8.F.4 Construct a function to model a linear relationship between two quantities. Determine the rate of change and initial value of the function from a description of a relationship or from two (x, y) values, including reading these from a table or from a graph. Interpret the rate of change and initial value of a linear function in terms of the situation it models, and in terms of its graph or a table of values.

MCC8.F.5 Describe qualitatively the functional relationship between two quantities by analyzing a graph (e.g., where the function is increasing or decreasing, linear or nonlinear). Sketch a graph that exhibits the qualitative features of a function that has been described verbally.

MCC8.SP.1 Construct and interpret scatter plots for bivariate measurement data to investigate patterns of association between two quantities. Describe patterns such as clustering, outliers, positive or negative association, linear association, and nonlinear association.

MCC8.SP.2 Know that straight lines are widely used to model relationships between two quantitative variables.

MCC8.SP.3 Use the equation of a linear model to solve problems in the context of bivariate measurement data, interpreting the slope and intercept.

MCC8.SP.4 Understand that patterns of association can also be seen in bivariate categorical data by displaying frequencies and relative frequencies in a two way table. Construct and interpret a two way table summarizing data on two categorical variables collected from the same subjects. Use relative frequencies calculated for rows or columns to describe possible association between the two variables.

Additional MCCS incorporated in Unit 6:

MCC8.EE.7 *Solve linear equations in one variable.*

MCC8.EE.7a Give examples of linear equations in one variable with one solution, infinitely many solutions, or no solutions. Show which of these possibilities is the case by successively transforming the given equation into simpler forms, until an equivalent equation of the form *x = a, a = a,* or *a = b* results (where *a* and *b* are different numbers).

MCC8.EE.7b Solve linear equations with rational number coefficients, including equations whose solutions require expanding expressions using the distributive property and collecting like terms.

Unit 7: Solving Systems of Equations

MCCS addressed in Unit 7:

MCC8.EE.8 Analyze and solve pairs of simultaneous linear equations.

MCC8.EE.8a Understand that solutions to a system of two linear equations in two variables correspond to points of intersection of their graphs, because points of intersection satisfy both equations simultaneously.

MCC8.EE.8b Solve systems of two linear equations in two variables algebraically, and estimate solutions by graphing the equations. Solve simple cases by inspection.

MCC8.EE.8c Solve real world and mathematical problems leading to two linear equations in two variables.

Additional MCCS incorporated in Unit 7:

MCC8.EE.7 Solve linear equations in one variable.

MCC8.EE.7a Give examples of linear equations in one variable with one solution, infinitely many solutions, or no solutions. Show which of these possibilities is the case by successively transforming the given equation into simpler forms, until an equivalent equation of the form *x = a, a = a,* or *a = b* results (where *a* and *b* are different numbers).

MCC8.EE.7b Solve linear equations with rational number coefficients, including equations whose solutions require expanding expressions using the distributive property and collecting like terms.

Unit 8: Show What We Know

MCCS addressed in Unit 8:
ALL

Additional MCCS incorporated in Unit 8:
PLUS High School Prep Review

- Inequalities
- Exponent rules
- Word problems
- Expressions
- Exponential graphs
- Graphing calculators

Transition Standards to be addressed

MCC7.SP.7 *Develop a probability model and use it to find probabilities of events. Compare probabilities from a model to observed frequencies; if the agreement is not good, explain possible sources of the discrepancy.*

> **MCC7.SP.7a** *Develop a uniform probability model by assigning equal probability to all outcomes, and use the model to determine probabilities of events.*

> **MCC7.SP.7b** *Develop a probability model (which may not be uniform) by observing frequencies in data generated from a chance process.*

MCC7.SP.8 *Find probabilities of compound events using organized lists, tables, tree diagrams, and simulation.*

> **MCC7.SP.8a** *Understand that, just as with simple events, the probability of a compound event is the fraction of outcomes in the sample space for which the compound event occurs.*

> **MCC7.SP.8b** *Represent sample spaces for compound events using methods such as organized lists, tables and tree diagrams. For an event described in everyday language (e.g., "rolling double sixes"), identify the outcomes in the sample space which compose the event.*

> **MCC7.SP.8c** *Design and use a simulation to generate frequencies for compound events.*

UNIT 1

Transformations, Congruence, and Similarity

Essential Question

HOW can you use different measurements to solve real-life problems?

Chapter 1
Transformations

In this chapter, you will describe the effect of translations, reflections, rotations, and dilations on geometric figures.

Chapter 2
Congruence and Similarity

In this chapter, you will describe transformations that produce congruent and similar figures.

Chapter 1
Transformations

 Essential Question

HOW can we best show or describe the change in position of a figure?

 Common Core GPS

Content Standards
MCC8.G.1, MCC8.G.1a, MCC8.G.1b, MCC8.G.1c, MCC8.G.3, MCC8.G.5

Mathematical Practices
1, 2, 3, 4, 5, 7, 8

 Math in the Real World

Nature Line symmetry occurs frequently in nature. A figure has line symmetry when a line can be drawn so that one half of the figure is a mirror image of the other other half.

On the figure below, draw the line of symmetry.

FOLDABLES®
Study Organizer

1 Cut out the correct Foldable from the FL pages in the back of this book.

2 Place your Foldable on the Key Concept page toward the end of this chapter.

3 Use the Foldable throughout this chapter to help you learn about transformations.

Vocabulary

alternate exterior angles	exterior angles	regular polygon
alternate interior angles	image	remote interior angles
angle of rotation	interior angles	rotation
center of dilation	line of reflection	rotational symmetry
center of rotation	parallel lines	transformation
congruent	perpendicular lines	translation
corresponding angles	polygon	transversal
dilation	preimage	triangle
equiangular	reflection	

Review Vocabulary

The Coordinate Plane The x- and y-axes divide the coordinate plane into four regions called quadrants. Label the axes and the quadrants on the coordinate plane shown.

Quadrilateral ABCD has vertices A(1, 1), B(3, 5), C(4, 7), and D(2, 6).

1. In what quadrant is ABCD located? _____

2. Suppose you multiplied the coordinates of ABCD by $\frac{3}{4}$. In what quadrant would the new figure be located? _____

3. Suppose the x-coordinates in ABCD are multiplied by −1. In what quadrant would the new figure be located? _____

4. Suppose you switched the x- and y-coordinates from Exercise 3. In what quadrant would the new figure be located? _____

When Will You Use This?

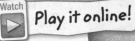

Try the Quick Check below.
Or, take the Online Readiness Quiz.

Check ✓

Common Core Review MCC6.G.3, MCC7.NS.1

Example 1

Two vertices of a rectangle are $J(3, 2)$ and $K(1, 2)$. The length of the rectangle is 4 units. Graph the rectangle and label the other two vertices.

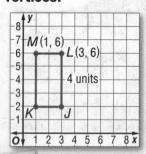

Example 2

Find $2 + (-6)$.

$2 + (-6) = -4$

$|2| - |-6| = -4$
The sum is negative because $|-6| > |2|$.

Coordinate Plane Graph each figure and label the missing vertices.

Show your work.

1. rectangle with vertices:
$B(-3, 3)$, $C(-3, 0)$; side length: 6 units

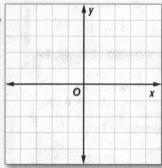

2. triangle with vertices:
$Q(-2, -4)$, $R(2, -4)$; height: 4 units

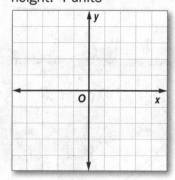

3. square with vertices:
$G(5, 0)$, $H(0, 5)$; side lengths: 5 units

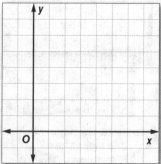

Integers Add.

4. $-5 + 3 =$ _____

5. $7 + (-9) =$ _____

6. $-4 + (-9) =$ _____

7. $-2 + 8 =$ _____

8. $-8 + (-6) =$ _____

9. $0 + (-6) =$ _____

10. $-8 + 2 =$ _____

11. $3 + (-1) =$ _____

How Did You Do? Which problems did you answer correctly in the Quick Check? Shade those exercise numbers below.

① ② ③ ④ ⑤ ⑥ ⑦ ⑧ ⑨ ⑩ ⑪

Inquiry WHAT are the angle relationships formed when a third line intersects two parallel lines?

CCGPS Content Standards
MCC8.G.5

Mathematical Practices
1, 3, 5

Newspapers A newspaper route has two parallel streets. The streets are cut by another street as shown in the figure.

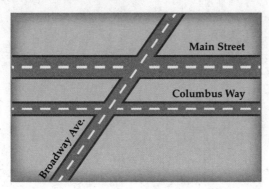

Investigation

Parallel lines have special angle relationships. You will examine those relationships in this investigation.

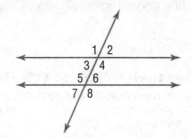

Step 1 Use a protractor and angle relationships you have previously learned to find the measure of each numbered angle and record it in the table.

Angle	1	2	3	4	5	6	7	8
Measure								

Step 2 Color the angles that have the same measure.

Step 3 Describe the position of the angles with the same measure.

_____

_____

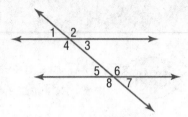

CCGPS **Use Math Tools** Work with a partner. If the measure of ∠1 in the figure at the right is 40°, determine the measure of each given angle without using a protractor. Then check your answers by measuring with a protractor.

1. ∠2 _____

2. ∠3 _____

3. ∠4 _____

4. ∠5 _____

5. ∠6 _____

6. ∠7 _____

7. ∠8 _____

Analyze

Refer to the figure above.

8. What is the relationship between the two horizontal lines?

_____

9. What do you notice about the measures of angles that are side by side?

_____

10. CCGPS **Reason Inductively** Congruent angles are angles that have the same measure. Describe the position of the congruent angles.

_____

_____

Reflect

11. CCGPS **Make a Conjecture** Draw a set of parallel lines cut by another line. Estimate the measures of the eight angles formed. Check your estimates by measuring each angle with a protractor.

12. **Inquiry** WHAT are the angle relationships formed when a third line intersects two parallel lines?

_____

_____

_____

What You'll Learn

Scan the lesson. Predict two things you will learn about parallel lines cut by a transversal.

- _____
  _____

- _____
  _____

Vocabulary Start-Up

When two lines intersect in a plane and form right angles they are called **perpendicular lines**. Two lines are called **parallel lines** when they are in the same plane and do not intersect.

Complete the graphic organizer.

	Parallel Lines	Perpendicular Lines
Symbols	‖	⊥
Define it in your own words		
Draw it		
Describe a real-world example of it		

Essential Question

HOW can algebraic concepts be applied to geometry?

Vocabulary

perpendicular lines
parallel lines
transversal
interior angles
exterior angles
alternate interior angles
alternate exterior angles
corresponding angles

Math Symbols
‖ is parallel to
⊥ is perpendicular to
$m\angle 1$ the measure of $\angle 1$

Common Core GPS

Content Standards
MCC8.G.5

Mathematical Practices
1, 3, 4

Real-World Link

A gymnastic event in the Summer Olympics involves the parallel bars. The women compete on uneven parallel bars and the men compete on the parallel bars like the one shown. Circle the parallel lines shown in the photo at the right.

Transversals and Angles

A line that intersects two or more lines is called a **transversal**, and eight angles are formed.

Interior angles lie inside the lines.
Examples: ∠3, ∠4, ∠5, ∠6

Exterior angles lie outside the lines.
Examples: ∠1, ∠2, ∠7, ∠8

Alternate interior angles are interior angles that lie on opposite sides of the transversal. When the lines are parallel, their measures are equal. **Examples:** $m\angle 4 = m\angle 6$, $m\angle 3 = m\angle 5$

Alternate exterior angles are exterior angles that lie on opposite sides of the transversal. When the lines are parallel, their measures are equal. **Examples:** $m\angle 1 = m\angle 7$, $m\angle 2 = m\angle 8$

Corresponding angles are those angles that are in the same position on the two lines in relation to the transversal. When the lines are parallel, their measures are equal. **Examples:** $m\angle 1 = m\angle 5$, $m\angle 2 = m\angle 6$, $m\angle 4 = m\angle 8$, $m\angle 3 = m\angle 7$

Angles
Read $m\angle 1$ as the measure of angle 1.

Parallel and Perpendicular Lines
Read $m \perp n$ as line m is perpendicular to line n.
Read $p \parallel q$ as line p is parallel to line q.

Special notation is used to indicate perpendicular and parallel lines.

A red right angle symbol indicates that lines *m* and *n* are perpendicular.

$m \perp n$

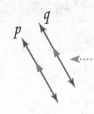

Red arrowheads indicate that lines *p* and *q* are parallel.

$p \parallel q$

Examples

Tutor

Classify each pair of angles in the figure as *alternate interior*, *alternate exterior*, or *corresponding*.

1. ∠1 and ∠7

∠1 and ∠7 are exterior angles that lie on opposite sides of the transversal. They are alternate exterior angles.

2. ∠2 and ∠6

∠2 and ∠6 are in the same position on the two lines. They are corresponding angles.

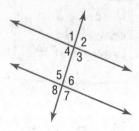

Work Zone

a. Classify the relationship between
∠4 and ∠6. Explain.

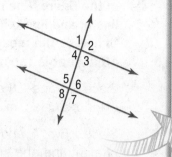

a. _____

Find Missing Angle Measures

When two parallel lines are cut by a transversal, special angle relationships exist. If you know the measure of one of the angles, you can find the measures of all of the angles. Suppose you know that $m\angle 1 = 50°$. You can use that to find the measures of angles 2, 3, and 4.

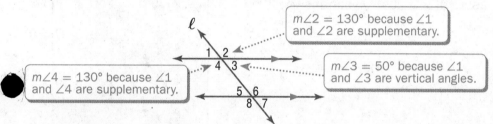

$m\angle 2 = 130°$ because $\angle 1$ and $\angle 2$ are supplementary.

$m\angle 3 = 50°$ because $\angle 1$ and $\angle 3$ are vertical angles.

$m\angle 4 = 130°$ because $\angle 1$ and $\angle 4$ are supplementary.

STOP and Reflect

In the figure, how do you know that $m\angle 5 = 50°$? Explain below.

Example

3. A furniture designer built the bookcase shown. Line *a* is parallel to line *b*. If $m\angle 2 = 105°$, find $m\angle 6$ and $m\angle 3$. Justify your answer.

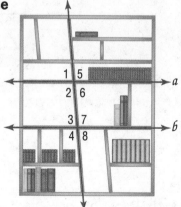

Tutor

Since ∠2 and ∠6 are supplementary, the sum of their measures is 180°. $m\angle 6 = 180° - 105°$ or $75°$

Since ∠6 and ∠3 are interior angles that lie on opposite sides of the transversal, they are alternate interior angles. The measures of alternate interior angles are equal. $m\angle 3 = 75°$

Got It? **Do this problem to find out.**

b. Refer to the situation above. Find $m\angle 4$. Justify your answer.

b. _____

Example

Tutor

4. In the figure, line *m* is parallel to line *n*, and line *q* is perpendicular to line *p*. The measure of ∠1 is 40°. What is the measure of ∠7?

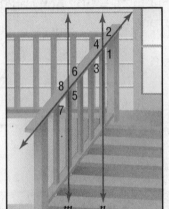

Since ∠1 and ∠6 are alternate exterior angles, *m*∠6 = 40°.

Since ∠6, ∠7, and ∠8 form a straight line, the sum of their measures is 180°.

40 + 90 + *m*∠7 = 180

So, *m*∠7 is 50°.

Guided Practice

Check ✓

1. Refer to the porch stairs shown. Line *m* is parallel to line *n* and *m*∠7 is 35°. Find the measure of ∠1. Justify your answer. (Example 3)

_____

_____

_____

_____

Refer to the figure at the right. Line *a* is parallel to line *b* and *m*∠2 is 135°. Find each given angle measure. Justify your answer. (Examples 1, 2, and 4)

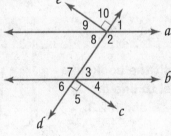

2. *m*∠9 _____

_____

3. *m*∠7 _____

_____

4.  **Building on the Essential Question** How are the measures of the angles related when parallel lines are cut by a transversal?

_____

_____

Rate Yourself!

How confident are you about lines and angles? Check the box that applies.

For more help, go online to access a Personal Tutor.

Independent Practice

Go online for Step-by-Step Solutions   eHelp

Classify each pair of angles as *alternate interior, alternate exterior,* or *corresponding.* (Examples 1 and 2)

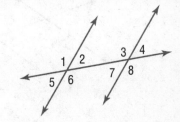

1. ∠2 and ∠4 _____

2. ∠4 and ∠5 _____

3 In the flag shown at the right, line *a* is parallel to line *b*. If *m*∠1 = 150°, find *m*∠4 and *m*∠7. Justify

your answers. (Example 3) _____

_____

_____

_____

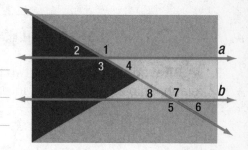

Refer to the figure at the right. Line *s* is parallel to line *t*, *m*∠2 is 110° and *m*∠11 is 137°. Find each given angle measure. Justify your answer. (Example 4)

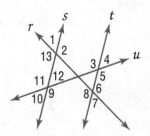

4. *m*∠7 _____

_____

5. *m*∠8 _____

_____

6. *m*∠3 _____

_____

7. The parallel lines shown are cut by a transversal. Find the value of *x*.

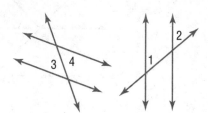

a. Angles 1 and 2 are corresponding angles, *m*∠1 = 45°,

and *m*∠2 = (x + 25)°. _____

b. Angles 3 and 4 are alternate interior angles, *m*∠3 = 2x°,

and *m*∠4 = 80°. _____

8. Describe a method you could use to find the value of *x* in the figure at the right without using a protractor.

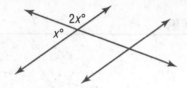

_____

_____

H.O.T. Problems Higher Order Thinking

9. **CCGPS** **Reason Inductively** If two parallel lines are cut by a transversal, what relationship exists between interior angles that are on the same side of

the transversal? _____

10. **CCGPS** **Persevere with Problems** Quadrilateral *ABCD* is a parallelogram. Make a conjecture about the relationship of

∠1 and ∠2. Justify your reasoning. _____

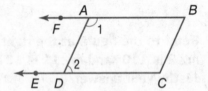

_____

_____

_____

_____

Georgia Test Practice

11. In the figure below, line *x* is parallel to line *y* and line *z* is perpendicular to $\overrightarrow{AB}$. The measure of ∠1 is 50°. What is the measure of ∠2?

Ⓐ 40°   Ⓒ 90°

Ⓑ 50°   Ⓓ 130°

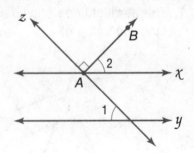

12. Which of the following is true when parallel lines are cut by a transversal?

Ⓐ Vertical angles are supplementary.

Ⓑ Alternate exterior angles are supplementary.

Ⓒ Alternate interior angles are complementary.

Ⓓ Corresponding angles have the same measure.

Extra Practice

Classify each pair of angles as *alternate interior*, *alternate exterior*, or *corresponding*.

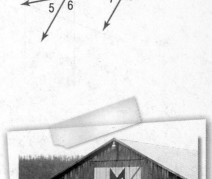

13. ∠3 and ∠6 *alternate interior*

 ∠3 and ∠6 are interior angles that lie on opposite sides of the transversal. They are alternate interior angles

14. ∠1 and ∠3 _____

15. ∠2 and ∠7 _____

16. In the quilt design on the barn at the right, line *a* is parallel to line *b*. If m∠1 = 120°, find m∠2 and m∠3.

Justify your answers. _____

_____

_____

Refer to the figure at the right. Line *s* is parallel to line *t*, m∠2 is 110° and m∠11 is 137°. Find each given angle measure. Justify your answer.

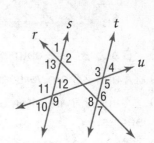

17. m∠6 _____

_____

18. m∠13 _____

_____

19. m∠4 _____

_____

20. **CCGPS** **Model with Mathematics** Draw a pair of parallel lines cut by a transversal. Estimate the measure of one angle and label it. Without using a protractor, label all the other angles with their approximate measure.

21. Lines *a* and *b* are parallel in the figure below. Find the value of *x*.

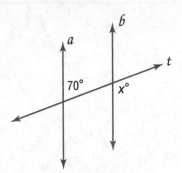

Ⓐ 70　　　　Ⓒ 100

Ⓑ 80　　　　Ⓓ 110

22. Which of the following statements is *not* true concerning ∠A, ∠B, and ∠C labeled on the glass pyramid at the Louvre in Paris, France?

Ⓕ ∠B and ∠C are obtuse angles.

Ⓖ ∠A and ∠C are vertical angles.

Ⓗ ∠A and ∠B are alternate interior angles.

Ⓘ ∠A and ∠C are congruent.

23. Short Response Lines *m* and *n* are parallel and cut by the transversal *p*. Name all pairs of corresponding angles.

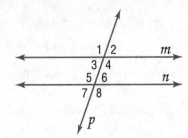

_____

_____

24. A poster has a triangular image with a base that measure 4 inches, and a height that measures 8 inches. What is the area of the poster? MCC6.G.1

_____

Classify each pair of angles as *complementary, supplementary*, or *neither*. MCC7.G.5

25. _____

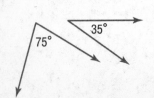

26. _____

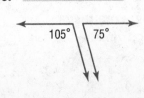

27. _____

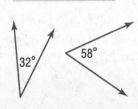

Inquiry WHAT is the relationship among the measures of the angles of a triangle?

CCGPS Content Standards
MCC8.G.5
Mathematical Practices
1, 3

Biking Lamont has a metal bracket that is in the shape of an angle that attaches a bag to the frame of a bike. The angle of the bracket measures 35°. Lamont wonders if it will fit into the frame of the bike by the handlebars.

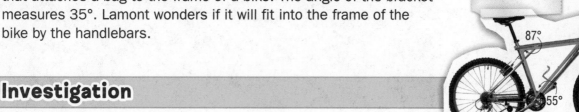

Investigation

Triangle means *three angles*. In this Investigation you will explore how the three angles of a triangle are related.

Step 1 On a separate piece of paper, draw a triangle like the one shown below.

Step 2 Label the corners 1, 2, and 3. Then tear off each corner.

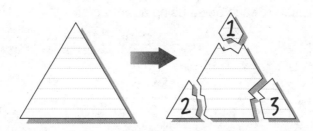

Step 3 Rearrange the torn pieces so that the corners all meet at one point. Label the torn pieces with 1, 2, and 3.

What does each torn corner represent?

_____

The point where these corners meet is the vertex of another angle. Classify this angle as *acute, right, obtuse,* or *straight.*

Explain. _____

Collaborate

Work with a partner. Repeat Steps 1–3 for each of the following triangles. Draw or tape your results in the space provided.

1.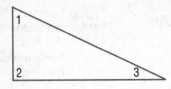

2.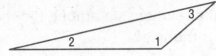

Show your work.

Analyze

3. **CCGPS** **Reason Inductively** What is the sum of the measures of the angles for

each of your triangles? _____

Verify your conjecture below by measuring each angle using a protractor.

Exercise 1: $m\angle 1 + m\angle 2 + m\angle 3 =$ _____

Exercise 2: $m\angle 1 + m\angle 2 + m\angle 3 =$ _____

Reflect

4. **CCGPS** **Justify Conclusions** Refer to the bicycle problem on the previous page.

Will the bracket fit exactly into Lamont's bike? Explain. _____

_____

5. **Inquiry** WHAT is the relationship among the measures of the angles of a

triangle? _____

Angles of Triangles

What You'll Learn

Scan the lesson. List two headings you would use to make an outline of the lesson.

- _____
  _____
  _____

- _____
  _____
  _____

 Real-World Link

STEM Caroline and Emily are building a bridge out of toothpicks for a science competition. Emily thinks the sides should be constructed using triangles. Use the activity to find the sum of the measures of the angles in a triangle.

 Collaborate **Lines *m* and *n* are parallel. Lines *p* and *r* are transversals that intersect at point *A*.**

1. What is true about the measures of ∠1 and ∠2? Explain.

   _____

   _____

2. What is true about the measures of ∠3 and ∠4? Explain.

   _____

   _____

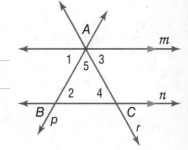

3. What kind of angle is formed by ∠1, ∠5, and ∠3? Write an equation representing the relationship between the 3 angles.

   _____

4. Use the information from Exercises 1, 2, and 3 to draw a conclusion about the sum of the measures of the angles of △*ABC*. Explain your reasoning.

   _____

   _____

Essential Question

HOW can algebraic concepts be applied to geometry?

Vocab **Vocabulary**

triangle
interior angle
exterior angle
remote interior angles

CCGPS **Common Core GPS**

Content Standards
MCC8.G.5
Mathematical Practices
1, 2, 3, 4

Key Concept ⟩ Angle Sum of a Triangle

Work Zone

Words	The sum of the measures of the interior angles of a triangle is 180°.	Model

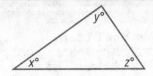

Symbols $x + y + z = 180°$

A **triangle** is formed by three line segments that intersect only at their endpoints. A point where the segments intersect is a vertex. The angle formed by the segments that lies inside the triangle is an **interior angle**.

Real World Example

  Tutor

1. **Find the value of x in the Antigua and Barbuda flag.**

$$x + 55 + 90 = \quad 180 \qquad \text{Write the equation.}$$

$$x + 145 = \quad 180 \qquad \text{Simplify.}$$

$$\underline{-145 = -145} \qquad \text{Subtract.}$$

$$x = \quad 35 \qquad \text{Simplify.}$$

The value of x is 35.

> *Show your work.*

Got It? Do this problem to find out.

a. In $\triangle XYZ$, if $m\angle X = 72°$ and $m\angle Y = 74°$, what is $m\angle Z$?

a. _____

Example

  Tutor

2. **The measures of the angles of $\triangle ABC$ are in the ratio 1:4:5. What are the measures of the angles?**

Let x represent the measure of angle A.

Then $4x$ and $5x$ represent angle B and angle C.

$$x + 4x + 5x = 180 \qquad \text{Write the equation.}$$

$$10x = 180 \qquad \text{Collect like terms.}$$

$$x = 18 \qquad \text{Division Property of Equality}$$

Since $x = 18$, $4x = 4(18)$ or 72, and $5x = 5(18)$ or 90.
The measures of the angles are 18°, 72°, and 90°.

Segments

$\overline{AB}$ is read as segment AB. So the sides of the triangle below are $\overline{AB}$, $\overline{AC}$, and $\overline{BC}$.

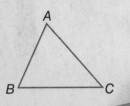

Show your work.

b. The measures of the angles of △LMN are in the ratio 2:4:6. What are the measures of the angles?

b. _____

Exterior Angles of a Triangle

Key Concept

Words The measure of an exterior angle of a triangle is equal to the sum of the measures of its two remote interior angles.

Model

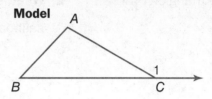

Symbols $m\angle A + m\angle B = m\angle 1$

In addition to its three interior angles, a triangle can have an **exterior angle** formed by one side of the triangle and the extension of the adjacent side. Each exterior angle of the triangle has two **remote interior angles** that are not adjacent to the exterior angle.

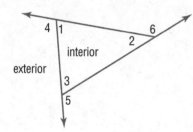

∠4 is an exterior angle of the triangle. Its two remote interior angles are ∠2 and ∠3.

$$m\angle 4 = m\angle 2 + m\angle 3$$

STOP and Reflect

Measure ∠2, ∠3, and ∠4 to verify that $m\angle 2 + m\angle 3 = m\angle 4$. Repeat the process for exterior angles 5 and 6. What is true about $m\angle 5$ and $m\angle 6$?

Example

Tutor

3. **Suppose $m\angle 4 = 135°$. Find the measure of ∠2.**

Angle 4 is an exterior angle. Its two remote interior angles are ∠2 and ∠LKM.

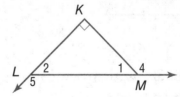

$m\angle 2 + m\angle LKM = m\angle 4$ Write the equation.

$\quad\quad x + 90° = 135°$ $m\angle 2 = x°, m\angle LKM = 90°, m\angle 4 = 135°$

$\quad\quad\quad\quad\quad x = 45°$ Subtraction Property of Equality

So, the $m\angle 2 = 45°$.

Show your work.

c. _____

c. Refer to the figure at the right.
Suppose m∠5 = 147°.
Find m∠1.

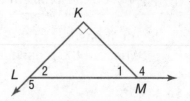

Guided Practice

Check ✓

1. Find the value of x in the triangle. (Example 1)

_____

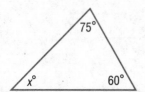

2. What is the value of x in the sail of the sailboat at the right? (Example 1) _____

3. The measures of the angles of △LMN are in the ratio 1:2:5. What are the measures of the angles? (Example 2)

_____

_____

4. Find the value of x in the triangle. (Example 3) _____

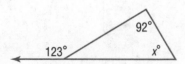

5. Ⓠ **Building on the Essential Question** How can you find the missing measure of an angle in a triangle if you know two of the interior angles?

_____

_____

_____

_____

Rate Yourself!

Are you ready to move on?
Shade the section that applies.

For more help, go online to access a Personal Tutor.

Tutor

Independent Practice

Go online for Step-by-Step Solutions

1. The diagram below shows the view of the top of Fountain Place in Dallas. What is the value of *x*? (Example 1) _____

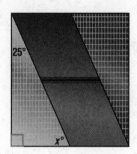

2. An A-frame picnic shelter at George Rogers Clark Historic Park in Ohio is shown below. What is the value of *x*? (Example 1) _____

3. The measures of the angles of △*RST* are in the ratio 2:4:9. What are the measures of the angles? (Example 2) _____

4. The measures of the angles of △*XYZ* are in the ratio 3:3:6. What are the measures of the angles? (Example 2) _____

Find the value of x in each triangle. (Example 3)

5. _____

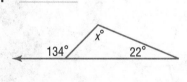

134° x° 22°

6. _____

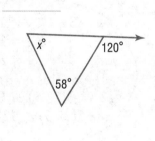

x° 120° 58°

7. _____

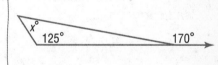

x° 125° 170°

8. In △*ABC* the measure of angle *A* is 2*x* + 3, the measure of angle *B* is 4*x* + 2, and the measure of angle *C* is 2*x* − 1. What are the measures of the angles? _____

9. (CCGPS) **Reason Abstractly** What is the measure of the third angle of a triangle if one angle measures 25° and the second angle measures 50°?

_____

Find the measures of the angles in each triangle.

10. _____

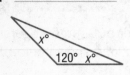

11. _____

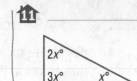

12. _____

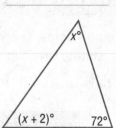

🔥 H.O.T. Problems Higher Order Thinking

13. **CCGPS** **Persevere with Problems** Use the figure at the right to informally prove that an exterior angle of a triangle is equal to the sum of its two remote interior angles.

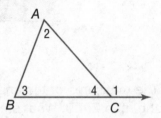

   Given: $\triangle ABC$; $\angle 1$ is an exterior angle.

   Prove: $m\angle 1 = m\angle 2 + m\angle 3$

   Proof: _____

   _____

   _____

   _____

   _____

14. **CCGPS** **Find the Error** Alma is finding the measures of the angles in a triangle that have the ratio 1:3:5. Circle her mistake and correct it.

> $x + 3x + 5x = 180$
> $8x = 180$
> $x = 22.5$
> The angles measure
> 22.5°, 3(22.5) or 67.5°,
> and 5(22.5) or 122.5°.

   _____

   _____

   _____

   _____

   _____

✏️ Georgia Test Practice

15. A triangle has angles measuring 25° and 60°. What is the measure of the triangle's third angle?

   (A) 15°   (C) 95°

   (B) 85°   (D) 115°

Extra Practice

Find the value of x in each triangle with the given angle measures.

16.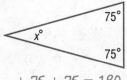

$x + 75 + 75 = 180$

(Homework Help)

$x + 75 + 75 = 180$

$x + 150 = 180$

$x = 30$

_____30_____

17.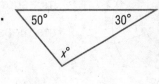

_____

18.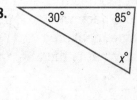

_____

19. 70°, 60°, x° _____

20. x°, 60°, 25° _____

21. x°, 35°, 25° _____

22. The measures of the angles of △DEF are in the ratio 2:4:4. What are the measures of the angles?

_____

23. The measures of the angles of △XYZ are in the ratio 4:5:6. What are the measures of the angles?

_____

Copy and Solve Find the value of x in each triangle. Show your work on a separate sheet of paper.

24.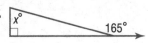

25.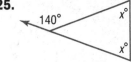

26.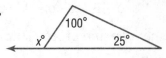

27. **CCGPS** **Reason Inductively** Apply what you know about angles and lines to find the values of x and y in the figure at the right.

x = _____   y = _____

28. When viewed from the front, the base of an upright fan has a triangular face with the angle measures shown. What is the value of x?

25° x 25°

Ⓐ 40   Ⓒ 105

Ⓑ 100   Ⓓ 130

29. What is always true about the relationship between the measures of two acute angles of any right triangle?

Ⓕ They are equivalent.

Ⓖ They are complementary.

Ⓗ They are supplementary.

Ⓘ They are scalene.

30. Short Response Triangle ABC is isosceles. The measure of $\angle B$ is 48° and the measures of $\angle A$ and $\angle C$ are equal. What is the measure of $\angle A$? _____

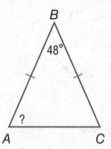

B

48°

?

A   C

31. The street maintenance vehicles for the city of Centerburg cannot safely make turns less than 70°. Should the proposed site of the new maintenance garage at the northeast corner of Park and Main be approved? Explain. MCC7.G.5

N↑   Main

Park   108°

_____

_____

32. $\angle A$ and $\angle B$ are complementary, and the measure of $\angle A$ is 39°. What is the measure of $\angle B$? MCC7.G.5 _____

Solve each equation. MCC6.EE.7

33. $x + 72 + 63 + 120 = 360$

34. $90 + 90 + (2x + 4) + (3x - 29) = 360$

Polygons and Angles

What You'll Learn

Scan the lesson. Write the definitions of polygon and regular polygon.

- _____
  _____
  _____

- _____
  _____

Essential Question

HOW can algebraic concepts be applied to geometry?

Vocabulary

polygon
equiangular
regular polygon

Common Core GPS

Content Standards
Extension of MCC8.G.5

Mathematical Practices
1, 3, 4

Vocabulary Start-Up

A **polygon** is a simple closed figure formed by three or more line segments. The segments intersect only at their endpoints.

A map of the United States is shown. List the states that are in the shape of a polygon. Then list the number of segments that form the polygon.

State	Number of Segments

Interior Angle Sum of a Polygon

Words   The sum of the measures of the interior angles of a polygon is $(n - 2)180$, where n represents the number of sides.

Symbols $S = (n - 2)180$

You can use the sum of the angle measures of a triangle to find the sum of the interior angle measures of various polygons. A polygon that is equilateral (all sides are the same length) and **equiangular** (all angles have the same measure) is called a **regular polygon**.

Number of Sides	Sketch of Figure	Number of Triangles	Sum of Angle Measures
3		1	$1(180°) = 180°$
4		2	$2(180°) = 360°$
5		3	$3(180°) = 540°$
6		4	$4(180°) = 720°$

Everyday Use
Deca- a prefix meaning ten, as in decade

Math Use
Decagon a polygon with ten sides

Example

Tutor

1. Find the sum of the measures of the interior angles of a decagon.

$S = (n - 2)\ 180$ Write an equation.

$S = (10 - 2)\ 180$ A decagon has 10 sides. Replace n with 10.

$S = (8)180$ or $1{,}440$ Simplify.

The sum of the measures of the interior angles of a decagon is $1{,}440°$.

Show your work.

Got It?   Do these problems to find out.

Find the sum of the interior angle measures of each polygon.

a. hexagon   **b.** octagon   **c.** 15-gon

a. _____

b. _____

c. _____

Example

 Tutor

2. Each chamber of a bee honeycomb is a regular hexagon. Find the measure of an interior angle of a regular hexagon.

Step 1 | Find the sum of the measures of the angles.

$S = (n - 2)180$ Write an equation.

$S = (6 - 2)180$ Replace n with 6.

$S = (4)180$ or 720   Simplify.

The sum of the measures of the interior angles is 720°.

Step 2 | Divide 720 by 6, the number of interior angles, to find the measure of one interior angle. So, the measure of one interior angle of a regular hexagon is 720° ÷ 6 or 120°.

Show your work.

Got It? Do these problems to find out.

Find the measure of one interior angle in each regular polygon. Round to the nearest tenth if necessary.

    d. octagon   **e.** heptagon   **f.** 20-gon

d. _____

e. _____

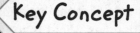

f. _____

Exterior Angles of a Polygon

Key Concept

Words	In a polygon, the sum of the measures of the exterior angles, one at each vertex, is 360°.	**Model**
Symbols	$m\angle 1 + m\angle 2 + m\angle 3 + m\angle 4 + m\angle 5 = 360°$	

Regardless of the number of sides in a polygon, the sum of the exterior angle measures is equal to 360°.

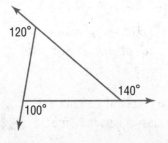

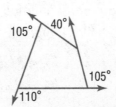

$120 + 100 + 140 = 360°$ $105 + 110 + 105 + 40 = 360°$

 **and Reflect**

Draw another quadrilateral and a pentagon. Extend the sides to show the exterior angles. Then find the sum of each figure's exterior angle measures.

Example

Tutor

3. Find the measure of an exterior angle in a regular hexagon.

Let x represent the measure of each exterior angle.

$6x = 360$ Write an equation. A hexagon has 6 exterior angles.

$x = 60$ Division Property of Equality

So, each exterior angle of a regular hexagon measures 60°.

g. _____

h. _____

i. _____

Show your Work.

Got It? Do these problems to find out.

Find the measure of an exterior angle of each regular polygon.

g. triangle   **h.** quadrilateral   **i.** octagon

Guided Practice

Check ✓

Find the sum of the interior angle measures of each polygon. (Example 1)

1. quadrilateral _____

2. nonagon _____

3. 12-gon _____

Show your work.

4. The quilt pattern shown is made of repeating equilateral triangles. What is the measure of one interior angle of an equilateral triangle? (Example 2)

_____

5. Find the measure of an exterior angle of a regular

pentagon. (Example 3) _____

6. **Building on the Essential Question** How can I find the sum of the interior angle measures of a polygon?

_____

_____

_____

Rate Yourself!

☐ I understand how to find the sum of the interior angle measures of a polygon.

▶▶ Great! You're ready to move on!

☐ I still have some questions about the angles of polygons.

▮▮ No Problem! Go online to access a Personal Tutor.   Tutor

Independent Practice

Go online for Step-by-Step Solutions

Find the sum of the interior angle measures of each polygon. (Example 1)

1. pentagon _____

2. 11-gon _____

3 13-gon _____

4. The soccer ball at the right consists of repeating regular pentagons and hexagons. Find the measure of one interior angle of a pentagon.

(Example 2) _____

Find the measure of an exterior angle of each regular polygon. (Example 3)

5 decagon _____

6. 20-gon _____

7. 15-gon _____

A tessellation is a repetitive pattern of polygons that fit together without overlapping and without gaps between them. For each tessellation, find the measure of each angle at the circled vertex. Then find the sum of the angles.

8.

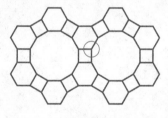

_____

9.

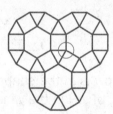

_____

Find the value of x in each figure.

10. _____

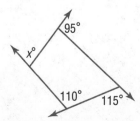

11. _____

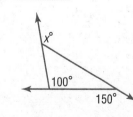

12. **CCGPS** **Reason Inductively** If the number of sides of a polygon increases by 1, what happens to the sum of the measures of the interior angles?

_____

_____

13. **CCGPS** **Persevere with Problems** How many sides does a regular polygon have if the measure of an interior angle is 160°? Justify your answer.

_____

_____

_____

_____

_____

 Georgia Test Practice

14. The sum of the measures of the interior angles of a regular polygon is 900°. How many sides does the polygon have?

Ⓐ 8

Ⓑ 7

Ⓒ 6

Ⓓ 5

15. A stained glass window is in the shape of a regular hexagon. What is the measure, in degrees, of ∠H in the window?

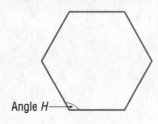

Angle H

Ⓕ 1,080

Ⓗ 180

Ⓖ 720

Ⓘ 120

Extra Practice

Find the sum of the interior angle measures of each polygon.

16. heptagon $900°$ _____

17. 14-gon _____

18. 24-gon _____

Homework Help

$$S = (n - 2)180$$
$$S = (7 - 2)180$$
$$S = 5 \cdot 180$$
$$S = 900$$

Find the measure of one interior angle in each regular polygon. Round to the nearest tenth if necessary.

19. nonagon _____

20. decagon _____

21. 19-gon _____

22. 16-gon _____

Find the measure of an exterior angle of each regular polygon.

23. nonagon _____

24. 12-gon _____

25. 18-gon _____

26. The surface of the dome of Spaceship Earth in Orlando consists of repeating equilateral triangles as shown. Find the measure of each angle in each outlined triangle. Then make a conjecture about the interior angle measures in equilateral triangles of different sizes.

_____

_____

_____

27. 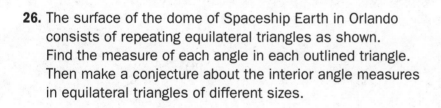 **Justify Conclusions** What is the sum of the interior angles of nonregular hexagons? Explain your reasoning to a classmate.

_____

_____

28. After the first two folds of an origami paper design, the paper is shaped like a square with two isosceles triangles removed from two adjacent corners.

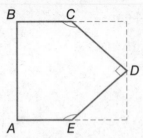

If angle *AED* is congruent to angle *BCD*, what is the measure of angle *AED*?

Ⓐ 45°   Ⓒ 135°

Ⓑ 90°   Ⓓ 160°

 Common Core Review

Classify each pair of angles as *complementary*, *supplementary*, or *neither*. MCC7.G.5

29. angle 1: 35° _____
    angle 2: 55°

30. angle 1: 62° _____
    angle 1: 108°

 Show your work.

Find the value of *x* in each triangle. MCC8.G.5

31. _____

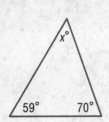

32. _____

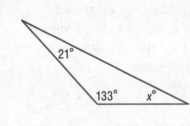

33. _____

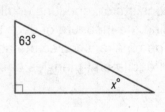

WHAT are some rigid motions of the plane?

 Content Standards
MCC8.G.1,
MCC8.G.1a,
MCC8.G.1b,
MCC8.G.1c
Mathematical Practices
1, 3

Animation Animated movies are created using frames. Each frame changes slightly from the previous one to create the impression of movement.

Investigation 1

In this Investigation, you will make animation frames using index cards.

Step 1 Arrange ten index cards in a pile. On the top card, draw a circle at the top right hand corner.

Step 2 On the next card, draw the same circle slightly down and to the left.

Step 3 Repeat this for three or four more cards until your circle is at the bottom of the card. Use the remainder of the cards to draw the circle up and to the left.

Step 4 Place a rubber band around the stack, hold the stack at the rubber band, and flip the cards from front to back.

Describe what you see when you flip the cards from front to back. _____

_____

Look at the circles on the first and second cards and then the second and third cards. How would you describe the change in the position of the circle from one card to the next?

_____

_____

Did the shape or size of the circle change when you moved it? If yes, describe the change. _____

Investigation 2

Step 1 Draw right angle *XYZ* on a piece of tracing paper. Place a dashed line on the paper as shown.

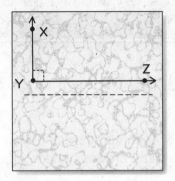

Step 2 Fold the paper along the dashed line. Trace the angle onto the folded portion of the paper. Unfold and label the angle *ABC* so that *A* matches up with *X*, *B* matches up with *Y*, and *C* matches up with *Z*. Tape the paper to your book.

Use a protractor to find the measure of ∠*XYZ* and ∠*ABC*. Did the measure of the angle change after the flip? _____

Use a centimeter ruler to measure the shortest distance from *X* and *A* to the dashed line. Repeat for *Y* and *B* and for *Z* and *C*. What do you notice?

_____

_____

_____

Investigation 3

Step 1 Place a piece of tracing paper over the trapezoid shown. Copy the trapezoid. Draw points *A*, *B*, and *C*. Draw $\overrightarrow{AB}$.

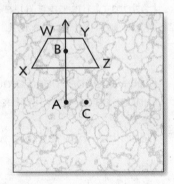

Step 2 Place the eraser end of your pencil on *A*. Turn the tracing paper until $\overrightarrow{AB}$ passes through *C*. Tape the paper to your book.

Did the shape of the trapezoid change when you moved it? If yes, describe the change. _____

Did the size of the trapezoid change when you moved it? If yes, describe the change. _____

 **Collaborate**

Work with a partner. Use a ruler to draw the image when each figure is moved as directed.

1. $\frac{1}{2}$ inch down and 1 inch to the left.

2. 1 inch up and 1 inch to the right.

Draw the image when each figure is flipped over line ℓ.

3.

4.

Draw the image when each pentagon is turned until $\overrightarrow{AB}$ passes through C.

5.

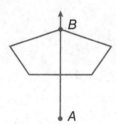

6.

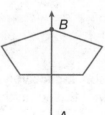

Analyze

For each pair of figures, describe a movement or movements that will place the blue figure on top of the green figure.

7.

Figure	Movement(s)

8.

Figure	Movement(s)

9. Refer to Investigation 1 and Exercises 1 and 2. Circle the word that best describes the movement of the figures: **flip** **slide** **turn**

10. Refer to Investigation 2 and Exercises 3 and 4. Circle the word that best describes the movement of the figures: **flip** **slide** **turn**

11. Refer to Investigation 3 and Exercises 5 and 6. Measure one side of the original figures. Then measure that same side after the turn. Did the length of the side change after you turned it? If yes, describe the change.

_____

12. **CCGPS** **Justify Conclusions** In Investigation 3, $\overline{WY}$ and $\overline{XZ}$ are parallel. Were the segments still parallel after the turn? Would they still be parallel after a slide? flip? Explain.

_____

_____

_____

13. **CCGPS** **Reason Inductively** Slides, flips, and turns are called *rigid motions of the plane*. Based on the Investigations, describe two characteristics of a rigid motion of the plane. _____

_____

_____

Reflect

14. **Inquiry** WHAT are some rigid motions of the plane? _____

_____

Translations

What You'll Learn

Scan the lesson. Predict two things you will learn about translations.

- _____
  _____

- _____
  _____

Vocabulary Start-Up

A **transformation** is an operation that maps an original geometric figure, the **preimage**, onto a new figure called the **image**. A **translation** slides a figure from one position to another without turning it.

Scan the lesson and complete the graphic organizer.

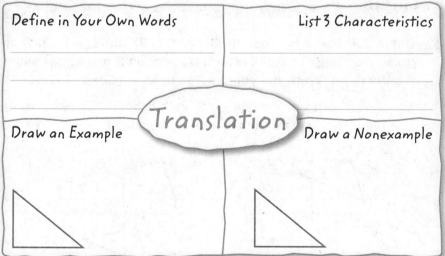

Define in Your Own Words

List 3 Characteristics

Translation

Draw an Example

Draw a Nonexample

 ### Real-World Link

Carmen created the design at the right on her computer.

1. Describe the motion involved in moving the design from A to A'.

   _____

2. Compare the size, shape, and orientation of the design piece in its original position to that of the piece in its new position.

   _____

Essential Question

HOW can we best show or describe the change in position of a figure?

Vocabulary

transformation
preimage
image
translation
congruent

Math Symbols
$(x, y) \rightarrow (x + a, y + b)$
A' is read A prime

 ### Common Core GPS

Content Standards
MCC8.G.1, MCC8.G.3

Mathematical Practices
1, 2, 3, 4, 8

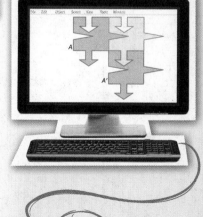

Translations in the Coordinate Plane

Prime Symbols
Use prime symbols for vertices in a transformed image.
$A \rightarrow A'$
$B \rightarrow B'$
$B \rightarrow B'$
A' is read A prime.

Words	When a figure is translated, the x-coordinate of the preimage changes by the value of the horizontal translation a. The y-coordinate of the preimage changes by the vertical translation b.

Model

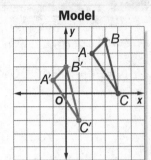

Symbols $(x, y) \rightarrow (x + a, y + b)$

When translating a figure, every point of the preimage is moved the same distance and in the same direction. The image and the preimage are congruent. **Congruent** figures have the same shape and same size. So, line segments in the preimage have the same length as line segments in the image. Angles in the preimage have the same measure as angles in the image.

Example

1. Graph △JKL with vertices $J(-3, 4)$, $K(1, 3)$, and $L(-4, 1)$. Then graph the image of △JKL after a translation 2 units right and 5 units down. Write the coordinates of its vertices.

Move each vertex of the triangle 2 units right and 5 units down. Use prime symbols for the vertices of the image.

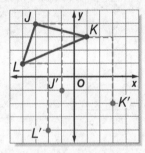
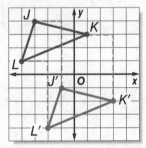

From the graph, the coordinates of the vertices of the image are $J'(-1, -1)$, $K'(3, -2)$, and $L'(-2, -4)$.

Got It? Do this problem to find out.

a. Graph △ABC with vertices $A(4, -3)$, $B(0, 2)$ and $C(5, 1)$. Then graph its image after a translation of 4 units left and 3 units up. Write the coordinates of the image.

a. _____

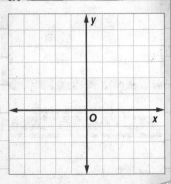

Example

2. Triangle *XYZ* has vertices *X*(−1, −2), *Y*(6, −3) and *Z*(2, −5).
Find the vertices of △*X′Y′Z′* after a translation of 2 units left
and 1 unit up.

Use a table. Add −2 to the *x*-coordinates and 1 to the
y-coordinates.

Vertices of △XYZ	(x + (−2), y + 1)	Vertices of △X′Y′Z′
X(−1, −2)	(−1 + (−2), −2 + 1)	X′(−3, −1)
Y(6, −3)	(6 + (−2), −3 + 1)	Y′(4, −2)
Z(2, −5)	(2 + (−2), −5 + 1)	Z′(0, −4)

So, the vertices of △*X′Y′Z′* are *X′*(−3, −1), *Y′*(4, −2), and *Z′*(0, −4).

Got It? Do this problem to find out.

Show
your
work.

b. Quadrilateral *ABCD* has vertices *A*(0, 0), *B*(2, 0), *C*(3, 4), and
D(0, 4). Find the vertices of quadrilateral *A′B′C′D′* after a
translation of 4 units right and 2 units down.

b. _____

Example

Tutor

3. A computer image is being translated to create the illusion of
movement. Use translation notation to describe the translation
from point *A* to point *B*.

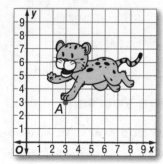

Point *A* is located at (3, 3). Point *B* is located at (2, 1).

$$(x, y) \longrightarrow (x + a, y + b)$$

$$(3, 3) \longrightarrow (3 + a, 3 + b) \longrightarrow (2, 1)$$

$$3 + a = 2 \qquad\qquad 3 + b = 1$$

$$a = -1 \qquad\qquad b = -2$$

So, the translation is $(x - 1, y - 2)$, 1 unit to the left and
2 units down.

Got It? Do this problem to find out.

c. Refer to the figure in Example 3. If point *A* was at (1, 5), use translation notation to describe the translation from point *A* to point *B*.

c. _____

Guided Practice

Graph △*XYZ* with vertices *X*(−4, −4), *Y*(−3, −1), and *Z*(2, −2). Then graph the image of △*XYZ* after each translation, and write the coordinates of its vertices. (Example 1)

1. 3 units right and 4 units up

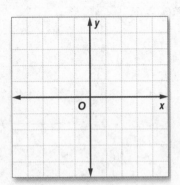

2. 2 units left and 3 units down

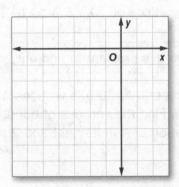

3. The baseball at the right was filmed using stop-motion animation so it appears to be thrown in the air. Use translation notation to describe the translation from point *A* to point *B*. (Example 3)

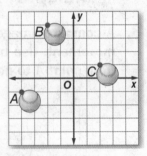

_____

4. Quadrilateral *DEFG* has vertices at *D*(1, 0), *E*(−2, −2), *F*(2, 4), and *G*(6, −3). Find the vertices of *D′E′F′G′* after a translation of 4 units right and 5 units down. (Example 2)

_____

5. ⓔ **Building on the Essential Question** How are figures translated on the coordinate plane?

_____

_____

_____

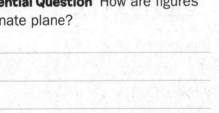

Rate Yourself!

Are you ready to move on? Shade the section that applies.

YES ? NO

For more help, go online to access a Personal Tutor.

Tutor

FOLDABLES Time to update your Foldable!

Independent Practice

Go online for Step-by-Step Solutions

Graph each figure with the given vertices. Then graph the image of the figure after the indicated translation, and write the coordinates of its vertices. (Example 1)

1 △ABC with vertices A(1, 2), B(3, 1), and C(3, 4) translated 2 units left and 1 unit up

2. rectangle JKLM with vertices J(−3, 2), K(3, 5), L(4, 3), and M(−2, 0) translated 1 unit right and 4 units down

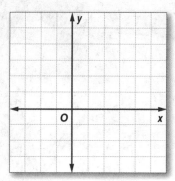

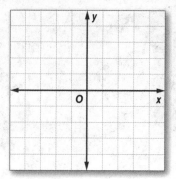

Triangle PQR has vertices P(0, 0), Q(5, −2), and R(−3, 6). Find the vertices of P′Q′R′ after each translation. (Example 2)

3. 6 units right and 5 units up _____

4. 8 units left and 1 unit down _____

Use the image of the race car at the right. (Example 3)

5. Use translation notation to describe the translation from point A to point B. _____

6. Use translation notation to describe the translation from point B to point C. _____

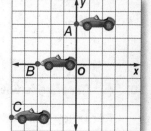

7 Quadrilateral KLMN has vertices K(−2, −2), L(1, 1), M(0, 4), and N(−3, 5). It is first translated by (x + 2, y − 1) and then translated by (x − 3, y + 4). When a figure is translated twice, a double prime symbol is used. Find the coordinates of quadrilateral K″L″M″N″ after both translations. _____

Show your work.

8. **CCGPS** **Model with Mathematics** Refer to the graphic novel frame below. List the five steps the girls should take and identify any transformations used in the dance steps. _____

_____

_____

H.O.T. Problems Higher Order Thinking

9. **CCGPS** **Reason Inductively** A figure is translated by $(x - 5, y + 7)$, then by $(x + 5, y - 7)$. Without graphing, what is the final position of the figure? Explain your reasoning to a classmate. _____

_____

_____

10. **CCGPS** **Persevere with Problems** What are the coordinates of the point (x, y) after being translated m units left and n units up? _____

Georgia Test Practice

11. If $\triangle PQR$ is translated 4 units right and 3 units up, what are the coordinates of R'?

 Ⓐ $(-1, -6)$ Ⓒ $(-1, 0)$

 Ⓑ $(7, 0)$ Ⓓ $(7, -6)$

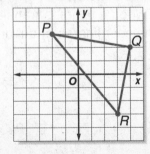

Extra Practice

Graph each figure with the given vertices. Then graph the image of the figure after the indicated translation, and write the coordinates of its vertices.

12. △HJK with vertices H(−1, 0), J(−2, −4) and K(1, −3) translated 3 units right and 3 units up

H'(2, 3), J'(1, −1), K'(4, 0)

Graph each point and connect them to form a triangle. Then move each point 3 units to the right and then 3 units up. Connect them to form △H'J'K'.

13. Rectangle KLMN with vertices K(1, −1), L(1, 1), M(5, 1), and N(5, −1) translated 4 units left and 3 units up

_____

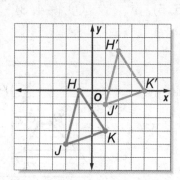

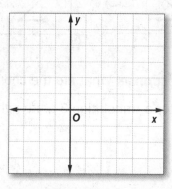

Quadrilateral ABCD has vertices A(−5, −1), B(−3, 0), C(2, −2), and D(0, −6). Find the vertices of A'B'C'D' after each translation.

14. 4 units up _____

15. 2 units right and 2 units down _____

16. Julio is in Colorado exploring part of the Denver Zoo as shown. He starts at the Felines exhibit and travels 3 units to the right and 5 units up. At which exhibit is Julio located? If the Felines exhibit is located at (3, 1), what are the coordinates of Julio's new location?

_____

17. **CCGPS** **Identify Repeated Reasoning** A diagram of a DNA double helix is shown below. Look for a pattern. On the diagram indicate where this pattern repeats or is translated. Find how many

translations of the original pattern are shown in the diagram. _____

18. Which graph shows a translation of the letter Z?

Ⓐ
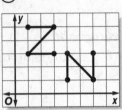

Ⓒ
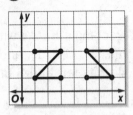

Ⓑ
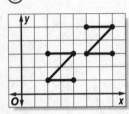

Ⓓ
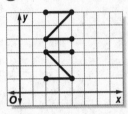

19. Point A is translated 4 units left and 3 units up. What are the coordinates of point A in its new position?

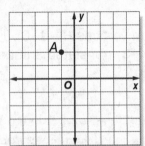

Ⓕ (4, 4)   Ⓗ (−5, −1)

Ⓖ (−5, 5)   Ⓘ (−4, 3)

20. Short Response What are the coordinates of C′ of trapezoid ABCD after a translation 3 units right and 7 units down? _____

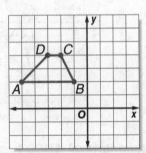

Common Core Review

Find each sum. MCC7.NS.1

21. $-5 + 12 =$ _____

22. $23 + (-3) =$ _____

23. $-36 + (-42) =$ _____

24. $256 + (-82) =$ _____

25. $-121 + (-119) =$ _____

26. $-452 + 97 =$ _____

Reflections

What You'll Learn

Scan the lesson. List two headings you would use to make an outline of the lesson.

- _____

- _____

Real-World Link

Art Pysanky is the ancient Ukrainian art of egg decorating. Many artists use flips and line symmetry to create their designs. Use the activity to create your own pysanky design.

Collaborate The template shown represents the front view of an egg. The template has been divided into four sections.

Step 1 To create your egg, draw a design in Quadrant II.

Step 2 To complete Quadrant I, draw the mirror image over the y-axis.

Step 3 Repeat Steps 2 and 3 to fill in Quadrants III and IV. You can create a new design or you can draw the mirror image over the x-axis.

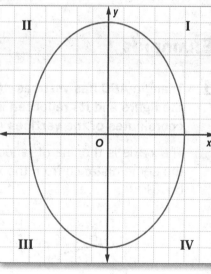

Add color to your design by using colored pencils or markers to complete the design.

1. *Line symmetry* is when a figure can be folded so one side is the mirror image of the other side. Does your pysanky have line symmetry? Explain. _____

_____

Essential Question

HOW can you best show or describe the change in position of a figure?

Vocabulary

reflection
line of reflection

Math Symbols

$(x, y) \rightarrow (x, -y)$
$(x, y) \rightarrow (-x, y)$

CCGPS Common Core GPS

Content Standards
MCC8.G.1, MCC8.G.3

Mathematical Practices
1, 3, 4, 7

Reflections in the Coordinate Plane

	Over the x-axis	Over the y-axis
Words	To reflect a figure over the x-axis, multiply the y-coordinates by −1.	To reflect a figure over the y-axis, multiply the x-coordinates by −1.
Symbols	$(x, y) \rightarrow (x, -y)$	$(x, y) \rightarrow (-x, y)$
Models	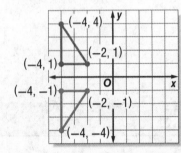	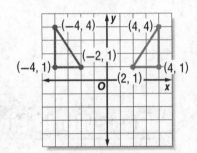

A **reflection** is a mirror image of the original figure. It is the result of a transformation of a figure over a line called a **line of reflection**. In a reflection, each point of the preimage and its image are the same distance from the line of reflection. So, in a reflection, the image is congruent to the preimage.

Examples

1. Triangle *ABC* has vertices *A*(5, 2), *B*(1, 3), and *C*(−1, 1). Graph the figure and its reflected image over the *x*-axis. Then find the coordinates of the vertices of the reflected image.

The *x*-axis is the line of reflection. So, plot each vertex of *A′B′C′* the same distance from the *x*-axis as its corresponding vertex on *ABC*.

Check

Check the coordinates of the image by multiplying the y-coordinates by −1.

$(x, y) \rightarrow (x, -y)$

$(5, 2) \rightarrow (5, -2)$

$(1, 3) \rightarrow (1, -3)$

$(-1, 1) \rightarrow (-1, -1)$ ✓

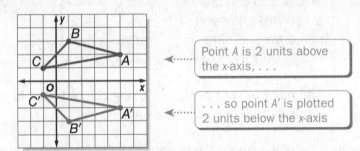

Point *A* is 2 units above the *x*-axis, . . .

. . . so point *A′* is plotted 2 units below the *x*-axis

The coordinates are *A′*(5, −2), *B′*(1, −3), and *C′*(−1, −1).

2. Quadrilateral *KLMN* has vertices *K*(2, 3), *L*(5, 1), *M*(4, −2), and *N*(1, −1). Graph the figure and its reflection over the *y*-axis. Then find the coordinates of the vertices of the reflected image.

The *y*-axis is the line of reflection. So, plot each vertex of *K′L′M′N′* the same distance from the *y*-axis as its corresponding vertex on *KLMN*.

Point *K′* is 2 units to the left of the *y*-axis.

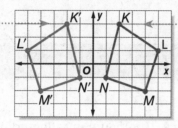

Point *K* is 2 units to the right of the *y*-axis.

The coordinates are *K′*(−2, 3), *L′*(−5, 1), *M′*(−4, −2), and *N′*(−1, −1).

Got It? Do this problem to find out.

a. Triangle *PQR* has vertices *P*(1, 5), *Q*(3, 7), and *R*(4, −1). Graph the figure and its reflection over the *y*-axis. Then find the coordinates of the reflected image.

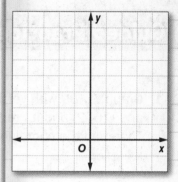

a. _____

Real World

Example

Tutor

3. The figure below is reflected over the *y*-axis. Find the coordinates of point *A′* and point *B′*. Then sketch the figure and its image on the coordinate plane.

Point *A* is located at (1, 4). Point *B* is located at (2, 1). Since the figure is being reflected over the *y*-axis, multiply the *x*-coordinates by −1.

$A(1, 4) \rightarrow A'(-1, 4)$ $B(2, 1) \rightarrow B'(-2, 1)$

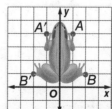

STOP and Reflect

Explain below how the *x*- and *y*-coordinates of an image relate to the *x*- and *y*-coordinates of the preimage after a reflection over the *y*-axis.

b. _____

Show your work.

Got It? Do this problem to find out.

b. The figure at the right is reflected over the *x*-axis. Find the coordinates of point *A′* and point *B′*. Then sketch the image on the coordinate plane.

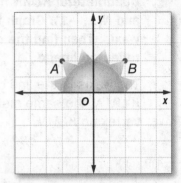

Check ✓

Guided Practice

1. Graph △*ABC* with vertices *A*(5, 1), *B*(1, 2), and *C*(6, 2) and its reflection over the *x*-axis. Then find the coordinates of the image.

(Examples 1 and 2)

_____

Show your work.

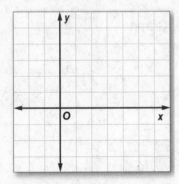

2. The figure is reflected over the *y*-axis. Find the coordinates of point *A′* and point *B′*. Then sketch the image on the coordinate plane.

(Example 3)

_____

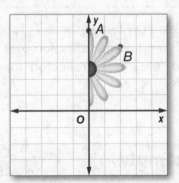

3. **Building on the Essential Question** How can you determine the coordinates of a figure after a reflection over either axis?

_____

_____

_____

Rate Yourself!

How well do you understand reflections? Circle the image that applies.

Clear   Somewhat Clear   Not So Clear

For more help, go online to access a Personal Tutor.

 Tutor

FOLDABLES Time to update your Foldable!

Name _____ My Homework _____

Go online for Step-by-Step Solutions

Graph each figure and its reflection over the indicated axis. Then find the coordinates of the reflected image. (Examples 1 and 2)

1 △GHJ with vertices G(4, 2), H(3, −4), and J(1, 1) over the y-axis

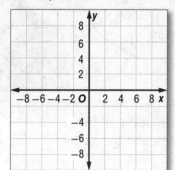

Show your work.

2. △MNP with vertices M(2, 1), N(−3, 1), and P(−1, 4) over the x-axis

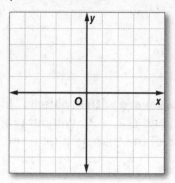

3. quadrilateral WXYZ with vertices W(−1, −1), X(4, 1), Y(4, 5), and Z(1, 7) over the x-axis

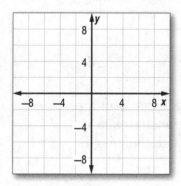

4. quadrilateral DEFG with vertices D(1, 0), E(1,−5), F(4, −1), and G(3, 2) over the y-axis

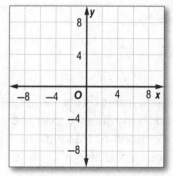

5. The figure at the right is reflected over the x-axis. Find the coordinates of point A′ and point B′. Then sketch the image on the coordinate plane. (Example 3)

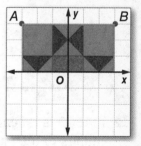

CCGPS Identify Structure The coordinates of a point and its image after a reflection are given. Describe the reflection as over the x-axis or y-axis.

6. A(−3, 5) → A′(3, 5) _____

7 M(3, 3) → M′(3, −3) _____

8. (CCGPS) **Find the Error** Roberto is finding the coordinates of the image of a triangle with vertices $A(1, 1)$, $B(4, 1)$ and $C(1, 5)$ after a reflection over the x-axis. Describe his mistake and correct it.

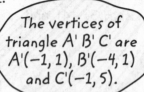

The vertices of triangle $A'B'C'$ are $A'(-1, 1)$, $B'(-4, 1)$ and $C'(-1, 5)$.

_____

_____

_____

9. (CCGPS) **Persevere with Problems** Triangle JKL has vertices $J(-7, 4)$, $K(7, 1)$, and $L(2, -2)$. Without graphing, find the new coordinates of the vertices of the triangle after a reflection first over the x-axis and then over the y-axis. _____

_____

10. (CCGPS) **Reason Inductively** Suppose you reflect a triangle in Quadrant I over the y-axis, then translate the image 2 units left and 3 units down. Is there a single transformation that maps the preimage onto the image? Explain your reasoning. _____

_____

11. (CCGPS) **Reason Inductively** Suppose you reflect a nonregular figure over the x-axis and then reflect it over the y-axis. Is there a single transformation using reflections or translations that maps the preimage onto the image? Explain your reasoning.

_____

_____

_____

 ## Georgia Test Practice

12. If $ABCD$ is reflected over the x-axis and translated 5 units to the right, which is the resulting image of point B?

Ⓐ $(-1, -2)$

Ⓑ $(-11, 2)$

Ⓒ $(-1, 2)$

Ⓓ $(11, 2)$

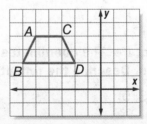

Extra Practice

Graph each figure and its reflection over the indicated axis. Then find the coordinates of the reflected image.

13. △*TUV* with vertices *T*(−4, −1), *U*(−2, −3), and *V*(4, −3) over the *x*-axis

Show your work.

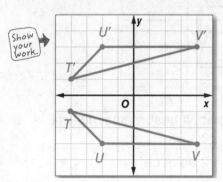

T'(−4, 1), *U'*(−2, 3), *V'*(4, 3)

14. square *ABCD* with vertices *A*(2, 4), *B*(−2, 4), *C*(−2, 8), and *D*(2, 8) over the *x*-axis

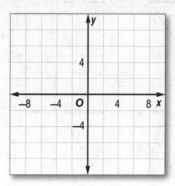

15. △*RST* with vertices *R*(−5, 3), *S*(−4, −2), and *T*(−2, 3) over the *y*-axis

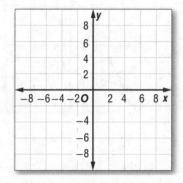

16. parallelogram *HIJK* with vertices *H*(−1, 3), *I*(−1, −1), *J*(2, −2), and *K*(2, 2) over the *y*-axis

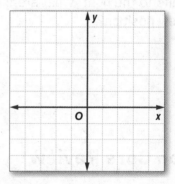

17. The figure at the right is reflected over the *y*-axis. Find the coordinates of point *A'* and point *B'*. Then sketch the image on the coordinate plane.

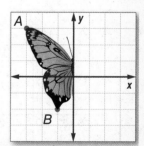

Identify Structure The coordinates of a point and its image after a reflection are given. Describe the reflection as over the *x*-axis or *y*-axis.

18. *X*(−1, −4) → *X'*(−1, 4) _____

19. *W*(−4, 0) → *W'*(4, 0) _____

20. Which of the following is the reflection of △*ABC* with vertices *A*(1, −1), *B*(4, −1), and *C*(2, −4) over the *x*-axis?

Ⓐ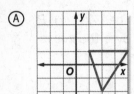

Ⓒ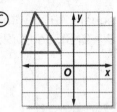

Ⓑ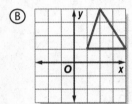

Ⓓ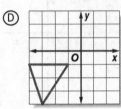

21. The figure shown was transformed from Quadrant II to Quadrant III.

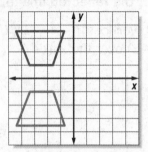

This transformation best represents which of the following?

Ⓕ translation 2 units up

Ⓖ translation 2 units down

Ⓗ reflection over the *x*-axis

Ⓘ reflection over the *y*-axis

22. Short Response Triangle *RST* is reflected over the *x*-axis and then translated 4 units to the right. What are the coordinates of point *R* in its new position?

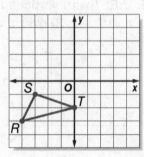

Common Core Review

Graph and label each figure on the coordinate plane. MCC6.G.3

23. △*CDE* with vertices *C*(−1, 1), *D*(−4, 0), *E*(0, −2)

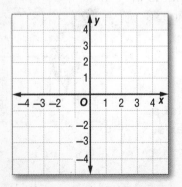

24. trapezoid *RSTU* with vertices *R*(−1, 3), *S*(2, 2), *T*(2, −1) and *U*(−1, −2)

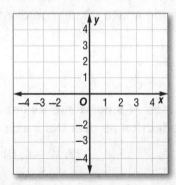

25. pentagon *LMNOP* with vertices *L*(0, 3), *M*(2, 2), *N*(2, 0), *O*(−2, 0), and *P*(−2, 2)

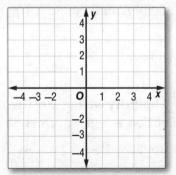

CCGPS Content Standards
MCC8.G.3
Mathematical Practices
1, 3, 4

Case #1 Black Belt Champion

Emily's school is 3 blocks east and 4 blocks south from her house. She is taking a martial arts class that is 2 blocks east and 6 blocks north from school.

What are two different ways that Emily can travel to go from martial arts class to her house?

Understand *What are the facts?*

You know the translations involved.

· School is 3 blocks east and 4 blocks south from her house.

· Martial arts class is 2 blocks east and 6 blocks north from school.

Plan *What is your strategy to solve this problem?*

Act out the situation on a coordinate plane. Plot Emily's house at (0, 0) and map out the route to her school and martial arts class. Then determine two translations that will take Emily from martial arts class to her house.

Solve *How can you apply the strategy?*

What are two different ways that Emily can travel to go from martial arts class to her house?

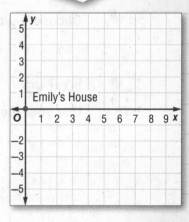

Emily's House

Check *Does the answer make sense?*

Begin with the point (0, 0) to represent Emily's house. Use translation notation to determine the route to school, martial arts class and then back home.

Analyze the Strategy Tutor

CCGPS **Make a Conjecture** Suppose Emily needed to drive 32 blocks east and 15 blocks north from school. Would it be more efficient using translation notation or acting the problem out on graph paper? Explain.

Case #2 Keep the Change

Shiro bought an apple juice and a bag of pretzels for $4.55.

If he paid the cashier with a $5 bill, in how many different ways can he receive his change if the cashier only gives him quarters, dimes, and nickels?

1 Understand

Read the problem. What are you being asked to find?

I need to find _____.

Underline key words and values. What information do you know?

Shiro's purchase was [   ] and he paid with a [   ] bill. The change

is in _____ , _____ , and _____ .

2 Plan

Choose a problem-solving strategy.

I will use the _____ strategy.

3 Solve

Use your problem-solving strategy to solve the problem.

Use counters or coins to represent _____ , _____ , and

_____ . Because Shiro received [   ] in change, use the

coins to find different combinations with a sum of [   ] . Record

each combination. Q = quarters, D = dimes, and N = nickels.

Combinations possible: 1Q, [   ] D; 1Q, 1D, [   ] N; 1Q, 4N; [   ] D, 1 N;

[   ] D, 3 N; 2 D, [   ] N; 1 D, 7 N; [   ] N.

So, _____.

4 Check

Use information from the problem to check your answer.

_____

Case #3 Photographs

Malcolm is taking a picture of the French Club's five officers. The club secretary will always stand on the left and the treasurer will always stand on the right.

How many different ways can he arrange the officers in a single row for the picture?

Case #4 Dancing in the Street

In a certain dance for a competition, a dancer makes the following series of steps: 2 steps back, 1 step to the right, 3 steps forward, 2 steps to the right. The series is repeated four times.

How does the dancer's final position compare to his original position?

Case #5 Fitness

The length of a basketball court is 84 feet. Kareem starts at one end of the court and runs 20 feet forward and then 8 feet back.

How many more times will he have to do this until he reaches the end of the basketball court?

Circle a strategy below to solve the problem.
• Make a table.
• Work backward.
• Look for a pattern.
• Guess, check, and revise.

Case #6 Parties

Abby sent a text message to three friends inviting each of them to a party. Each of those friends sent the message to three more friends.

How many people received the text message at the fourth stage?

Mid-Chapter Check

Vocabulary Check

1. **CCGPS** **Be Precise** Define *transformation* using the words *preimage* and *image*. (Lesson 4)

   _____

   _____

2. Describe the role of the line of reflection in a transformation. (Lesson 5)

   _____

   _____

Skills Check and Problem Solving

Graph each triangle with the given vertices. Then graph the image after the given transformation and write the coordinates of the image's vertices.
(Lessons 4 and 5)

3. △ABC with vertices A(3, 5), B(4,1), and C(1, 2); translation of 3 units left and 4 units down

4. △WXY with vertices W(−1, −2), X(0, −4), and Y(−3, −5); reflection over the x-axis followed by a reflection over the y-axis

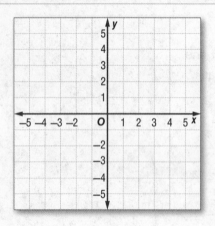

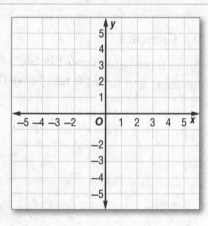

5. **Short Response** What is the sum of the measures, in degrees, of the interior angles of an octagon? (Lesson 3)

   _____

   _____

HOW can you identify rotational symmetry?

CCGPS Content Standards
MCC8.G.1

Mathematical Practices
1, 3

Logos Many products have logos so people can easily identify them. If you turn the first aid logo 180°, will the logo look the same as the original figure?

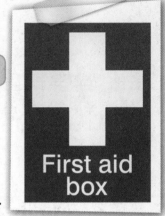

First aid box

Investigation

A figure has **rotational symmetry** if it can be rotated or turned less than 360° about its center so that the figure looks exactly as it does in its original position.

Step 1 Copy the outline of the first aid logo onto a piece of tracing paper. Label one vertex *A*.

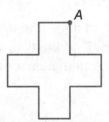

Step 2 Place the tracing paper over the outline in Step 1. Put your pencil point at the center of the figure to hold the tracing paper in place. Turn the tracing paper clockwise from its original position until the two figures match. Draw and label the new figure in the space provided.

Step 3 Continue turning the tracing paper until the logo is back to its original position. Does the figure have rotational symmetry? Explain.

_____

_____

Work with a partner. Determine whether the figure has rotational symmetry. Write yes or no.

1.   _____

2.  _____

Show your work.

3.  _____

4.  _____

Analyze

5. **CCGPS** **Reason Inductively** The degree measure of an angle through which the figure is rotated is called the **angle of rotation**. Find the first angle of rotation of the first aid logo by dividing 360° by the total number of times

   the figures matched. _____

6. List the other angles of rotation of the first aid logo by adding the measure of the first angle of rotation to the previous angle measure.

   Stop when you reach 360°. _____

7. What is the angle of rotation of each figure in Exercises 1–4? Write *no* if there is no rotational symmetry.

   Exercise 1 _____   Exercise 3 _____

   Exercise 2 _____   Exercise 4 _____

Reflect

8. **Inquiry** HOW can you identify rotational symmetry?

   _____

   _____

   _____

What You'll Learn

Scan the lesson. Predict two things you will learn about rotations.

- _____

  _____

- _____

  _____

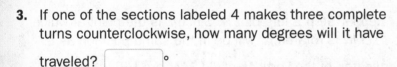
Real-World Link

Prizes Pablo is spinning the prize wheel shown.

1. A spin can be *clockwise* or *counterclockwise*. Define these two words in your own words.

   clockwise _____

   counterclockwise _____

2. If the section labeled 8 on the left part of the wheel spins 90° clockwise, where will it land? _____

3. If one of the sections labeled 4 makes three complete turns counterclockwise, how many degrees will it have traveled? [   ]°

4. Are there any points on the wheel that stay fixed, or do not move, when the wheel spins? If so, what are the points?

   _____

5. Does the center of the wheel change if the wheel is spun counterclockwise as opposed to clockwise? _____

6. Does the distance from the center to the edge change as it spins? Explain.

   _____

   _____

Essential Question

HOW can we best show or describe the change in position of a figure?

Vocabulary

rotation
center of rotation

Math Symbols

$(x, y) \rightarrow (y, -x)$
$(x, y) \rightarrow (-x, -y)$
$(x, y) \rightarrow (-y, x)$

Common Core GPS

Content Standards
MCC8.G.1, MCC8.G.3
Mathematical Practices
1, 3, 4, 7

Rotate a Figure About a Point

A **rotation** is a transformation in which a figure is rotated, or turned, about a fixed point. The **center of rotation** is the fixed point. A rotation does not change the size or shape of the figure. So, the preimage and the image are congruent.

Example

1. Triangle *LMN* with vertices *L*(5, 4), *M*(5, 7), and *N*(8, 7) represents a desk in Jackson's bedroom. He wants to rotate the desk counterclockwise 180° about vertex *L*. Graph the figure and its image. Then give the coordinates of the vertices for △*L'M'N'*.

Step 1   Graph the original triangle.

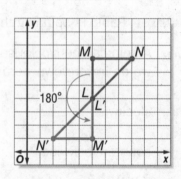

Step 2   Graph the rotated image. Use a protractor to measure an angle of 180° with *M* as one point on the ray and *L* as the vertex. Mark off a point the same length as $\overline{ML}$. Label this point *M'* as shown.

Step 3   Repeat Step 2 for point *N*. Since *L* is the point at which △*LMN* is rotated, *L'* will be in the same position as *L*.

So, the coordinates of the vertices of △*L'M'N'* are *L'*(5, 4), *M'*(5, 1), and *N'*(2, 1).

Got It?   Do this problem to find out.

a. Rectangle *ABCD* with vertices *A*(−7, 4), *B*(−7, 1), *C*(−2, 1), and *D*(−2, 4) represents the bed in Jackson's room. Graph the figure and its image after a clockwise rotation of 90° about vertex *C*. Then give the coordinates of the vertices for rectangle *A'B'C'D'*.

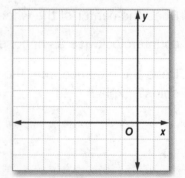

Rotations

Rotations can be described in degrees and direction. For example, 90° clockwise or 270° counterclockwise.

Show your work.

a. _____

Rotations About the Origin

Words   A rotation is a transformation around a fixed point. Each point of the original figure and its image are the same distance from the center of rotation.

Models   The rotations shown are clockwise rotations about the origin.

90° Rotation   **180° Rotation**   **270° Rotation**

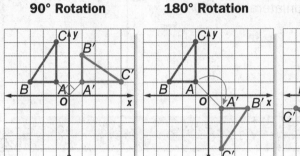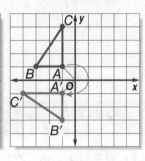

Symbols

$(x, y) \rightarrow (y, -x)$ $(x, y) \rightarrow (-x, -y)$ $(x, y) \rightarrow (-y, x)$

Figures can also be rotated about the origin.

Example

 Tutor

2. Triangle *DEF* has vertices *D*(−4, 4), *E*(−1, 2), and *F*(−3, 1). Graph the figure and its image after a clockwise rotation of 90° about the origin. Then give the coordinates of the vertices for △*D'E'F'*.

> **Step 1**   Graph △*DEF* on a coordinate plane.

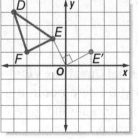

> **Step 2**   Sketch segment $\overline{EO}$ connecting point *E* to the origin. Sketch another segment, $\overline{E'O}$, so that the angle between point *E*, *O*, and *E'* measures 90° and the segment is the same length as $\overline{EO}$.

> **Step 3**   Repeat Step 2 for points *D* and *F*. Then connect the vertices to form △*D'E'F'*.

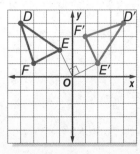

So, the coordinates of the vertices of △*D'E'F'* are *D'*(4, 4), *E'*(2, 1), and *F'*(1, 3).

Check
Check the coordinates of the image.
$(x, y) \rightarrow (y, -x)$
$(-4, 4) \rightarrow (4, 4)$
$(-1, 2) \rightarrow (2, 1)$
$(-3, 1) \rightarrow (1, 3)$ ✔

b. _____

Got It? Do this problem to find out.

b. Quadrilateral *MNPQ* has vertices *M*(2, 5), *N*(6, 4), *P*(6, 1), and *Q*(2, 1). Graph the figure and its image after a counterclockwise rotation of 270° about the origin. Then give the coordinates of the vertices for quadrilateral *M′N′P′Q′*.

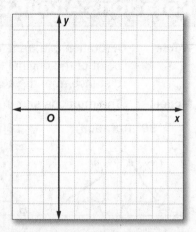

Guided Practice

Triangle *XYZ* has vertices *X*(3, −1), *Y*(5, −4), and *Z*(1, −5). Graph △*XYZ* and its image after each rotation. Then give the coordinates of the vertices for △*X′Y′Z′*. (Examples 1 and 2)

1. 270° counterclockwise about vertex *X*

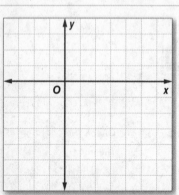

2. 180° clockwise about the origin

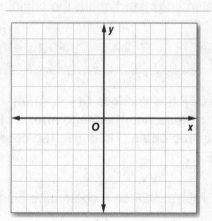

3. 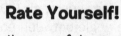 **Building on the Essential Question** What is the difference between rotating a figure about a given point that is a vertex and rotating the same figure about the origin if the rotation is less than 360°?

_____

_____

_____

_____

_____

_____

Rate Yourself!

How confident are you about rotations? Check the box that applies.

For more help, go online to access a Personal Tutor.

FOLDABLES *Time to update your Foldable!*

Independent Practice

Go online for Step-by-Step Solutions

1 Triangle *RST* represents the placement of Tyra's tricycle in the driveway and has vertices *R*(−7, 8), *S*(−7, 2), and *T*(−2, 2). Graph the figure and its rotated image after a clockwise rotation of 180° about the origin. Then give the coordinates of the vertices for triangle *R′S′T′*. (Example 2)

Show your work.

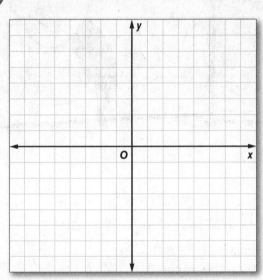

2. Quadrilateral *ABCD* has vertices at *A*(−3, −4), *B*(−1, −1), *C*(2, −2), and *D*(3, −4). Graph quadrilateral *ABCD* and its image after a 90° clockwise rotation about vertex *A*. Then give the coordinates of the vertices of the image. (Example 1)

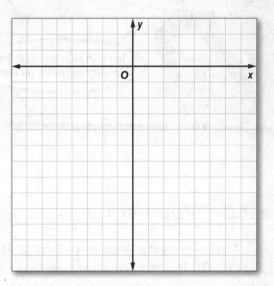

3. CCGPS **Model with Mathematics** A partial hubcap is shown. Copy and complete the figure so that the completed hubcap has rotational symmetry of 90°, 180°, and 270°.

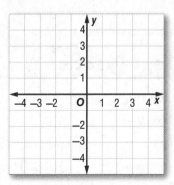

4. The right isosceles triangle *PQR* has vertices *P*(3, 3), *Q*(3, 1), and *R*(x, y) and is rotated 90° counterclockwise about the origin. Find the missing vertex of the triangle. Then graph the triangle and its image.

R(x, y) = *R*(_____, _____)

5 Which capital letters in VIRGINIA produce the same letter after being rotated 180°? _____

6. **Model with Mathematics** Refer to the graphic novel frame below. The last step is shown on grid 6. The girls make a clockwise rotation of 90° and begin the dance again. On a separate sheet of paper, expand the grid and mark the ending spot of the second series.

H.O.T. Problems Higher Order Thinking

7. **Persevere with Problems** Triangle *ABC* has vertices *A*(0, 4), *B*(0, −2), and *C*(2, 0). The triangle is reflected over the *x*-axis. Then the image is rotated 180° counterclockwise about the origin. What are the coordinates of the final image?

8. **Persevere with Problems** Triangle *QRS* is translated 7 units right, then rotated 90° clockwise about the origin. The vertices of triangle *Q″R″S″* are *Q″*(6, −1), *R″*(0, −1), and *S″*(0, −7). Find the coordinates of △*QRS*.

Georgia Test Practice

9. Square *JKLM* is rotated about the origin. Which of the following describes the rotation?

Ⓐ 90° clockwise

Ⓒ 180° clockwise

Ⓑ 90° counterclockwise

Ⓓ 270° counterclockwise

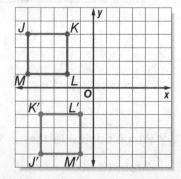

Extra Practice

10. Quadrilateral *ABCD* has vertices at *A*(−3, −4), *B*(−1, −1), *C*(2, −2), and *D*(3, −4). Graph quadrilateral *ABCD* and its image after a 180° counterclockwise rotation about vertex *D*. Then give the coordinates of the vertices of the image.

11. Quadrilateral *EFGH* has vertices *E*(1, −1), *F*(3, −5), *G*(7, −5), and *H*(6, −1). Graph the figure and its rotated image after a counterclockwise rotation of 90° about the origin. Then give the coordinates of the vertices for quadrilateral *E'F'G'H'*.

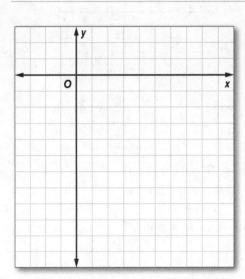

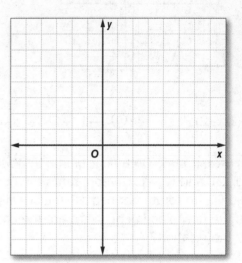

12. **CCGPS** **Identify Structure** Identify each transformation as a *translation*, *reflection*, or *rotation*.

a.

b.

c.

_____   _____   _____

Copy and Solve **Triangle *MNP* has vertices *M*(1, 4), *N*(3, 1), and *P*(5, 3). Find the vertices of *M'N'P'* after each rotation about the origin. Show your work on a separate piece of paper.**

13. 90° clockwise

14. 180° clockwise

15. 90° counterclockwise

16. If △ABC is rotated 90° counterclockwise about the origin, which is the resulting image of point C?

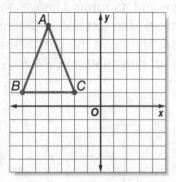

Ⓐ (2, −1)   Ⓒ (−2, −1)

Ⓑ (1, −2)   Ⓓ (−1, −2)

17. If △ABC is rotated 90° clockwise about point C, which is the resulting image of point B?

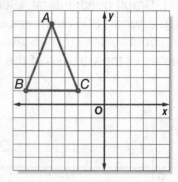

Ⓕ (6, 1)   Ⓗ (−2, 5)

Ⓖ (6, −1)   Ⓘ (−2, −3)

18. Short Response On a floor plan, *TUVW* with vertices *T*(−4, 0), *U*(−4, 2), *V*(−1, 2), and *W*(−1, 0) represents the bed in Chantal's bedroom. Chantal would like to rotate her bed 180° clockwise about point *V* to see if she likes the new placement. What are the coordinates of the image of point *T* after the rotation?

Common Core Review

19. Use the graph of △ABC shown at the right. MCC8.G.1
   a. What are the coordinates of △A′B′C′ when △ABC is reflected over the x-axis? _____
   b. Graph the image of △ABC after it is translated 2 units right and 1 unit up.

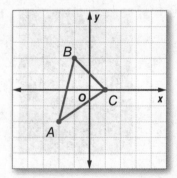

20. Triangle *FGH* has vertices *F*(−3, 7), *G*(−1, 5), and *H*(−2, 2). Find the vertices of its image after a translation of 4 units right and 2 units down followed by a reflection over the y-axis. MCC8.G.1

Inquiry WHAT are the results of a dilation of a triangle?

CCGPS Content Standards
Preparation for MCC8.G.3 and MCC8.G.4

Mathematical Practices
1, 3, 5

Murals One way to create murals on a wall is to use a drawing grid method. Artists draw a grid on the artwork to be copied and draw a similar grid on the wall. By transferring sections of the artwork, the mural is the same shape as the artwork, but a different size.

Investigation 1

In this Investigation, you will enlarge △ABC by a *scale factor* of 2 using grid paper. Point A will be the center point for the enlargement.

Step 1 On the grid shown below, $\overrightarrow{AB}$ is drawn to the edge of the grid. Draw $\overrightarrow{AC}$ in the same way.

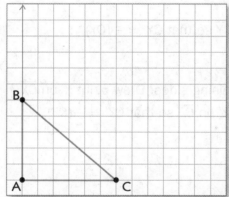

Step 2 Draw point B′ on $\overrightarrow{AB}$ so that AB′ = 2(AB). Draw point C′ on $\overrightarrow{AC}$ so that AC′ = 2(AC).

Step 3 Draw $\overline{B'C'}$ to complete △AB′C′.

What is the ratio of the length of $\overline{AB}$ to the length of $\overline{AB'}$? _____

What is the ratio of the length of $\overline{AC}$ to the length of $\overline{AC'}$? _____

Is △AB′C′ the same shape as △ABC? _____

Investigation 2

In Investigation 1, you used a dilation to transform △ABC by a scale factor of 2. A **dilation** is a transformation that enlarges or reduces a figure by a scale factor relative to a center point. That point is called the **center of dilation**.

In this Investigation, you will draw the image of △XYZ after a dilation with a scale factor of $\frac{1}{2}$. Point C will be the center of dilation.

Step 1 Triangle XYZ is shown below. Point C is the center of dilation. Using a ruler, draw line segments connecting C to each of the vertices of the triangle. $\overline{CY}$ is done for you.

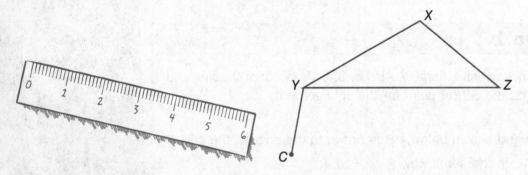

Step 2 Measure $\overline{CY}$. Draw point Y′ on $\overline{CY}$ so that $CY' = \frac{1}{2}(CY)$.

Step 3 Repeat Step 2 for the two remaining sides. Draw point X′ on $\overline{CX}$ so that $CX' = \frac{1}{2}(CX)$ and point Z′ on $\overline{CZ}$ so that $CZ' = \frac{1}{2}(CZ)$.

Step 4 Draw △X′Y′Z′.

Is △X′Y′Z′ the same shape as △XYZ? _____

Measure and compare the corresponding lengths on the original and new triangles. Describe the relationship between these

measurements. _____

_____

Measure and compare the corresponding angles on the original and new triangles. Describe the relationship between these

measurements. _____

_____

Work with a partner. Draw the image after a dilation with the given scale factor. Point *A* is the center of dilation.

1. scale factor: 3

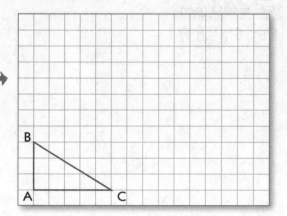

Show your work.

2. scale factor: $\frac{1}{3}$

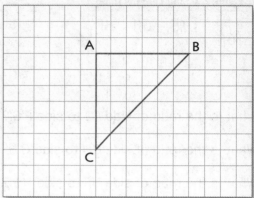

Work with a partner. Use a ruler to draw the image after a dilation with the given scale factor. Point *C* is the center of dilation.

3. scale factor: 3

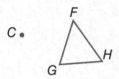

4. scale factor: $\frac{1}{5}$

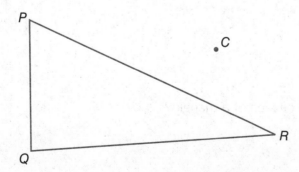

CCGPS **Use Math Tools** For each pair of figures from Exercise 3, measure the given side lengths in millimeters. Complete the table.

5.

Figure	Side Lengths (mm)		
	FG	GH	HF
△FGH			

6.

Figure	Side Lengths (mm)		
	F'G'	G'H'	H'F'
△F'G'H'			

7. What is the ratio of side *FG* to side *F'G'*? _____

8. What is the ratio of side *GH* to side *G'H'*? _____

9. What is the ratio of side *HF* to side *H'F'*? _____

10. Measure the angles of △FGH and △F'G'H' in Exercise 3 using a protractor.

Angle Measure (°)		
∠F	∠G	∠H
∠F'	∠G'	∠H'

Describe the relationship between the corresponding angles.

_____

_____

11. **CCGPS** **Reason Inductively** Based on the Investigations and Exercises, what can you conclude about the effects of a dilation on the sides and angles of a triangle?

_____

_____

_____

Reflect

12. **Inquiry** WHAT are the results of a dilation of a triangle?

_____

_____

What You'll Learn

Scan the lesson. List two real-world scenarios in which you would use a dilation.

- _____
- _____

Vocabulary Start-Up

A dilation uses a scale factor to enlarge or reduce a figure.

Scan the lesson and complete the graphic organizer.

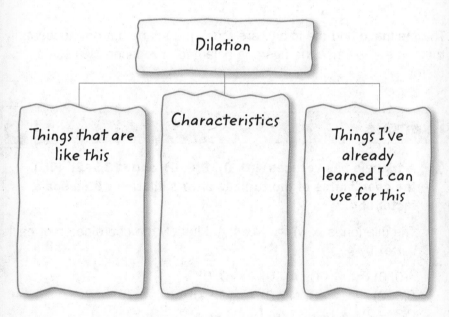

Dilation

Things that are like this

Characteristics

Things I've already learned I can use for this

Essential Question

HOW can we best show or describe the change in position of a figure?

Math Symbols

$(x, y) \longrightarrow (kx, ky)$

Common Core GPS

Content Standards
MCC8.G.3

Mathematical Practices
1, 3, 4

Real-World Link

Watch ▶

Photography Necie wants to insert a photo of her dog on her blog. The current size of the photo is 480 pixels by 640 pixels.

1. Suppose she wants to reduce the photo to 120 pixels by 160 pixels. Compare and contrast the original photo and the reduction. _____

2. What is the scale factor from the original to the reduction? _____

Dilations in the Coordinate Plane

Words A dilation with a scale factor of *k* will be:

- an enlargement, or an image larger than the original, if *k* > 1,

- a reduction, or an image smaller than the original, if 0 < *k* < 1,

- the same as the original figure if *k* = 1.

Model

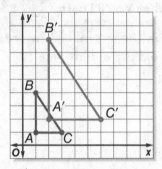

When the center of dilation in the coordinate plane is the origin, each coordinate of the preimage is multiplied by the scale factor *k* to find the coordinates of the image.

Symbols $(x, y) \longrightarrow (kx, ky)$

The preimage and the image are the same shape but not necessarily the same size since the figure is enlarged or reduced by a scale factor.

Example

1. **A triangle has vertices A(0, 0), B(8, 0), and C(3, −2). Find the coordinates of the triangle after a dilation with a scale factor of 4.**

The dilation is $(x, y) \longrightarrow (4x, 4y)$. Multiply the coordinates of each vertex by 4.

$A(0, 0) \longrightarrow (4 \cdot 0, \ 4 \cdot 0) \longrightarrow (0, 0)$
$B(8, 0) \longrightarrow (4 \cdot 8, \ 4 \cdot 0) \longrightarrow (32, 0)$
$C(3, -2) \longrightarrow [4 \cdot 3, \ 4 \cdot (-2)] \longrightarrow (12, -8)$

So, the coordinates after the dilation are A′(0, 0), B′(32, 0), and C′(12, −8).

Got It? Do this problem to find out.

a. A figure has vertices W(−2, 4), X(1, 4), Y(−3, −1), and Z(3, −1). Find the coordinates of the figure after a dilation with a scale factor of 2.

a. _____

Example

2. A figure has vertices J(3, 8), K(10, 6), and L(8, 2). Graph the figure and the image of the figure after a dilation with a scale factor of $\frac{1}{2}$.

The dilation is $(x, y) \rightarrow \left(\frac{1}{2}x, \frac{1}{2}y\right)$. Multiply the coordinates of each vertex by $\frac{1}{2}$. Then graph both figures on the coordinate plane.

$J(3, 8) \rightarrow \left(\frac{1}{2} \cdot 3, \frac{1}{2} \cdot 8\right) \rightarrow J'\left(\frac{3}{2}, 4\right)$

$K(10, 6) \rightarrow \left(\frac{1}{2} \cdot 10, \frac{1}{2} \cdot 6\right) \rightarrow K'(5, 3)$

$L(8, 2) \rightarrow \left(\frac{1}{2} \cdot 8, \frac{1}{2} \cdot 2\right) \rightarrow L'(4, 1)$

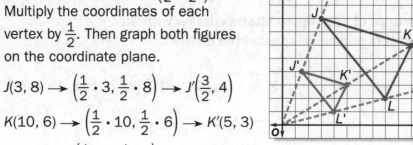

Check Draw lines throught the origin and each of the vertices of the original figure. The vertices of the dilation should lie on those same lines. ✓

Got It? Do these problems to find out.

b. A figure has vertices F(−1, 1), G(1, 1), H(2, −1), and I(−1, −1). Graph the figure and the image of the figure after a dilation with a scale factor of 3.

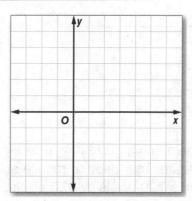

Example

3. Through a microscope, the image of a grain of sand with a 0.25-millimeter diameter appears to have a diameter of 11.25 millimeters. What is the scale factor of the dilation?

Write a ratio comparing the diameters of the two images.

$\dfrac{\text{diameter in dilation}}{\text{diameter in original}} = \dfrac{11.25}{0.25}$

$= 45$

So, the scale factor of the dilation is 45.

Show
your
work.

c. _____

Got It? Do this problem to find out.

c. Lucas wants to enlarge a 3- by 5-inch photo to a $7\frac{1}{2}$- by $12\frac{1}{2}$-inch photo. What is the scale factor of the dilation?

Guided Practice

Check ✓

Find the coordinates of the vertices of each figure after a dilation with the given scale factor _k_. Then graph the original image and the dilation.
(Examples 1 and 2)

1. $A(3, 5)$, $B(0, 4)$, $C(-2, -2)$; $k = 2$

2. $J(0, -4)$, $K(0, 6)$, $L(4, 4)$, $M(4, 2)$; $k = \frac{1}{4}$

_____

Show
your
work.

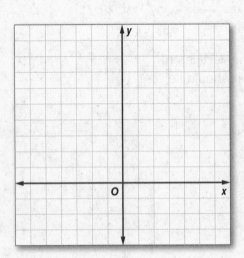

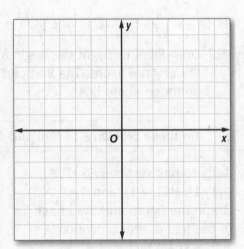

3. **STEM** Mrs. Bowen's homeroom is creating a Web page for their school's Intranet site. They need to reduce a scanned photograph so it is 720 pixels by 320 pixels. If the scanned photograph is 1,080 pixels by 480 pixels, what is the scale factor of the dilation? (Example 3) _____

4. **Building on the Essential Question** How are dilations similar to scale drawings?

_____

_____

_____

Rate Yourself!

☐ I understand how to dilate a figure.

▶▶ Great! You're ready to move on!

☐ I still have some questions about how to dilate a figure.

❚❚ No Problem! Go online to access a Personal Tutor.

Tutor 💬

FOLDABLES Time to update your Foldable!

Name _____ My Homework _____

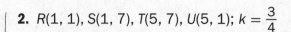
Find the coordinates of the vertices of each figure after a dilation with the given scale factor *k*. Then graph the original image and the dilation.
(Examples 1 and 2)

1. C(1, 4), A(2, 2), T(5, 5); k = 2

2. R(1, 1), S(1, 7), T(5, 7), U(5, 1); $k = \frac{3}{4}$

 Show your work.

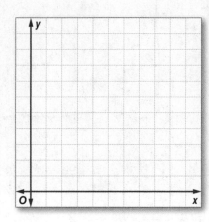

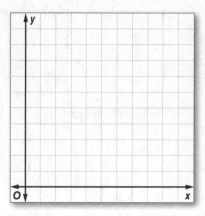

3. A graphic designer created a logo on $8\frac{1}{2}$- by 11-inch paper. In order to be placed on a business card, the logo needs to be $1\frac{7}{10}$ inches by $2\frac{1}{5}$ inches. What is the scale factor of the dilation? (Example 3)

_____

4. Darian wants to build a regulation-size pool table that is 9 feet in length. The plans he ordered are 18 by 36 inches. What is the scale factor of the dilation he must use to build the regulation pool table? (Example 3)

_____

5. A triangle has vertices A(−2, 3), B(0, 0), and C(1, 1).

    a. Find the coordinates of the triangle if it is reflected over the x-axis, then dilated by a scale factor of 3.

    _____

    b. Find the coordinates if the original triangle is dilated by a scale factor of 3, then reflected over the x-axis.

    _____

    c. Are the two transformations commutative? Explain.

    _____

6. **Model with Mathematics** In each part of the graphic organizer, sketch an image of pentagon *MNOPQ* after a dilation within the given parameters.

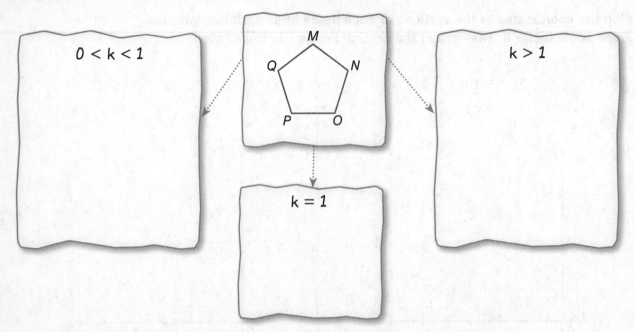

H.O.T. Problems Higher Order Thinking

7. **Make a Conjecture** A figure has a vertex at the point $(-4, -6)$. The figure is dilated with the center at the origin with a scale factor of 5. The resulting image is then dilated with a scale factor of $\frac{3}{5}$.

a. What are the coordinates of the vertex in the final image? _____

b. How do they compare with those of the original image?

_____

c. Can you predict the scale factor of a compound dilation? Explain.

_____

_____

8. **Persevere with Problems** The coordinates of two triangles are shown in the table. Is △*WXY* a dilation of △*ABC*? Explain.

WXY		ABC	
W	(a, b)	A	$(4a, 2b)$
X	(a, c)	B	$(4a, 2c)$
Y	(d, b)	C	$(4d, 2b)$

_____

_____

Georgia Test Practice

9. A line segment has endpoints $Q(-5, -6)$ and $P(-5, 1)$. Which of the following figures is the image after a dilation?

Ⓐ $Q'(-5, 6)$, $P'(-5, -1)$ Ⓒ $Q'(-10, -12)$, $P'(-10, 2)$

Ⓑ $Q'(5, -6)$, $P'(5, 1)$ Ⓓ $Q'(-6, -5)$, $P'(1, -5)$

Extra Practice

Find the coordinates of the vertices of each figure after a dilation with the given scale factor *k*. Then graph the original image and the dilation.

10. $R(5, 5)$, $S(5, 10)$, $T(10, 10)$, $U(10, 5)$; $k = \frac{2}{5}$

$R'(2, 2)$, $S'(2, 4)$, $T'(4, 4)$, $U'(4, 2)$

Multiply each coordinate in each ordered pair by scale factor. Then graph the two figures.

Homework Help

$R(5, 5) \rightarrow \left(\frac{2}{5} \cdot 5, \frac{2}{5} \cdot 5\right) \rightarrow R'(2, 2)$

$S(5, 10) \rightarrow \left(\frac{2}{5} \cdot 5, \frac{2}{5} \cdot 10\right) \rightarrow S'(2, 4)$

$T(10, 10) \rightarrow \left(\frac{2}{5} \cdot 10, \frac{2}{5} \cdot 10\right) \rightarrow T'(4, 4)$

$U(10, 5) \rightarrow \left(\frac{2}{5} \cdot 10, \frac{2}{5} \cdot 5\right) \rightarrow U'(4, 2)$

11. $V(-3, 4)$, $X(-2, 0)$, $W(1, 2)$; $k = 3$

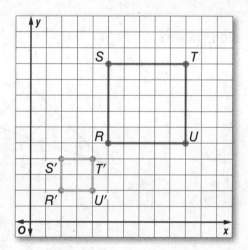

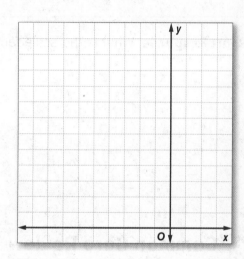

12. To place a picture in his class newsletter, Joaquin must reduce the picture by a scale factor of 0.3. Find the dimensions of the reduced picture if the original is 15 centimeters wide and 10 centimeters high.

_____

13. **CCGPS** **Multiple Representations** Triangle *XYZ* has vertices $X(0, 0)$, $Y(3, 1)$ and $Z(2, 3)$.

a. **Numbers** Find the coordinates of the image of $\triangle XYZ$ after a dilation with a scale factor of -2.

_____

b. **Algebra** Graph $\triangle XYZ$ and the image on the coordinate plane.

c. **Words** Describe the locations of $\triangle XYZ$ and $\triangle X'Y'Z'$ using transformations.

_____

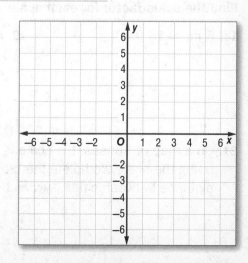

14. Square *B* is the result of a dilation of square *A*.

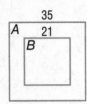

What scale factor was used to dilate square *A* to square *B*?

Ⓐ $\frac{1}{7}$ Ⓒ $\frac{5}{3}$

Ⓑ $\frac{3}{5}$ Ⓓ 7

15. Quadrilateral *WXYZ* is the result of a dilation of quadrilateral *LMNP*.

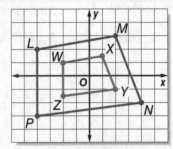

Which number best represents the scale factor used to change quadrilateral *LMNP* into quadrilateral *WXYZ*?

Ⓕ 3   Ⓗ $\frac{1}{2}$

Ⓖ 2   Ⓘ $\frac{1}{3}$

16. Short Response What is the scale factor of the dilation shown?

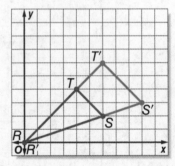

_____

17. A model airplane is built with a wing span of 18 inches. The actual wing span of the airplane is 90 feet. Find the scale. MCC7.G.1

_____

Find the scale factor for each scale. MCC7.G.1

18. 6 in. = 10 ft _____

19. 4 cm = 2.5 mm _____

20. 5 ft = 15 yd _____

21. On a map of Kansas, the scale is 1 in. = 50 miles. Using the scale, complete the table showing the distance between cities. MCC7.G.1

Cities	Map	Actual
Wichita to Topeka	$2\frac{3}{4}$ in.	
Salina to Kansas City		150 mi

21ST CENTURY CAREER
in Computer Animation

Computer Animator

Have you ever wondered how they make animated movies look so realistic? Computer animators use computer technology and apply their artistic skills to make inanimate objects come alive. If you are interested in computer animation, you should practice drawing, study human and animal movement, and take math classes every year in high school. Tony DeRose, a computer scientist at an animation studio said, "Trigonometry helps rotate and move characters, algebra creates the special effects that make images shine and sparkle, and calculus helps light up a scene."

College & Career READINESS

Explore college and careers at ccr.mcgraw-hill.com

Is This the Career for You?

Are you interested in a career as a computer animator? Take some of the following courses in high school.

◆ 2-D Animation
◆ Algebra
◆ Calculus
◆ Trigonometry

Turn the page to find out how math relates to a career in Computer Animation.

An Animation Sensation

Use Figures 1–3 to solve each problem.

1. In Figure 1, the car is translated 8 units left and 5 units down so that it appears to be moving. What are the coordinates of A' and B' after the translation? _____

2. In Figure 1, the car is translated so that A' has coordinates $(-7, 2)$. Describe the translation as an ordered pair. Then find the coordinates of point B'. _____

_____

3. In Figure 1, the car is reflected over the x-axis in order to make its reflection appear in a pond. What are the coordinates of A' and B' after the reflection? _____

_____

4. In Figure 2, the artist uses rotation to show the girl's golf swing. Describe the coordinates of G' if the golf club is rotated 90° clockwise about point H. _____

5. The character in Figure 3 is enlarged by a scale factor of $\frac{5}{2}$. What are the coordinates of Q' and R' after the dilation? _____

_____

6. The character in Figure 3 is reduced in size by a scale factor of $\frac{2}{3}$. What is the number of units between S' and T', the width of the character's face, after the dilation? _____

_____

Figure 1

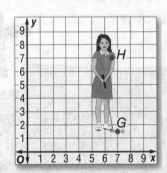

Figure 2

Figure 3

Career Project

It's time to update your career portfolio! Choose a movie that was completely or partially computer animated. Use the Internet to research how technology was used to create the scenes in the movie. Describe any challenges that the computer animators faced.

_____

_____

_____

_____

What are some short term goals you need to achieve to become a computer animator?

- _____
- _____
- _____
- _____

Vocabulary Check

Unscramble each of the clue words. After unscrambling all of the terms, use the numbered letters to find the name of a geometric operation.

GONUENRTC [ ][ ][ ][ ][ ][ ][ ][ ][ ]
　　　　　　　　7　　　　　　　　11

TLODNIIA [ ][ ][ ][ ][ ][ ][ ][ ]
　　　　　　3　　　　　14

GEIMA [ ][ ][ ][ ][ ]
　　　12　9　10

PEERIGAM [ ][ ][ ][ ][ ][ ][ ][ ]
　　　　8

TIFROLCENE [ ][ ][ ][ ][ ][ ][ ][ ][ ][ ]
　　　　　　6　　　　　　　　4

NOTTIRAO [ ][ ][ ][ ][ ][ ][ ][ ]
　　　　13　1

LAOTANSTRIN [ ][ ][ ][ ][ ][ ][ ][ ][ ][ ][ ]
　　　　2　　　5

[ ][ ][ ][ ][ ][ ][ ][ ][ ][ ][ ][ ][ ][ ][ ]
 1 2 3 4 5 6 7 8 9 10 11 12 13 14 5

Complete each sentence using one or more of the unscrambled words above.

1. _____ is another name for a slide.

2. The image produced by enlarging or reducing a figure is called
   a _____.

3. A _____ is an operation that maps an original
   geometric figure, the _____, onto a new figure called
   the _____.

4. A _____ is the mirror image of the original figure.

Use Your FOLDABLES

Use your Foldable to help review the chapter.

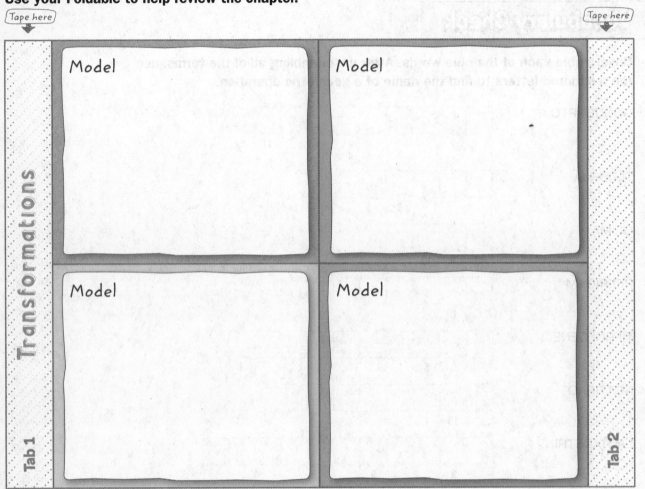

Tape here

Tape here

Transformations

Tab 1

Tab 2

Model

Model

Model

Model

Got it?

The problems below may or may not contain an error. If the problem is correct, write a "✓" by the answer. If the problem is not correct, write an "X" over the answer and correct the problem.

Use the figure at the right.

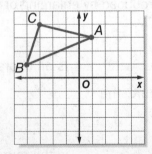

1. The coordinates of point *A* after a dilation with a scale factor of 2 are (2, 6).

2. The coordinates of point *A* after a reflection over the *y*-axis are (1, −3).

3. The coordinates of point *A* after a clockwise rotation 90° about the origin are (3, −1).

4. The coordinates of point *A* after a translation of 3 units left and 2 units up are (2, 5).

1. In chess, a knight moves two spaces up and one space to the left. If the starting point is represented by P(1, 4), what are the coordinates of its stopping point? (Lesson 4) _____

Show your work.

2. Ella wants rearrange the furniture in her bedroom. Quadrilateral *TUVW* represents a floor pillow in her room and has vertices T(−4, 0), U(−4, 2), V(−2, 0), and W(−2, 2). If she reflects the pillow over the *y*-axis, what are the coordinates of the final image? (Lesson 5)

_____

3. On a floor plan of Dylan's patio, a flagpole is represented by the origin and the corners of a picnic table are represented by the points P(1, 3), Q(3, 3), R(3, −1), and S(1, −1). Plot the picnic table and its image after a 180° clockwise rotation about the flagpole. Then give the coordinates of the vertices of the image. (Lesson 6)

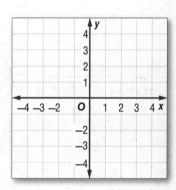

_____

_____

4. Alex wants to paint a figure on one side of a bookcase. He needs to enlarge a pattern of pentagon *ABCDE* by a scale factor of 3. The vertices of *ABCDE* are A(−1, 1), B(0, 2), C(1, 1), D(1, −1), and E(−1, −1). Graph the pentagon and the image after the dilation. Then give the coordinates of the vertices of the image. (Lesson 7)

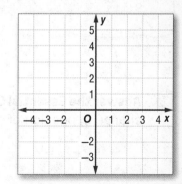

_____

_____

Reflect

 Answering the Essential Question

Use what you learned about transformations to complete the graphic organizer. Determine if you would demonstrate each transformation by using words, symbols, or models. Then give an example using your method for each transformation.

translation

reflection

Essential Question

HOW can we best show or describe the change in position of a figure?

rotation

dilation

Answer the Essential Question. HOW can we best show or describe the change in position of a figure?

_____

_____

_____

Chapter 2

Congruence and Similarity

 Essential Question

HOW can you determine congruence and similarity?

 Common Core GPS

Content Standards
MCC8.G.1, MCC8.G.1a, MCC8.G.1b, MCC8.G.2, MCC8.G.4, MCC8.G.5, MCC8.EE.6

Mathematical Practices
1, 2, 3, 4, 5, 7

 Math in the Real World

Models The wingspan of a model of a 737 commercial aircraft is 6.75 inches. The scale for the model is 1 inch = 200 inches.

Use the scale to find the wingspan in inches of the actual 737 aircraft. Then convert the inches to feet.

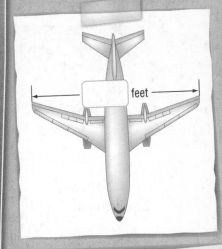

FOLDABLES
Study Organizer

1 Cut out the correct Foldable from the FL pages in the back of this book.

2 Place your Foldable on the Key Concept page toward the end of this chapter.

3 Use the Foldable throughout this chapter to help you learn about congruence and similarity.

Vocabulary

composition of transformations   scale factor

corresponding parts   similar

indirect measurement   similar polygons

Study Skill: Use a Web

Use a Web A *web* can help you understand how math concepts are related to each other. To make a web, write the major topic in the center of a piece of paper. Then, draw "arms" from the center for as many categories as you need.

Here is a partial web for the major topic of triangles. Complete the web by adding descriptions for the classifications by sides. Then add the classifications by angles.

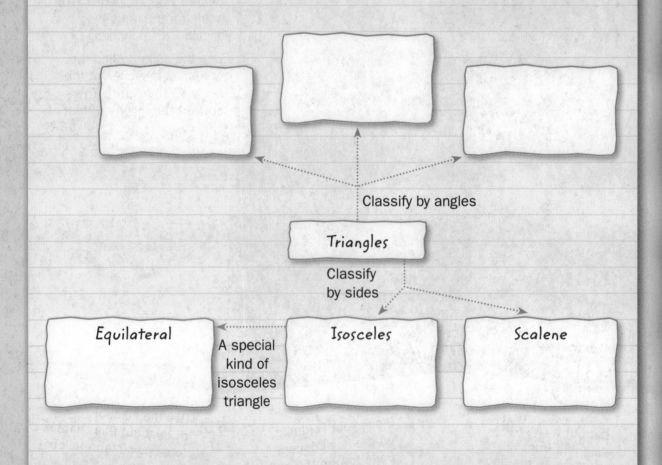

Are You Ready?

Try the Quick Check below.
Or, take the Online Readiness Quiz.

Check ✓

CCGPS **Quick Review**

Common Core Review MCC7.RP.2, MCC8.EE.5

Example 1

Solve $\frac{w}{12} = \frac{5}{6}$.

$$\frac{w}{12} = \frac{5}{6}$$ Write the proportion.

$6 \times w = 12 \times 5$ Find cross products.

$6w = 60$ Simplify.

$w = 10$ Division Property of Equality

Example 2

Find the slope of the line that passes through (3, 8) and (−1, 0).

$$m = \frac{y_2 - y_1}{x_2 - x_1}$$ Slope formula

$$m = \frac{0 - 8}{-1 - 3}$$ $(x_1, y_1) = (3, 8); (x_2, y_2) = (-1, 0)$

$$m = \frac{-8}{-4} \text{ or } 2$$ Simplify.

Quick Check

Proportions Solve each proportion.

1. $\frac{x}{15} = \frac{7}{30}$ _____

2. $\frac{4}{9} = \frac{14}{y}$ _____

3. $\frac{12}{z} = \frac{30}{37}$ _____

Show your work.

4. $\frac{8}{15} = \frac{m}{21}$ _____

5. $\frac{n}{5} = \frac{18}{45}$ _____

6. $\frac{3}{7} = \frac{21}{p}$ _____

Find Slope Find the slope of the line that passes through each pair of points.

7. $(-1, 1), (-3, 7)$ _____

8. $(2, 0), (0, 2)$ _____

9. $(-6, -1), (-3, 4)$ _____

How Did You Do?

Which problems did you answer correctly in the Quick Check?
Shade those exercise numbers below.

① ② ③ ④ ⑤ ⑥ ⑦ ⑧ ⑨

Inquiry HOW does a combination of transformations differ from a single transformation? How are they the same?

CCGPS Content Standards
MCC8.G.2

Mathematical Practices
1, 3

Graphic Arts Graphic artists often use several transformations to create designs. When a transformation is applied to a figure and then another transformation is applied to the image, the result is called a **composition of transformations.**

Investigation 1

Step 1 Fold the page in your book vertically into three sections along the dotted lines.

Step 2 Draw the reflection of the arrow over the fold in the middle section.

Step 3 Draw a reflection of the 2nd arrow over the fold in the right-hand section.

Step 4 Repeat Steps 2 and 3 with the pentagon.

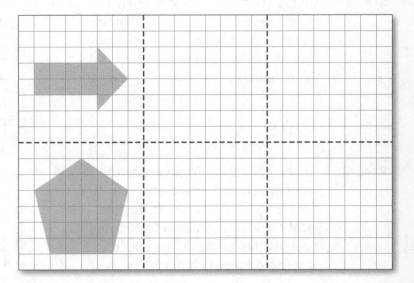

How are the original figures and the final figures related?

_____

_____

Would the final images be the same as the original figure if the second reflection was reflected over the horizontal line? Explain.

_____

_____

_____

Investigation 2

In this Investigation, you will use a translation and a reflection to create a decorative border.

Step 1 Draw a figure on the coordinate plane shown, close to the origin.

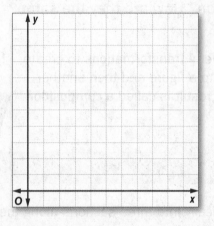

Step 2 On the coordinate plane in Step 1, translate your figure. Lightly draw the image since it will not be in its final location. In this example, the red figure is translated 2 units to the right.

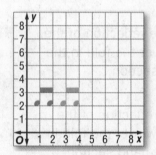

Step 3 On the coordinate plane in Step 1, reflect the drawn image across a horizontal line. This will be the final location so you can draw this in your book. In this example, the image is reflected across the line $y = 2$.

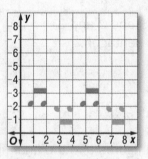

Step 4 Repeat the process to create your border.

How are the size and shape of the original figure related to the size and shape of the images?

Suppose you wanted your border to run up the side of the page instead of across the bottom of the page. Describe what transformations you might use to do this.

92 Chapter 2 Congruence and Similarity

Copyright © by The McGraw-Hill Companies, Inc.

Collaborate

Work with a partner. Describe the transformations combined to create the outlined patterns shown in Exercises 1-4.

1.

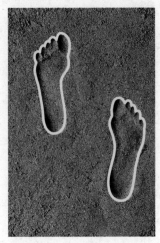

2.

Show your work.

3.

4.

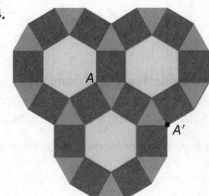

5. Draw a figure on the coordinate plane shown. Use a reflection and a rotation to create a logo for a company.

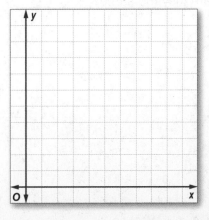

In some cases, a composition of transformations is the same as a single transformation. Draw the composition of transformations described. Then identify the single transformation that would produce the same image as each composition.

6. $\overline{AB}$ is reflected across the y-axis, then reflected across the x-axis.

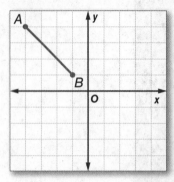

_____

_____

7. $\triangle XYZ$ is reflected across line m and then reflected across line n.

_____

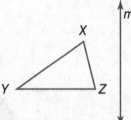

8. **CCGPS** **Reason Inductively** The transformations in the Investigations and Exercises have been translations, reflections, and rotations which preserve distance. Describe what would happen to the position, size, and shape of a figure if a composition of transformations included a dilation.

_____

_____

 Reflect

9. **Inquiry** HOW does a combination of transformations differ from a single transformation? How are they the same?

_____

_____

_____

_____

Congruence and Transformations

What You'll Learn

Scan the lesson. Predict two things you will learn about congruence and transformations.

• _____

   _____

• _____

   _____

 Essential Question

HOW can you determine congruence and similarity?

 Common Core GPS

Content Standards
MCC8.G.1, MCC8.G.1a,
MCC8.G.1b, MCC8.G.2

Mathematical Practices
1, 3, 4

 ## Real-World Link

Braille The letter R in the Braille alphabet consists of four large dots and 2 smaller dots in the pattern shown. Circle the letter with the same shape as the letter R.

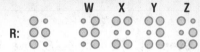

  Collaborate How can you determine whether two figures are the same size and shape?

Step 1 Copy the figure shown on tracing paper two times. Cut out both figures. Label the figures *A* and *B*.

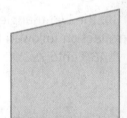

Step 2 Place Figure *B* on top of Figure *A*. Are the side lengths the same? the angle measures?

_____

Are the figures the same size and shape? _____

Step 3 Translate Figure *B* up and over on your desk. How can you move Figure *A* on top of Figure *B* so all sides and angles match?

_____

_____

Step 4 Flip Figure *B* over. How can you move Figure *A* on top of Figure *B* so all sides and angles match?

_____

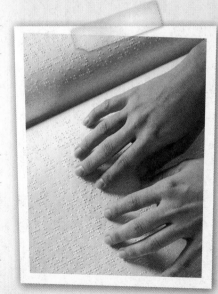

Identify Congruence

On the previous page, you matched Figure A to Figure B by a translation and a reflection. Two figures are congruent if the second can be obtained from the first by a series of rotations, reflections, and/or translations.

Examples

Determine if the two figures are congruent by using transformations. Explain your reasoning.

1.

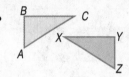

Transformations

Translations, reflections and rotations are called isometries. In an isometry, the distance between two points in an image is the same as the distance in the preimage.

iso / metry

↓ ↓

same distance

Step 1 Reflect △*ABC* over a vertical line. Label the vertices of the image *A'*, *B'*, and *C'*.

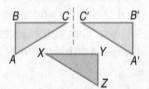

Step 2 Translate △*A'B'C'* until all sides and angles match △*XYZ*.

So, the two triangles are congruent because a reflection followed by a translation will map △*ABC* onto △*ZYX*.

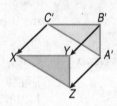

- -

2.

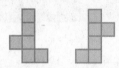

Reflect the red figure over a vertical line.

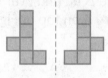

Even if the reflected figure is translated up and over, it will not match the green figure exactly. The two figures are not congruent.

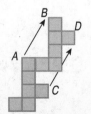

Got It? Do these problems to find out.

a.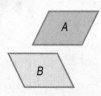

b.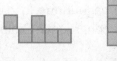

a. _____

b. _____

Determine the Transformations

If you have two congruent figures, you can determine the transformation, or series of transformations, that maps one figure onto the other by analyzing the orientation or relative position of the figures.

Translation	Reflection	Rotation
• length is the same • orientation is the same	• length is the same • orientation is reversed	• length is the same • orientation is changed

Show your work.

STOP and Reflect

How does analyzing the orientation of two figures help determine what transformations map one figure onto another? Explain below.

Real World Example

Tutor

3. **Ms. Martinez created the logo shown. What transformations did she use if the letter "d" is the preimage and the letter "p" is the image? Are the two figures congruent?**

Step 1 Start with the preimage. Rotations or reflections change orientation. Rotate the letter "d" 180° about point A.

Step 2 Translate the new image up.

Ms. Martinez used a rotation and translation to create the logo. The letters are congruent because images produced by a rotation and translation have the same shape and size.

Got It? Do this problem to find out.

c. What transformations could be used if the letter "W" is the preimage and the letter "M" is the image in the logo shown? Are the two figures congruent? Explain.

Guided Practice

Determine if the two figures are congruent by using transformations. Explain your reasoning. (Examples 1 and 2)

1.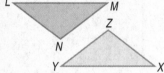

Show your work.

_____
_____
_____

2.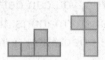

_____
_____
_____

3. The Boyd Box Company uses the logo shown. What transformations could be used if the red trapezoid is the preimage and the blue trapezoid is the image? Are the two figures congruent? Explain. (Example 3)

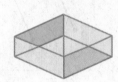

_____
_____
_____

4. **Building on the Essential Question** Why do translations, reflections, and rotations create congruent images?

_____
_____
_____
_____

Rate Yourself!

How confident are you about the relationship between congruence and transformations? Check the box that applies.

For more help, go online to access a Personal Tutor.

Tutor

FOLDABLES Time to update your Foldable!

Independent Practice

Go online for Step-by-Step Solutions eHelp

Determine if the two figures are congruent by using transformations. Explain your reasoning. (Examples 1 and 2)

1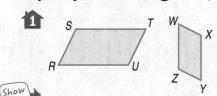

Show your work.

_____

_____

_____

2.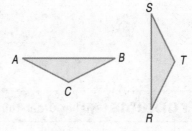

_____

_____

_____

3 Nilda purchased some custom printed stationery with her initials. What transformations could be used if the letter "Z" is the preimage and the letter "N" is the image in the design shown? Are the two figures

congruent? Explain. (Example 3) _____

_____

_____

4. (CCGPS) **Multiple Representations** One way to identify congruent triangles is to prove their matching sides have the same measure. Triangle *CDE* has vertices at (1, 4), (1, 1), and (5, 1).

a. **Graphs** Graph △*CDE*.

b. **Numbers** Find the lengths of the sides of △*CDE*.

_____

c. **Geometry** Reflect △*CDE* over the *y*-axis, then translate it 2 units left. Label the vertices of the image *C'D'E'*. Write the coordinates of △*C'D'E'* below.

_____

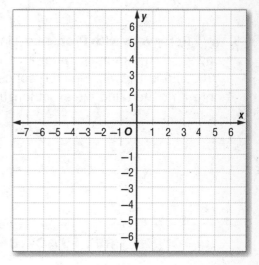

d. **Numbers** Find the lengths of the sides of △*C'D'E'*.

_____

e. **Words** Are the two triangles congruent? Justify your response.

_____

5. Graph △GHJ with vertices at G(0, 1), H(4, 0), and J(4, 1). Then graph the image of the triangle after a translation of 3 units up followed by a reflection over the y-axis. Find the lengths of each side of the preimage and the image. Then determine if the two figures are congruent.

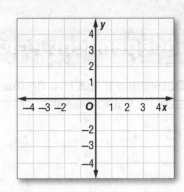

H.O.T. Problems Higher Order Thinking

6. **Model with Mathematics** Create a design in the space at right, using a series of transformations that produce congruent figures. Exchange designs with a classmate and determine what transformations were used to create their design.

> Show your work.

7. CCGPS **Persevere with Problems** Angle ABC has points A(−3, 4), B(−2, 1) and C(2, 2). Find the coordinates of the image of the angle after a 90° clockwise rotation about the origin, a translation of 2 units up, and a reflection over the y-axis.

8. CCGPS **Persevere with Problems** Line segment XY has endpoints at X(3, 1) and Y(−2, 0). Its image after a series of transformations has endpoints at X'(0, 1) and Y'(5, 0). Find the series of transformations that maps $\overline{XY}$ onto $\overline{X'Y'}$. Then find the exact length of both segments.

Georgia Test Practice

9. Triangle MNO is congruent to triangle RST.

Which series of transformations maps △MNO onto △RST?

Ⓐ 90° clockwise rotation about M then a reflection

Ⓑ translation then a dilation

Ⓒ 90° clockwise rotation about M then a translation

Ⓓ reflection then a translation

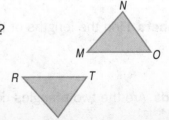

Extra Practice

Determine if the two figures are congruent by using transformations. Explain your reasoning.

10.

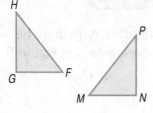

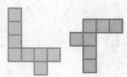

The two figures are not congruent because no sequence of
transformations will map the green figure onto the red figure exactly.

11.

H *P* *G* *F* *M* *N*

_____

_____

_____

12.

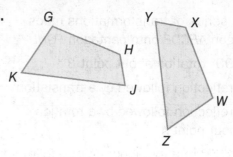

_____

_____

_____

13. Simon is illustrating a graphic novel for a friend. He is using the two thought bubbles shown. What transformations did he use if Figure A is the preimage and Figure B is the image?

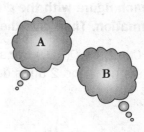

_____

14. **CCGPS** **Model with Mathematics** Graph △*PQR* with vertices at *P*(0, 0), *Q*(2, 0), and *R*(0, 2). Then graph the image of the triangle after a reflection over the *x*-axis followed by a dilation with a scale factor of 2. Find the lengths of each side of the preimage and the image. Then determine if the two figures are congruent.

_____

_____

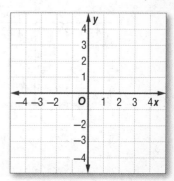

15. Pentagon *ABCDE* is congruent to pentagon *FGHIJ*.

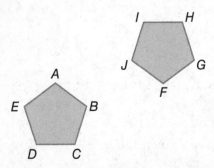

Which series of transformations maps pentagon *ABCDE* onto pentagon *FGHIJ*?

Ⓐ a 90° rotation about point *B*

Ⓑ a reflection followed by a translation

Ⓒ a reflection followed by a rotation about point *A*

Ⓓ a 180° rotation about point *C* followed by a reflection

16. Short Response Gregory is creating a mosaic for art class. He started by using triangular tiles as shown.

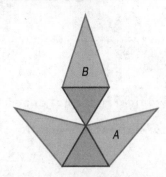

What are possible transformations he used if Figure A is the preimage and Figure B is the image?

_____

Common Core Review

Graph each figure with the given vertices and its image after the indicated transformation. Then give the coordinates of the final image. MCC8.G.1, MCC8.G.3

17. $\overline{CD}$: *C*(−2, 4), *D*(0, 0) translation of 3 units right and 2 units down

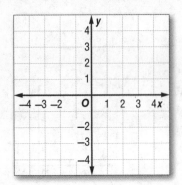

18. △*XYZ*: *X*(−1, 1), *Y*(3, 1), *Z*(1, 3) reflection over the *y*-axis

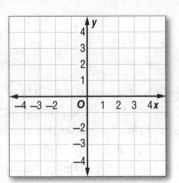

Inquiry WHICH three pairs of corresponding parts can be used to show that two triangles are congruent?

 Content Standards
MCC8.G.2

Mathematical Practices
1, 3

Bridges While driving past a bridge with his family, Henry noticed that the bridge truss was made up of congruent triangles.

Investigation 1

In this Investigation, you will investigate whether it is possible to show that two triangles are congruent without showing that all six pairs of corresponding parts are congruent.

Step 1 Copy the sides of the triangle shown onto a piece of patty paper and cut them out.

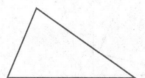

Step 2 Arrange and tape the pieces together so that they form a triangle.

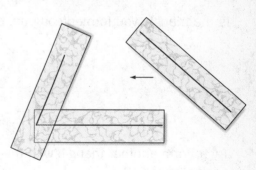

Is the triangle you formed congruent to the original triangle? Explain. _____

_____

Rotate the triangle you formed 180°. Is the triangle congruent to the original triangle? Explain. _____

_____

Try to form another triangle with the given sides. Is it congruent to the original triangle? _____

Step 1 Draw a triangle on a piece of patty paper. Copy each angle of the triangle onto a separate piece of patty paper. Extend each side of each angle to the edge of the patty paper.

 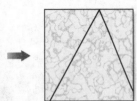 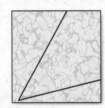 

Step 2 Arrange and tape the pieces together so that they form a triangle.

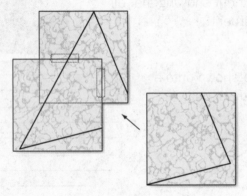

Is the triangle you formed congruent to the original triangle? Explain.

_____

_____

_____

Try to form another triangle with the given angles. Is it congruent to the original triangle?

A *counterexample* disproves a statement by showing an example of when the statement is not true. Based on your investigation, is the following statement true? If not, provide a counterexample.

If the angles of one triangle are congruent to the angles of another triangle, the two triangles are congruent.

_____

Collaborate

1. Draw a triangle on a piece of patty paper. Copy two sides of the triangle and the angle between them onto separate pieces of patty paper and cut them out. Arrange and tape pieces together so that the two sides are joined to form the rays of the angle. Connect the two rays to form a triangle.

   a. Is the triangle you formed congruent to the original triangle?

   Explain. ______________________________

   ____

   b. Try to form another triangle with the given sides and angle. Is it congruent to the original triangle? ______________

2. Determine if two triangles with the following congruent parts are congruent. If not, draw a counterexample.

Show your work.

Various Parts	Congruent?	Counterexample
3 angles	No	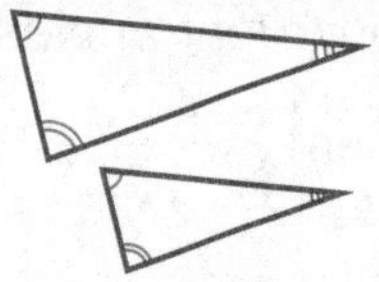
2 sides		
2 angles and 1 side		
2 angles and the side between the 2 angles		
2 angles		
3 sides		

Analyze

3. **CCGPS** **Make a Conjecture** Use patty paper to investigate the relationship between two triangles with the given information. Make a conjecture about whether each of these cases can be used to show that two triangles are congruent.

Case 1 two pairs of congruent sides and a pair of congruent angles not between them _____

_____

_____

Case 2 two pairs of congruent angles and the pair of congruent sides between them _____

_____

_____

Case 3 two pairs of congruent angles and a pair of congruent sides not between them _____

_____

_____

Reflect

4. Based on Investigation 1, can three pairs of congruent sides be used to show that two triangles are congruent? _____

5. Based on Investigation 2, can three pairs of congruent angles be used to show that two triangles are congruent? _____

6. Based on Exercise 1, can two pairs of congruent sides and the pair of congruent angles between them be used to show that two triangles are congruent? _____

7. **Inquiry** WHICH three pairs of corresponding parts can be used to show that two triangles are congruent?

_____

_____

_____

Congruence

What You'll Learn

Scan the lesson. List two headings you would use to make an outline of the lesson.

- _____
  _____
  _____

- _____
  _____

 Essential Question

HOW can you determine congruence and similarity?

Vocab
 Vocabulary

corresponding parts

Math Symbols
≅ is congruent to

Common Core GPS

Content Standards
MCC8.G.2

Mathematical Practices
1, 2, 3, 4

Real-World Link

Crafts Lauren is creating a quilt using the geometric pattern shown. She wants to make sure that all of the triangles in the pattern are the same shape and size.

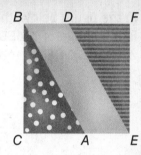

1. What would Lauren need to do to show the two triangles are congruent?

   _____
   _____

2. Complete the lists of the parts of △ABC and △DEF. Then draw lines between the corresponding parts of each triangle.

   $\overline{CB}$ _____ $\overline{BA}$ ∠BAC ∠ABC ∠ _____

   _____ $\overline{ED}$ _____ ∠ _____ ∠ _____ ∠EDF

3. Suppose you cut out the two triangles and laid one on top of the other so the parts of the same measures were matched up. What is true about the triangles?

   _____

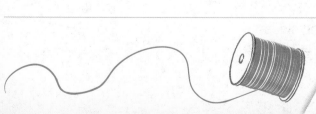

Corresponding Parts of Congruent Figures

Congruence
To indicate that sides are congruent, an equal number of tick marks is drawn on the corresponding sides. To show that angles are congruent, an equal number of arcs is drawn on the corresponding angles.

Words   If two figures are congruent, their corresponding sides are congruent and their corresponding angles are congruent.

Model

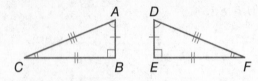

Symbols $\triangle ABC \cong \triangle DEF$

Congruent Angles: $\angle A \cong \angle D$; $\angle B \cong \angle E$; $\angle C \cong \angle F$

Congruent Sides: $\overline{AB} \cong \overline{DE}$; $\overline{BC} \cong \overline{EF}$; $\overline{CA} \cong \overline{FD}$

In the figure below, the two triangles are congruent because $\triangle DEF$ is the image of $\triangle ABC$ reflected over line m. The notation $\triangle ABC \cong \triangle DEF$ is read *triangle ABC is congruent to triangle DEF*.

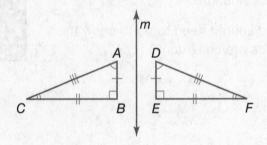

The parts of congruent figures that *match* or correspond, are called **corresponding parts**.

Example

Tutor

1. **Write congruence statements comparing the corresponding parts in the congruent triangles shown.**

   Use the matching arcs and tick marks to identify the corresponding parts.

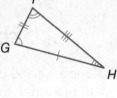

   Corresponding angles:
   $\angle J \cong \angle G$, $\angle L \cong \angle I$, $\angle K \cong \angle H$

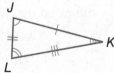

   Corresponding sides:
   $\overline{JK} \cong \overline{GH}$, $\overline{KL} \cong \overline{HI}$, $\overline{LJ} \cong \overline{IG}$

Got It? Do this problem to find out.

a.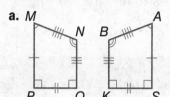

Show your work.

a. _____

Example

Tutor

2. Triangle *ABC* is congruent to △*XYZ*.
Write congruence statements
comparing the corresponding parts.
Then determine which transformations
map △*ABC* onto △*XYZ*.

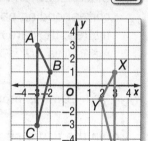

Step 1 Analyze the figures to determine
which angles and sides of the
figures correspond.

Corresponding angles: $\angle A \cong \angle X$, $\angle B \cong \angle Y$, $\angle C \cong \angle Z$
Corresponding sides: $\overline{AB} \cong \overline{XY}$, $\overline{BC} \cong \overline{YZ}$, $\overline{CA} \cong \overline{ZX}$

Step 2 Determine any changes in the orientation of the triangles.
The orientation is reversed so at least one of the
transformations is a reflection. If you reflect △*ABC* over
the *y*-axis and then translate it down 2 units it coincides
with △*XYZ*.

The transformations that map △*ABC* onto △*XYZ* consist
of a reflection over the *y*-axis followed by a translation of
2 units down.

STOP and Reflect

When writing congruence
statements, why is it
important to match up
corresponding points in
the statement?

Got It? Do this problem to find out.

b. Parallelogram *WXYZ* is congruent to
parallelogram *KLMN*. Write congruence
statements comparing the corresponding
parts. Then determine which
transformation(s) map parallelogram
WXYZ onto parallelogram *KLMN*.

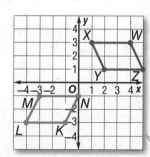

b. _____

Find Missing Measures

You can use properties of congruent figures to find the missing measures of angles and sides in a figure.

Example

3. Miley is using a brace to support a tabletop. In the figure, $\triangle BCE \cong DFG$. If $m\angle CEB = 50°$, what is the measure of $\angle FGD$?

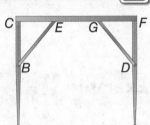

Since $\angle CEB$ and $\angle FGD$ are corresponding parts in congruent figures, they are congruent. So, $\angle FGD$ measures 50°.

Got It? Do this problem to find out.

c. _____

c. In the figure shown above, the length of $\overline{CE}$ is 2 feet. What is the length of $\overline{FG}$?

Guided Practice

1. Triangle *RST* is congruent to $\triangle UVW$. Write congruence statements comparing the corresponding parts. Then determine which transformation(s) map $\triangle RST$ onto $\triangle UVW$. (Examples 1 and 2)

_____

_____

_____

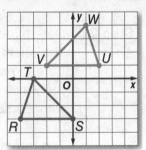

2. In the table design shown in Example 3, suppose $BE = 18$ inches. What is *DG*? (Example 3)

_____

3.  **Building on the Essential Question** How can the coordinate plane help you determine that corresponding

sides are congruent? _____

_____

_____

Rate Yourself!

How confident are you about congruence? Check the box that applies.

☐ ☐ ☐ ☐ ☐

For more help, go online to access a Personal Tutor.

FOLDABLES Time to update your Foldable!

Independent Practice

Go online for Step-by-Step Solutions

eHelp

Write congruence statements comparing the corresponding parts in each set of congruent figures. (Example 1)

1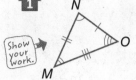

_____

_____

2.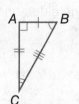

_____

_____

3 Parallelograms *UVWX* and *HJIK* are congruent. Write congruence statements comparing the corresponding parts. Then determine which transformation(s) map parallelogram *UVWX* onto parallelogram *HJIK*. (Example 2)

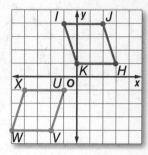

_____

_____

_____

4. In the umbrella shown at the right, △*JLK* ≅ △*NLM*. (Example 3)

  a. If m∠*JKL* = 66°, then m∠*NML* = _____.

  b. If *MN* = 15 inches, then *KJ* = _____ inches.

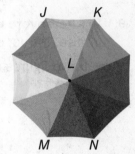

5. ⒸⒸⒼⓅⓈ **Reason Abstractly** In the figure, △*ABC* ≅ △*EBD*.

  a. On the figure, draw arc and tic marks to identify the corresponding parts.

  b. Find the value of *x*.

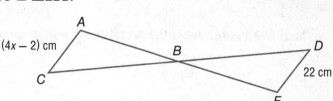

_____

6. In the figure at the right, △*EFG* ≅ △*LMN*. Find the value of *x*. Then describe the transformations that map △*EFG* onto △*LMN*.

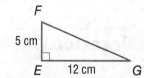 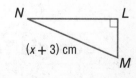

_____

_____

7. CCGPS **Make a Conjecture** Hexagon *ABCDEF* has six congruent sides.

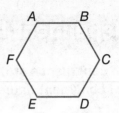

  a. Draw $\overline{CA}$, $\overline{CF}$, and $\overline{CE}$.

  b. How many triangles were formed? _____

  c. Make a conjecture about which triangles are congruent. Test your conjecture by measuring the sides and angles of the triangles.

  _____

  _____

 ## H.O.T. Problems Higher Order Thinking

8. CCGPS **Find the Error** Mandar is making a congruence statement for the congruent triangles shown. Find his mistake and correct it.

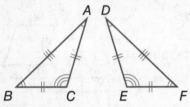

Triangle ABC is congruent to triangle DEF.

  _____

  _____

  _____

9. CCGPS **Persevere with Problems** Determine whether each statement is *true* or *false*. If true, explain your reasoning. If false, give a counterexample.

  a. If two figures are congruent, their perimeters are equal.

  _____

  _____

  _____

  b. If two figures have the same perimeter, they are congruent.

  _____

  _____

  _____

  _____

 ## Georgia Test Practice

10. Which of the following statements is *not* true if $\triangle CDE \cong \triangle FGH$?

  Ⓐ $\angle C \cong \angle F$ Ⓒ $\overline{CE} \cong \overline{HG}$

  Ⓑ $\angle H \cong \angle E$ Ⓓ $\overline{DC} \cong \overline{GF}$

Extra Practice

Write congruence statements comparing the corresponding parts in each set of congruent figures.

11.

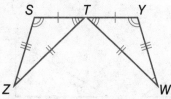

Use the matching arcs and tick marks to identify the corresponding parts.

Corresponding angles:

$\angle S \cong \angle Y$, $\angle STZ \cong \angle YTW$, $\angle Z \cong \angle W$

Corresponding sides:

$\overline{SZ} \cong \overline{YW}$, $\overline{ZT} \cong \overline{WT}$, $\overline{TS} \cong \overline{TY}$

12.

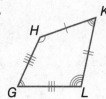
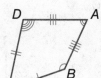

_____

_____

13. Quadrilaterals *KLMN* and *FGHJ* are congruent. Write congruence statements comparing the corresponding parts. Then determine which transformation(s) map quadrilateral *KLMN* onto quadrilateral *FGHJ*.

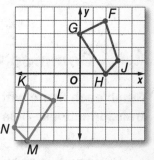

_____

_____

_____

_____

_____

14. In the quilt design shown, $\triangle ABC \cong \triangle ADE$. What is the measure of $\angle BCA$?

_____

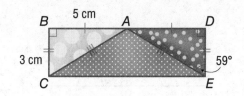

15. **Reason Abstractly** In the figure, $\triangle LZP \cong \triangle NZM$.

a. On the figure, draw arc and tic marks to identify the corresponding parts.

b. Find the value of *x.* _____

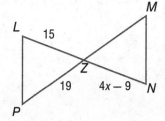

16. Wires stretching from the top of a telephone pole to the ground create two congruent triangles, △PQR and △SQR. Find QS.

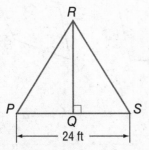

Ⓐ 12 ft

Ⓑ 24 ft

Ⓒ 48 ft

Ⓓ 65 ft

17. Short Response Triangle *ABC* is congruent to triangle *DEF*. Write congruence statements comparing the corresponding parts.

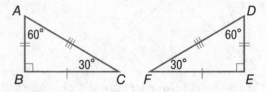

_____

_____

CCGPS Common Core Review

Graph each figure with the given vertices and its image after the indicated transformations. Then give the coordinates of the final image. MCC8.G.3

18. △*ABC*: *A*(−4, 2), *B*(−2, −3), *C*(−4, −3); 90° counterclockwise rotation about *A* followed by a translation of 4 units to the right

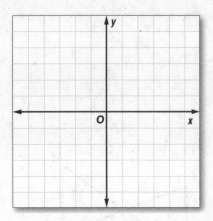

19. quadrilateral *RSTU*: *R*(4, 3), *S*(5, −1), *T*(4, −3), *U*(3, −1); reflection over the *x*-axis followed by a reflection over the *y*-axis

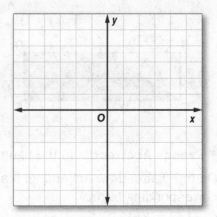

Inquiry HOW can technology help you show the relationship between transformations and congruence?

CCGPS Content Standards MCC8.G.2

Mathematical Practices 1, 3, 5

Kaleidoscope While looking through a kaleidoscope at a flower, Evan noticed that some of the images were a result of a reflection followed by a rotation.

Investigation

You can use The Geometer's Sketchpad® to perform transformations on a two-dimensional figure.

Step 1 First, click on **Graph**. Go to **Grid Form** and click on **Square Grid**. Next, plot triangle *ABC* by clicking on **Graph** and then **Plot Points**. Enter the coordinates (3, 3), and then click **Plot**. Repeat the process for (1, 1) and (1, 4). Then click **Done**. Right click on point (3, 3) and click **Label Plotted Point**. Type **A** in the box provided and then click **OK**. Repeat this process for points *B*(1, 1) and *C*(1, 4).

Step 2 Using the line segment tool, [/] , click on one point and then another. A line segment will appear between those two points. Repeat until you have drawn a triangle like the one shown.

Step 3 To reflect △*ABC* over the *x*-axis, use the selection arrow to click on the three points and three line segments that make up the triangle. Then double click on the *x*-axis. Use the pull-down menu under **Transform**. Click on **Reflect**. The program will automatically label the points of the image when you right click on a point and click **Label Plotted Point**. Draw the reflection on the grid shown.

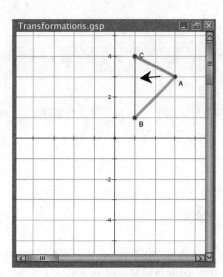

Step 4 Rotate △*A′B′C′* by using the pull-down menu under **Transform**. Click **Rotate**. Type 270 when asked for the angle of rotation. Add labels to the points. Draw the rotation on the grid shown.

Collaborate

Work with a partner. Once you have completed the transformations, draw the images that appear on your display.

1. Graph quadrilateral *QRST* with vertices of *Q*(−5, −4), *R*(−4, −1), *S*(−2, −1), and *T*(−1, −3). Rotate the quadrilateral 180° about the origin and then reflect the image over the *y*-axis.

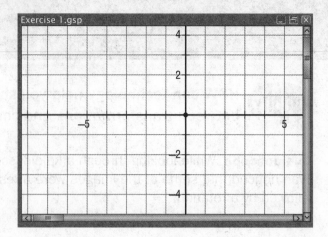

Analyze

CCGPS **Use Math Tools** **Work with a partner.**

2. You can use The Geometer's Sketchpad® to measure the side lengths and angle measures of a figure. Use quadrilateral *QRST* from Exercise 1. Click on points *S* and *T*. On the MENU bar, click **Measure** and then **Distance**.

   What is *ST*? _____

3. You can also measure angles. Click on *S*, *T*, and *Q*. On the MENU bar, click

   Measure and then **Angle**. What is *m∠STQ*? _____

4. Show that quadrilateral *QRST* is congruent to quadrilateral *Q″R″S″T″* by measuring the sides and angles of each figure. Record the measures in

   the table. Compare the corresponding parts. _____

_____

QR	Q″R″	RS	R″S″	ST	S″T″	TQ	T″Q″

∠QRS	∠Q″R″S″	∠RST	∠R″S″T″	∠STQ	∠S″T″Q″	∠TQR	∠T″Q″ R″

Reflect

5. **Inquiry** HOW can technology help you show the relationship between transformations and congruence?

_____

_____

CCGPS **Content Standards**
MCC8.G.5
Mathematical Practices
1, 3, 4

Case #1 Hammer Time

Christy wants to make shelves to store her game system and other electronics in her room. She will make brackets in the shape of right triangles to hold the shelves. Since it is a right triangle, one of the angles measure 90°.

What is the relationship of the other two angles in a right triangle?

1 Understand *What are the facts?*

The bracket is in the shape of a right triangle, so one of the angles measures 90°.

2 Plan *What is your strategy to solve this problem?*

Draw several right triangles, measure each angle, and look for a pattern.

3 Solve *How can you apply the strategy?*

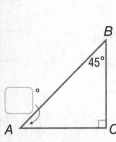 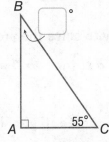 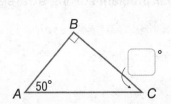

It appears that the sum of the measures of the acute angles of a right

triangle is ☐. So, the acute angles are _____.

4 Check *Does the answer make sense?*

You can try several more examples to see whether your conjecture appears to be true. But at this point, it is just a conjecture, not an actual proof.

Analyze the Strategy 💬 Tutor

CCGPS **Justify Conclusions** Inductive reasoning is the process of making a conjecture after observing several examples. Did Christy use inductive

reasoning? Explain. _____

Case #2 Bike-A-Thon

Jacob is participating in a biking fundraiser to the lake.
After 45 miles, he is $\frac{5}{6}$ of the way there.

How many more miles does he need to travel to reach the lake?

1 Understand

Read the problem. What are you being asked to find?

I need to find _____ .

Underline key words and values. What information do you know?

Jacob has biked _____ of the way to the lake. This is equal

to _____ .

2 Plan

Choose a problem-solving strategy.

I will use the _____ strategy.

3 Solve

Use your problem-solving strategy to solve the problem.

Draw a line that represents the distance to the lake. Divide the line
into 6 equal parts.

45 miles   distance left

_____ of the 6 parts = 45 so

each part is _____ miles.

_____ + _____ + _____ +

_____ + _____ = 45

The distance to the lake is

45 + _____ = _____ miles.

So, Jacob has _____ left to ride.

4 Check

Use information from the problem to check your answer.

_____

Randy Faris/CORBIS   Copyright © The McGraw-Hill Companies, Inc.

Collaborate Work with a small group to solve the following cases.
Show your work on a separate piece of paper.

Case #3 Diagonal Dilemma

Draw several rectangles and their diagonals. Measure the lengths of their diagonals.

What seems to be true about the measures of the lengths of the diagonals of a rectangle?

_____

Case #4 Geometry

A stock clerk is piling baseballs in the shape of a square-based pyramid as shown.

If the pyramid is to have five layers, how many baseballs will he need?

_____

Case #5 Scrapbooks

A scrapbook page measures 12 inches long by 12 inches wide.

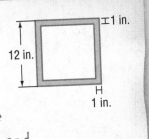

How many 3-inch by 5-inch horizontal photographs can be placed on the page if $\frac{1}{2}$ inch is placed between each photo and at least 1 inch is left as a margin on all four sides?

Circle a strategy below to solve the problem.

- Guess, check, and revise.
- Look for a pattern.
- Determine reasonable answers.
- Act it out.

Case #6 Geometry

The sides of a triangle are in the ratio 2:3:4. The perimeter of the triangle is 81 feet.

What is the length of each side?

_____

Mid-Chapter Check

Vocabulary Check

1. What transformations can be used to show two figures are congruent? (Lesson 1)

_____

2. List two attributes of two congruent polygons. (Lesson 2)

_____

_____

Skills Check and Problem Solving

Determine if the two figures are congruent by using transformations. Explain your reasoning. (Lesson 1)

3.

4.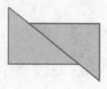

5.

Show your work.

_____   _____   _____

_____   _____   _____

_____   _____   _____

_____   _____   _____

6. Jordan is creating the logo shown using a pentagon and five congruent triangles. Triangle *WAX* is congruent to triangle *YBZ*. Describe the transformations that map △*WAX* onto △*YBZ*. If *WX* measures 5 inches, what is the length of *YZ*? (Lesson 2)

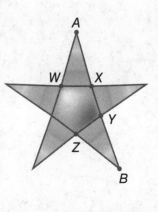

_____

7. **Georgia Test Practice** Trapezoid *MNOP* is congruent to trapezoid *QROP*. Which transformation maps *MNOP* onto *QROP*? (Lesson 2)

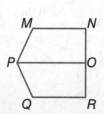

  Ⓐ translation   Ⓒ rotation

  Ⓑ reflection   Ⓓ dilation

Inquiry HOW are two triangles related if they have the same shape but different sizes?

CCGPS **Content Standards** Preparation for MCC8.G.4

Mathematical Practices 1, 3

Farms While flying in an airplane, Ariel looked out the window and saw roads and a field like the one shown. She wondered if there was a relationship between the two triangles she saw.

Investigation

To determine if there is a relationship between the two triangles, use the diagram shown.

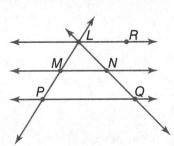

$\overleftrightarrow{LR} \parallel \overleftrightarrow{MN} \parallel \overleftrightarrow{PQ}$
$\overleftrightarrow{LP}$ and $\overleftrightarrow{LQ}$ are transversals.

Step 1 Measure and record the lengths of the line segments in centimeters and angles in degrees in the table.

△LPQ		△LMN	
LP =	m∠L = °	LM =	m∠L = °
LQ =	m∠P = °	LN =	m∠M = °
PQ =	m∠Q = °	MN =	m∠N = °

What do you notice about the measure of the corresponding angles of the triangles? _____

Step 2 Express the lengths of the corresponding sides of the triangles as ratios.

$\frac{LP}{LM} =$ _____ $\frac{LQ}{LN} =$ _____ $\frac{PQ}{MN} =$ _____

What do you notice about the ratios of the corresponding sides of the triangles? _____

Collaborate

Work with a partner.

1. **CCGPS** **Model with Mathematics** Triangle *ABC* is a right triangle with $m\angle A = 53°$. On the grid, draw and label a different right triangle, *XYZ*, using the given angle *X*, which also measures 53°.

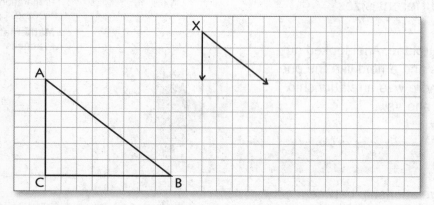

Show your work.

a. What do you notice about the shape of the triangles? _____

_____

b. What is the measure of $\angle B$? _____

c. What is the measure of the angle that corresponds to $\angle B$

in $\triangle XYZ$? _____

d. Express the lengths of the corresponding sides of the triangles as ratios.

e. What do you notice about the ratios? _____

 ## Analyze

2. **Reason Inductively** The two triangles in the Investigation and in Exercise 1 are called *similar triangles*. Based on your discoveries, what properties do similar triangles have?

_____

_____

 ## Reflect

3. **Inquiry** HOW are two triangles related if they have the same shape but different sizes?

_____

Similarity and Transformations

What You'll Learn

Scan the lesson. List two real-world scenarios in which you would use similarity.

- _____
- _____

Essential Question

HOW can you determine congruence and similarity?

Vocabulary

similar

Common Core GPS

Content Standards
MCC8.G.4

Mathematical Practices
1, 3, 4, 7

Vocabulary Start-Up

Recall that a dilation changes the size of a figure by a scale factor, but does not change the shape of the figure. Since the size is changed, the image and the preimage are not congruent.

Complete the graphic organizer. Consider each word on the Rating Scale and place a check ✓ in the appropriate column next to the word. If you do not know the meaning of a word, find the meaning in the glossary or on the Internet.

| Word | Rating Scale | | | |
	Know it well	Have seen or heard it	No clue	What it means
dilation				
scale factor				
similar figures				

Real-World Link

A *fractal* is a geometric image that can be divided into parts that are smaller copies of the whole. The photo at the right is an example of a fractal.

1. Circle two different size parts of the figure that are smaller copies of the whole.

Identify Similarity

Two figures are **similar** if the second can be obtained from the first by a sequence of transformations and dilations.

Examples

1. **Determine if the two triangles are similar by using transformations.**

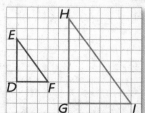

Since the orientation of the figures is the same, one of the transformations is a translation.

Step 1 Translate △*DEF* down 2 units and 5 units to the right so *D* maps onto *G*.

Step 2 Write ratios comparing the lengths of each side.

$$\frac{HG}{ED} = \frac{8}{4} \text{ or } \frac{2}{1} \qquad \frac{GI}{DF} = \frac{6}{3} \text{ or } \frac{2}{1} \qquad \frac{IH}{FE} = \frac{10}{5} \text{ or } \frac{2}{1}$$

Since the ratios are equal, △*HGI* is the dilated image of △*EDF*. So, the two triangles are similar because a translation and a dilation maps △*EDF* onto △*HGI*.

2. **Determine if the two rectangles are similar by using transformations.**

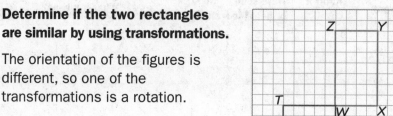

The orientation of the figures is different, so one of the transformations is a rotation.

Step 1 Rotate rectangle *VWTU* 90° clockwise about *W* so that it is oriented the same way as rectangle *WXYZ*.

Step 2 Write ratios comparing the lengths of each side.

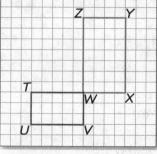

$$\frac{WT}{XY} = \frac{5}{7} \qquad \frac{TU}{YZ} = \frac{3}{4}$$

$$\frac{UV}{ZW} = \frac{5}{7} \qquad \frac{VW}{WX} = \frac{3}{4}$$

The ratios are not equal. So, the two rectangles are not similar since a dilation did not occur.

Got It? Do these problems to find out.

a.
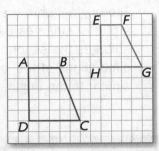

b.

Use the Scale Factor

Similar figures have the same shape, but may have different sizes. The sizes of the two figures are related to the scale factor of the dilation.

If the scale factor of the dilation is ...	then the dilated figure is ...
between 0 and 1	smaller than the original
equal to 1	the same size as the original
greater than 1	larger than the original

Example

 Tutor

3. Ken enlarges the photo shown by a scale factor of 2 for his webpage. He then enlarges the webpage photo by a scale factor of 1.5 to print. If the original photo is 2 inches by 3 inches, what are the dimensions of the print? Are the enlarged photos similar to the original?

 STOP and Reflect

List below at least two topics in mathematics that use a scale factor.

Multiply each dimension of the original photo by 2 to find the dimensions of the webpage photo.

2 in. × 2 = 4 in.   3 in. × 2 = 6 in.

So, the webpage photo will be 4 inches by 6 inches. Multiply the dimensions of that photo by 1.5 to find the dimensions of the print.

4 in. × 1.5 = 6 in.   6 in. × 1.5 = 9 in.

The printed photo will be 6 inches by 9 inches. All three photos are similar since each enlargement was the result of a dilation.

Got It? Do this problem to find out.

c. _____

c. An art show offers different size prints of the same painting. The original print measures 24 centimeters by 30 centimeters. A printer enlarges the original by a scale factor of 1.5, and then enlarges the second image by a scale factor of 3. What are the dimensions of the largest print? Are both of the enlarged prints similar to the original?

Guided Practice

Check ✓

Determine if the two figures are similar by using transformations. Explain your reasoning. (Examples 1 and 2)

1.

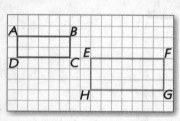

Show your work.

_____

_____

2.

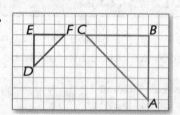

_____

_____

3. A T-shirt iron-on measures 2 inches by 1 inch. It is enlarged by a scale factor of 3 for the back of the shirt. The second iron-on is enlarged by a scale factor of 2 for the front of the shirt. What are the dimensions of the largest iron-on? Are both of the enlarged iron-ons similar to the

original? (Example 3) _____

4. ⓔ **Building on the Essential Question** What is the difference between using transformations to create similar figures versus using transformations to create congruent figures?

_____

_____

_____

_____

Rate Yourself!

How confident are you about similar figures? Shade the ring on the target.

For more help, go online to access a Personal Tutor.

Tutor

FOLDABLES _Time to update your Foldable!_

Independent Practice

Go online for Step-by-Step Solutions

Determine if the two figures are similar by using transformations. Explain your reasoning. (Examples 1 and 2)

1.
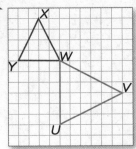

Show your work.

_____

_____

2.
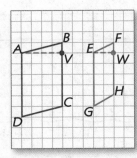

_____

_____

_____

3 Felisa is creating a scrapbook of her family. A photo of her grandmother measures 3 inches by 5 inches. She enlarges it by a scale factor of 1.5 to place in the scrapbook. Then she enlarges the second photo by a scale factor of 1.5 to place on the cover of the scrapbook. What are the dimensions of the photo for the cover of the scrapbook? Are all of the photos similar? (Example 3) _____

CCGPS **Persevere with Problems Each preimage and image are similar. Describe a sequence of transformations that maps the preimage onto the image.**

4.
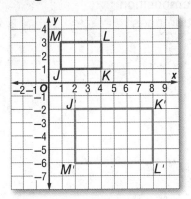

_____

_____

_____

5.
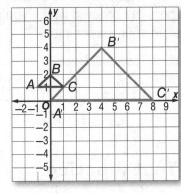

_____

_____

_____

6. **CCGPS** **Identify Structure** Use the graphic organizer to compare and contrast similar and congruent figures.

	Similar Figures	Congruent Figures
Side Measures		
Angle Measures		
Transformations Used		

H.O.T. Problems Higher Order Thinking

7. **CCGPS** **Persevere with Problems** Using at least one dilation, describe a series of transformations where the image is congruent to the preimage.

_____

_____

_____

8. **CCGPS** **Model with Mathematics** The image of △DEF after two transformations has vertices at D′(3, 3), E′(6, 3) and F′(3, −6). If the two triangles are similar, determine what two transformations map △DEF onto △D′E′F′.

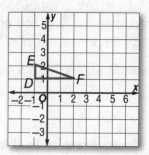

_____

_____

_____

9. **CCGPS** **Construct an Argument** *True* or *false*. If a dilation is in a composition of transformations, the order in which you perform the composition does not matter. Explain your reasoning.

_____

_____

_____

Georgia Test Practice

10. Trapezoid *ABCD* is similar to trapezoid *PQRS*. Which series of transformations maps point *C* onto point *R*?

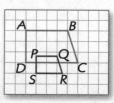

Ⓐ rotation then a dilation   Ⓒ translation then a dilation

Ⓑ reflection then a dilation   Ⓓ two dilations

Extra Practice

**Determine if the two figures are similar by using transformations.
Explain your reasoning.**

11.

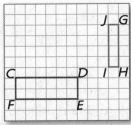

no; The ratios of the side lengths are
not equal.

Find the ratios of the side lengths.
$\frac{CD}{GH} = \frac{6}{4}$ and $\frac{DE}{JG} = \frac{2}{1}$; $\frac{6}{4} \neq \frac{2}{1}$, so the two
figures are not similar.

12.

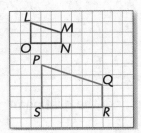

_____

_____

_____

_____

_____

13. Shannon is making three different sizes of blankets from the same
material. The first measures 2.5 feet by 2 feet. She wants to enlarge it by
a scale factor of 2 to make the second blanket. Then she will enlarge the
second one by a scale factor of 1.5 to make the third blanket. What are
the dimensions of the third blanket? Are all of the blankets similar?

_____

14. **CCGPS** **Model with Mathematics** In the figure shown,
trapezoid *RSTU* has vertices *R*(1, 3), *S*(4, 3), *T*(3, 1),
and *U*(2, 1).

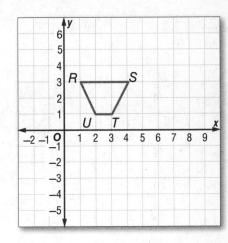

  a. Draw the image of *RSTU* after a translation
  of 2 units down followed by a dilation with a scale
  factor of 2. Label the vertices *ABCD*.

  b. Draw the image of *RSTU* after a dilation with a scale
  factor of 2, followed by a translation of 2 units down.
  Label the vertices *EFGH*.

  c. Which figures are similar? Which figures are congruent?

  _____

  _____

  d. Are *ABCD* and *EFGH* in the same location? If they are
  not, what transformation would map *ABCD* onto *EFGH*?

  _____

  _____

15. Triangle *DEF* is the image of △*ABC* after a sequence of transformations.

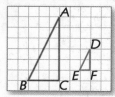

What is the scale factor of the dilation in the sequence?

Ⓐ 3

Ⓑ $\frac{1}{3}$

Ⓒ $-\frac{1}{3}$

Ⓓ −3

16. Which transformation produces similar figures that are enlargements or reductions?

Ⓕ translation

Ⓖ rotation

Ⓗ reflection

Ⓘ dilation

17. Short Response Figure B is produced after Figure A is reflected over the *y*-axis and then dilated by a scale factor of $\frac{3}{4}$. What is the ratio comparing the lengths of the sides of Figure A to Figure B? _____

Common Core Review

Find the coordinates of the vertices of each figure after a dilation with the given scale factor *k*. Then graph the original image and the dilation. MCC8.G.3

18. *M*(0, 0), *N*(−1, 1), *O*(2, 3); *k* = 2

_____

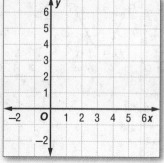

19. *A*(−3, 3), *B*(3, 3), *C*(3, −3); $k = \frac{2}{3}$

_____

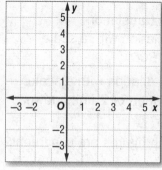

20. *G*(4, 4), *H*(2, −4), *I*(−4, −4), *J*(0, 2); $k = \frac{1}{2}$

_____

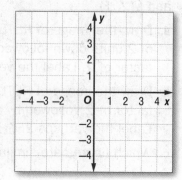

Properties of Similar Polygons

What You'll Learn

Scan the lesson. List two headings you would use to make an outline of the lesson.

- _____

- _____

Real-World Link

Photos Elsa is printing pictures at a photo kiosk in the store. She can choose between 4 × 6 prints or 5 × 7 prints. Are the side lengths of the two prints proportional? Explain. _____

 Essential Question

HOW can you determine congruence and similarity?

Vocabulary

similar polygons
scale factor

Math Symbols
~ is similar to

 Common Core GPS

Content Standards
MCC8.G.4

Mathematical Practices
1, 2, 3, 4

 Collaborate Follow the steps to discover how the triangles are related.

1. Using a centimeter ruler, measure the sides of the two triangles. Then, use a protractor to measure the angles. Write the results in the table.

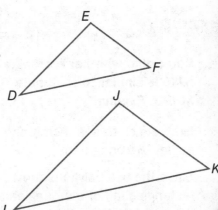

Figure	Side Length (cm)			Angle Measure (°)		
	DE	EF	FD	∠D	∠E	∠F
△EFD						
	LJ	JK	KL	∠L	∠J	∠K
△LJK						

2. Are the side lengths proportional? Explain.

_____

3. What do you notice about the angles of the two triangles?

Similar Polygons

Words If two polygons are similar, then
- their corresponding angles are congruent and
- the measures of their corresponding sides are proportional.

Model

$$\triangle ABC \sim \triangle XYZ$$

Symbols $\angle A \cong \angle X$, $\angle B \cong \angle Y$, $\angle C \cong \angle Z$, and $\frac{AB}{XY} = \frac{BC}{YZ} = \frac{AC}{XZ}$

Polygons that have the same shape are called **similar polygons**. In the Key Concept box, triangle *ABC* is similar to triangle *XYZ*. This is written as $\triangle ABC \sim \triangle XYZ$. The parts of similar figures that "match" are called corresponding parts.

Example

Watch | Tutor

1. **Determine whether rectangle *HJKL* is similar to rectangle *MNPQ*. Explain.**

First, check to see if corresponding angles are congruent.

Since the two polygons are rectangles, all of their angles are right angles. Therefore, all corresponding angles are congruent.

Common Error
Do not assume that two rectangles are similar just because their corresponding angles are congruent. Their corresponding sides must also be proportional.

Next, check to see if corresponding sides are proportional.

$$\frac{HJ}{MN} = \frac{7}{10} \qquad \frac{JK}{NP} = \frac{3}{6} \text{ or } \frac{1}{2} \qquad \frac{KL}{PQ} = \frac{7}{10} \qquad \frac{LH}{QM} = \frac{3}{6} \text{ or } \frac{1}{2}$$

Since $\frac{7}{10}$ and $\frac{1}{2}$ are not equivalent, the rectangles are *not* similar.

Show your work.

Got It? **Do this problem to find out.**

a. _____

a. Determine whether $\triangle ABC$ is similar to $\triangle XYZ$. Explain.

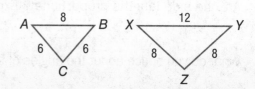

Find Missing Measures

Scale factor is the ratio of the lengths of two corresponding sides of two similar polygons. You can use the scale factor of similar figures to find missing measures.

Example

2. Quadrilateral *WXYZ* is similar to quadrilateral *ABCD*.

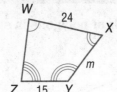

a. Describe the transformations that map *WXYZ* onto *ABCD*.

Since the figures are similar, they are not the same size. Choose two corresponding sides and determine what transformations will map one onto the other. A translation followed by a dilation will map $\overline{AB}$ onto $\overline{WX}$.

b. Find the missing measure.

Method 1

Find the scale factor from quadrilateral *ABCD* to quadrilateral *WXYZ*.

$$\text{scale factor: } \frac{YZ}{CD} = \frac{15}{10} \text{ or } \frac{3}{2}$$

So, a length on polygon *WXYZ* is $\frac{3}{2}$ times as long as the corresponding length on polygon *ABCD*. Let *m* represent the measure of $\overline{XY}$.

$m = \frac{3}{2}(12)$ Write the equation.

$m = 18$ Multiply.

Method 2

Set up a proportion to find the missing measure.

$\dfrac{XY}{BC} = \dfrac{YZ}{CD}$ Write the proportion.

$\dfrac{m}{12} = \dfrac{15}{10}$ $XY = m, BC = 12, YZ = 15, CD = 10$

$m \cdot 10 = 12 \cdot 15$ Find the cross products.

$10m = 180$ Simplify.

$m = 18$ Division Property of Equality

Got It? Do these problems to find out.

b. _____

Find each missing measure.

b. WZ

c. AB

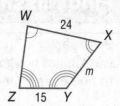

c. _____

Guided Practice

Determine whether each pair of polygons is similar. Explain. (Example 1)

1.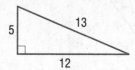

2.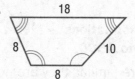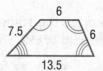

_____

_____

3. The two triangles are similar. (Example 2)

 a. Determine the transformations that map one figure onto the other.

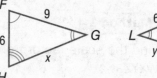

_____

 b. Find the missing side measures. _____

4. The two triangles are similar. (Example 2)

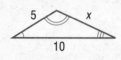

 a. Determine the transformations that map one figure onto the other.

_____

 b. Find the missing side measure. _____

5. @ **Building on the Essential Question** How does the scale factor of a dilation relate to the ratio of two of the corresponding sides of the preimage and the image?

_____

_____

Rate Yourself!

Are you ready to move on?
Shade the section that applies.

I have a few questions.

I'm ready to move on.

I have a lot of questions.

For more help, go online to access a Personal Tutor.

 Tutor

FOLDABLES Time to update your Foldable!

Independent Practice

eHelp

Go online for Step-by-Step Solutions

Determine whether each pair of polygons is similar. Explain. (Example 1)

1
3   7

4

8

Show your work.

2.
3 3   5 5

3 3   5 5

_____   _____
_____   _____
_____   _____

Each pair of polygons is similar. Determine the transformations that map one figure onto the other. Then find the missing side measures. (Example 2)

3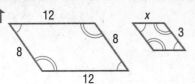
12

8   8

8

12

x

3

4.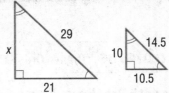
29

x

21

14.5

10

10.5

_____   _____
_____   _____

5. 🔵 **Persevere with Problems** The figures at the right are similar.

a. Find the area of both figures.

_____

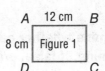
A 12 cm B

8 cm Figure 1

D   C

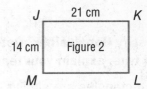
J   21 cm   K

14 cm   Figure 2

M   L

b. Compare the scale factor of the side lengths and the ratio of the areas.

_____
_____
_____

6. **STEM** The scale factor from the model of a human inner ear to the actual ear is 55:2. If one of the bones of the model is 8.25 centimeters long, how long is the actual bone in a human ear? _____

7. **Model with Mathematics** Refer to the graphic novel frame below. The brochure says that the rope is 500 feet long. Use the properties of similar triangles to find the parasailer's height above the water. _____

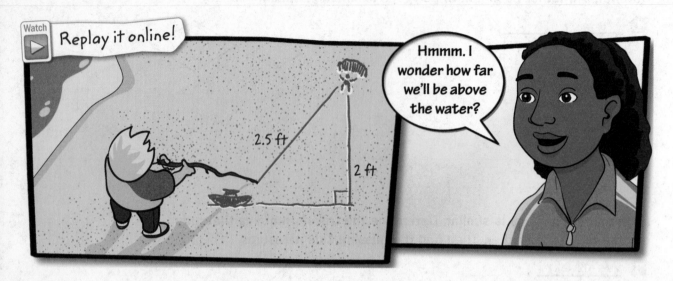

H.O.T. Problems Higher Order Thinking

8. **Persevere with Problems** Suppose two rectangles are similar with a scale factor of 2. What is the ratio of their areas? Explain. _____

_____

_____

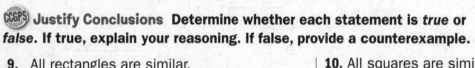**Justify Conclusions** Determine whether each statement is *true* or *false*. If true, explain your reasoning. If false, provide a counterexample.

9. All rectangles are similar.

_____

_____

_____

_____

10. All squares are similar.

_____

_____

_____

Georgia Test Practice

11. Quadrilateral *RSTU* is similar to quadrilateral *WXYZ*. Which of the following statements is *not* always true?

Ⓐ ∠*RST* ≅ ∠*WXY*

Ⓒ ∠*TUR* ≅ ∠*YZW*

Ⓑ $\frac{ST}{XY} = \frac{TU}{YZ}$

Ⓓ $\overline{RS} = \overline{WX}$

Extra Practice

Determine whether each pair of polygons is similar. Explain.

12.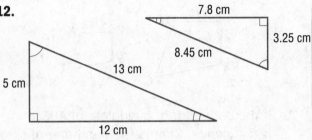

7.8 cm

3.25 cm

8.45 cm

13 cm

5 cm

12 cm

13.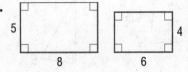

5   4

8   6

Homework
Help

→ As indicated by the arc marks, corresponding angles are congruent. Check to see if the corresponding sides are proportional.

$$\frac{3.25}{5} = \frac{8.45}{13} = \frac{7.8}{12}$$

The sides are proportional so the triangles are similar.

14. The two figures are similar. Determine the transformations that map one figure onto the other. Then find the missing side length.

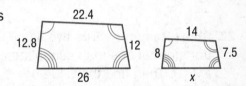

22.4

12.8   12

26

14

8   7.5

x

15. **Model with Mathematics**
Mrs. Henderson wants to build a fence around the rectangular garden in her backyard. In the scale drawing, the perimeter of the garden is 14 inches. If the actual length of $\overline{AB}$ is 20 feet, how many feet of fencing will she need?

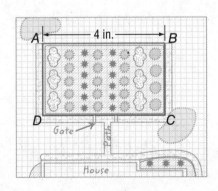

A |← 4 in. →| B

Gate

House

16. Isaiah is making a mosaic using different pieces of tile. The tiles shown at the right are similar. If the perimeter of the larger tile is 23 centimeters, what is the perimeter of the smaller tile?

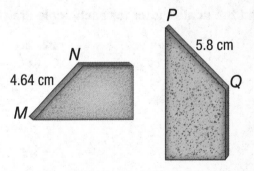

P

5.8 cm

N

4.64 cm

M

Q

17. Triangle *FGH* is similar to triangle *RST*.

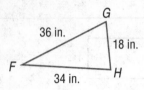
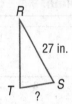

What is the length of $\overline{TS}$?

Ⓐ $13\frac{1}{2}$ inches   Ⓒ 24 inches

Ⓑ $22\frac{2}{3}$ inches   Ⓓ $25\frac{1}{2}$ inches

18. △*DEF* ∼ △*GHI*. What is the value of *GH* if *EF* = 6 meters, *DE* = 9 meters, and *HI* = 10 meters?

Ⓕ 5.4 m   Ⓗ 15 m

Ⓖ 9 m   Ⓘ 19.4 m

19. Quadrilateral *ABCD* is similar to quadrilateral *WXYZ*.

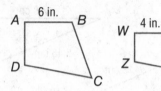

If the perimeter of quadrilateral *ABCD* is 54 inches, what is the perimeter of quadrilateral *WXYZ*?

Ⓐ 13.5 inches   Ⓒ 27 inches

Ⓑ 24 inches   Ⓓ 36 inches

20. **Short Response** The two figures are similar. Determine what transformations map quadrilateral *FGHJ* onto quadrilateral *LMNO*. Then find the value of *x*.

_____

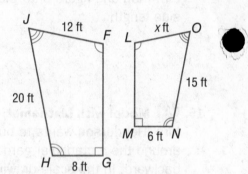

Find the scale factor for each scale drawing. MCC7.G.1

21. 6 in. = 12 ft _____

22. 20 cm = 10 m _____

23. 18 in. = 3 ft _____

24. 8 cm = 2.5 mm _____

25. 2 in. = 0.25 mi _____

26. 8 ft = 24 yd _____

Similar Triangles and Indirect Measurement

What You'll Learn

Scan the lesson. List two real-world scenarios in which you would use indirect measurement.

- _____
  _____

- _____
  _____

Essential Question

HOW can you determine congruence and similarity?

Vocabulary

indirect measurement

Common Core GPS

Content Standards
MCC8.G.5

Mathematical Practices
1, 3, 4, 7

Vocabulary Start-Up

Indirect measurement allows you to use properties of similar polygons to find distances or lengths that are difficult to measure directly.

Complete the graphic organizer. List three real-world examples in the Venn diagram for each method of measurement.

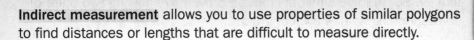

Direct Measurement
your arm

Indirect Measurement
Statue of Liberty's arm

Write the name of an object that could be measured by either

method. _____

Real-World Link

Shadows Legend says that Thales, the first Greek mathematician, was the first to determine the height of the pyramids by examining the shadows made by the Sun.

1. What appears to be true about the corresponding

   angles in the two triangles? _____

2. If the corresponding sides are proportional, what could you

   conclude about the triangles? _____

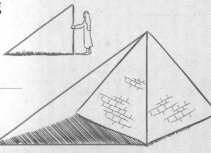

Lesson 5 Similar Triangles and Indirect Measurement **139**

Angle-Angle (AA) Similarity

Words   If two angles of one triangle are congruent to two angles of another triangle, then the triangles are similar.

Symbols   If $\angle A \cong \angle F$ and $\angle B \cong \angle G$, then $\triangle ABC \sim \triangle FGH$.

Model

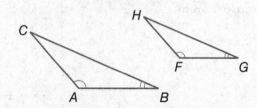

Work Zone

In the figure below, $\angle X \cong \angle P$ and $\angle Y \cong \angle Q$. If you extend the sides of each figure to form a triangle, you can see the two triangles are similar. So, triangle similarity can be proven by showing two pairs of corresponding angles are congruent.

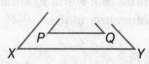
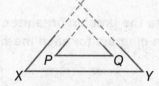

STOP and Reflect

What do you know about the third pair of angles in the triangle?

Example

Tutor

1. **Determine whether the triangles are similar. If so, write a similarity statement.**

Angle A and $\angle E$ have the same measure, so they are congruent. Since $180 - 62 - 48 = 70$, $\angle G$ measures 70°. Two angles of $\triangle EFG$ are congruent to two angles of $\triangle ABC$, so $\triangle ABC \sim \triangle EFG$.

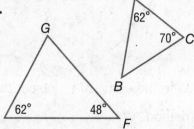

Show your work.

Got It?   Do this problem to find out.

a. _____

a.

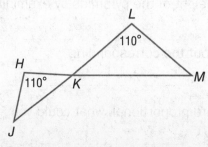

Use Indirect Measurement

One type of indirect measurement is *shadow reckoning*. Two objects and their shadows form two sides of right triangles. In shadow problems, you can assume that the angles formed by the Sun's rays with two objects at the same location are congruent. Since two pairs of corresponding angles are congruent, the two right triangles are similar. You can also use similar triangles that do not involve shadows to find missing measures.

Examples

2. **A fire hydrant 2.5 feet high casts a 5-foot shadow. How tall is a street light that casts a 26-foot shadow at the same time? Let *h* represent the height of the street light.**

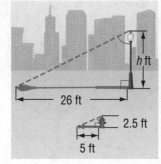

Shadow			**Height**
hydrant →	$\dfrac{5}{26}$	$=\dfrac{2.5}{h}$	← hydrant
street light →			← street light

$$5h = 26 \cdot 2.5 \qquad \text{Find the cross products.}$$

$$5h = 65 \qquad \text{Multiply.}$$

$$\frac{5h}{5} = \frac{65}{5} \qquad \text{Divide each side by 5.}$$

$$h = 13$$

The street light is 13 feet tall.

3. **In the figure at the right, triangle *DBA* is similar to triangle *ECA*. Ramon wants to know the distance across the lake.**

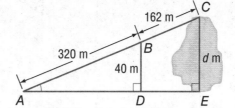

$$\frac{AB}{AC} = \frac{BD}{CE} \qquad \overline{AB} \text{ corresponds to } \overline{AC} \text{ and } \overline{BD} \text{ corresponds to } \overline{CE}.$$

$$\frac{320}{482} = \frac{40}{d} \qquad \text{Replace } AB \text{ with 320, } AC \text{ with 482, and } BD \text{ with 40.}$$

$$320d = 482 \cdot 40 \qquad \text{Find the cross products.}$$

$$\frac{320d}{320} = \frac{19,280}{320} \qquad \text{Multiply. Then divide each side by 320.}$$

$$d = 60.25$$

The distance across the lake is 60.25 meters.

b. _____

Show your work.

Got It? Do this problem to find out.

b. At the same time a 2-meter street sign casts a 3-meter shadow, a nearby telephone pole casts a 12.3-meter shadow. How tall is the telephone pole?

Guided Practice

Check ✓

Determine whether the triangles are similar. If so, write a similarity statement. (Example 1)

1.

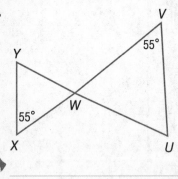

Show your work.

_____

_____

2.

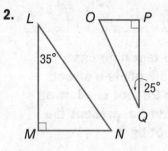

_____

_____

3. How tall is the tree? (Example 2) _____

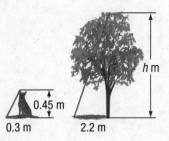

4. Find the distance from the house to the street light. (Example 3) _____

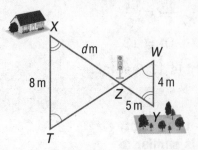

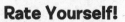

5. (e) **Building on the Essential Question** How do similar triangles make it easier to measure very tall objects?

_____

_____

_____

_____

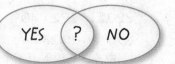

Rate Yourself!

Are you ready to move on? Shade the section that applies.

YES ? NO

For more help, go online to access a Personal Tutor.

Tutor

Independent Practice

Go online for Step-by-Step Solutions

Determine whether the triangles are similar. If so, write a similarity statement. (Example 1)

1.

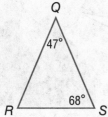
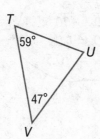

_____

_____

2.

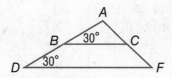

_____

_____

3. How tall is the building? (Example 2)

_____

50 ft   12.5 ft

h ft   50 ft

4. How tall is the taller flagpole? (Example 2)

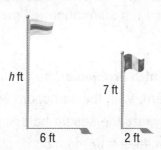

h ft   7 ft

6 ft   2 ft

5. How far is it from the log ride to the pirate ship? (Example 3) _____

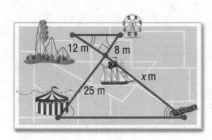

12 m   8 m

25 m   *x* m

6. Find the height of the brace. (Example 3)

_____

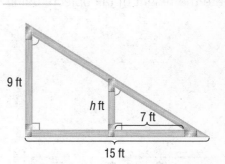

9 ft

h ft   7 ft

15 ft

7. **CCGPS** **Reason Abstractly** The Giant Wheel at Cedar Point in Ohio is one of the tallest Ferris wheels in the country at 136 feet tall. If the Giant Wheel casts a 34-foot shadow, write and solve a proportion to find the height of a nearby man who casts a $1\frac{1}{2}$-foot shadow.

_____

_____

8. CCGPS **Find the Error** Sara is finding the height of the lighthouse shown in the diagram. Find her mistake and correct it.

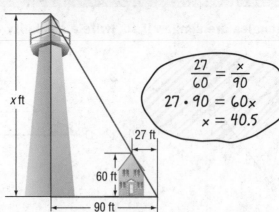

$$\frac{27}{60} = \frac{x}{90}$$
$$27 \cdot 90 = 60x$$
$$x = 40.5$$

_____

_____

_____

_____

9. CCGPS **Model with Mathematics** On a separate sheet of paper, draw two different triangles so that each one contains both of the angles shown. Then verify that they are similar by determining which transformation will map one onto the other.

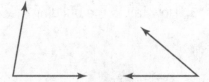

10. CCGPS **Persevere with Problems** You cut a square hole $\frac{1}{4}$ inch wide in a piece of cardboard. With the cardboard 30 inches from your face, the moon fits exactly into the square hole. If the moon is about 240,000 miles from Earth, estimate the moon's diameter.

_____

11. CCGPS **Identify Structure** What measures must be known in order to calculate the height of tall objects using shadow reckoning?

_____

_____

_____

✏️ **Georgia Test Practice**

12. Mila must determine the height of the statue to make a scale drawing of it. Mila is $4\frac{1}{2}$ feet tall, and her shadow is 6 feet long. At the same time, the statue's shadow is 12 feet long. What is the height of the statue?

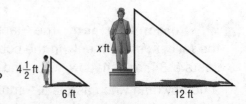

Ⓐ $8\frac{1}{4}$ ft

Ⓒ $13\frac{1}{2}$ ft

Ⓑ 9 ft

Ⓓ 24 ft

Extra Practice

13. What is the height of the tree? _90 ft_

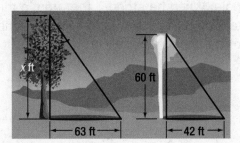

x ft

60 ft

← 63 ft →   ← 42 ft →

Homework Help

The triangles are similar. Write and solve a proportion.

$$\frac{63}{42} = \frac{x}{60}$$

$$63 \cdot 60 = 42x$$

$$90 = x$$

14. Find the distance across the river. _____

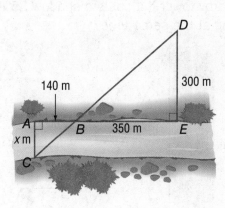

140 m

300 m

A   B   350 m   E

x m

C

15. About how long is the log that goes across the creeks? _____

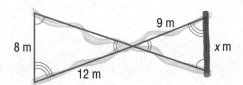

9 m

8 m   x m

12 m

16. How deep is the water 62 meters from the shore?

_____

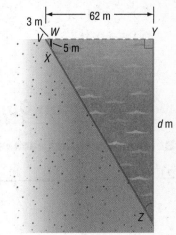

3 m   62 m

V   W   Y

5 m

X

d m

Z

17. In the diagram shown at the right, $\triangle ABC \sim \triangle EDC$.

a. Write a proportion that could be used to solve for the height h of the flag pole. _____

b. What information would you need to know in order to solve this proportion?

_____

_____

_____

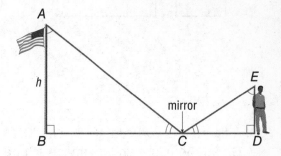

A

h

B   mirror   C   D

E

18. **CCGPS** **Model with Mathematics** A 78-inch-tall man casts a shadow that is 54 inches long. At the same time, a nearby building casts a 48-foot-long shadow. Write and solve a proportion to find the height of the building.

_____

19. Horatio is 6 feet tall and casts a shadow 3 feet long. What is the height in feet of a nearby tower if it casts a shadow 25 feet long at the same time?

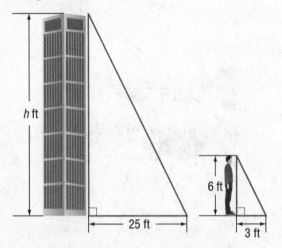

Ⓐ 12.5 feet   Ⓒ 125 feet

Ⓑ 50 feet   Ⓓ 500 feet

20. As shown below, Lenno used similiar triangles to find the height of a telephone pole. When he stood 7 feet from a mirror laying on the ground, he could see the top of the pole in the mirror.

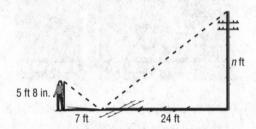

Which is closest to the height of the telephone pole?

Ⓕ 50 ft   Ⓗ 20 ft

Ⓖ 40 ft   Ⓘ 10 ft

 Common Core Review

Determine whether each pair of polygons is similar. Explain. MCC8.G.4

21.

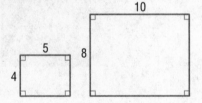

_____

_____

22.

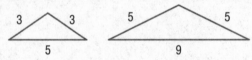

_____

_____

23. A figure has vertices $A(-3, 1)$, $B(0, 2)$, and $C(2, -2)$. Graph the figure and its image after a dilation with a scale factor of 3. Then give the coordinates of the final image. MCC8.G.3

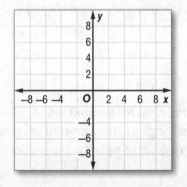

_____

Area and Perimeter of Similar Figures

What You'll Learn

Scan the lesson. Predict two things you will learn about the perimeter and area of similar figures.

- _____
- _____

Essential Question

HOW can you determine congruence and similarity?

CCGPS **Common Core GPS**

Content Standards
Extension of MCC8.G.4

Mathematical Practices
1, 2, 3, 4

Real-World Link

Watch ▶

Games Four square is a ball game played on a hard surface. The court is a 16-foot by 16-foot square divided into four equal squares.

1. Use the figure to draw a four square court. Divide each side in half. Draw lines to divide the court into four equal squares. Is each smaller square similar or congruent to the larger square? Explain. _____

2. What is the perimeter of the larger square drawn above? the smaller square? [ ] centimeters; [ ] centimeters

3. How is the perimeter of one of the smaller squares related to the perimeter of the larger square and the scale factor?

_____

Perimeter and Area of Similar Figures

Work Zone

Perimeter

Words If figure *B* is similar to figure *A* by a scale factor, then the perimeter of *B* is equal to the perimeter of *A* times the scale factor.

Symbols $\dfrac{\text{perimeter of}}{\text{figure } B} = \dfrac{\text{perimeter of}}{\text{figure } A} \cdot$ scale factor

Models

a

Figure A

Area

Words If figure *B* is similar to figure *A* by a scale factor, then the area of *B* is equal to the area of *A* times the square of the scale factor.

Symbols $\dfrac{\text{area of}}{\text{figure } B} = \dfrac{\text{area of}}{\text{figure } A} \cdot$ (scale factor)^2

b

Figure B

In similar figures, the perimeters are related by the scale factor, *k*. What about area? The area of one similar figure is equal to the area of the other similar figure times the *square* of the scale factor, or k^2.

Example

1. **Two rectangles are similar. One has a length of 6 inches and a perimeter of 24 inches. The other has a length of 7 inches. What is the perimeter of this rectangle?**

The scale factor is $\dfrac{7}{6}$. The perimeter of the original is 24 inches.

$x = 24\left(\dfrac{7}{6}\right)$ Multiply by the scale factor.

$x = \dfrac{\overset{4}{24}}{1}\left(\dfrac{7}{\underset{1}{6}}\right)$ Divide out common factors.

$x = 28$ Simplify.

So, the perimeter of the new rectangle is 28 inches.

Got It? Do this problem to find out.

a. Triangle *LMN* is similar to triangle *PQR*. If the perimeter of △*LMN* is 64 meters, what is the perimeter of △*PQR*?

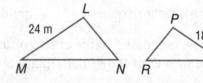

a. _____

Example

2. In a scale drawing, the perimeter of the garden is **64 inches**. The actual length of $\overline{AB}$ is **18 feet**. What is the perimeter of the actual garden?

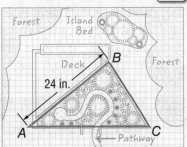

Step 1 The actual length is proportional to the length in the drawing with a ratio of $\frac{18\ ft}{24\ in.}$. Find the scale factor.

$\frac{18\ ft}{24\ in.} = \frac{216\ in.}{24\ in.}$ or $\frac{9}{1}$ Convert feet to inches and divide out units.

Step 2 Find the perimeter of the actual garden.

perimeter of garden = perimeter of drawing • scale factor

$P = 64 \cdot 9$ or 576 Substitute. Then simplify.

The perimeter of the actual garden is 576 inches or 48 feet.

Got It? Do this problem to find out.

b. Two quilting squares are shown. The scale factor is 3:2. What is the perimeter of square *TUVW*?

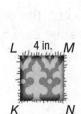

Show your work.

b. _____

Example

3. The Eddingtons have a 5-foot by 8-foot porch on the front of their house. They are building a similar porch on the back with double the dimensions. Find the area of the back porch.

The scale factor is 2.

The area of the front porch is (5)(8) or 40 square feet.

$x = 40(2)^2$ Multiply by the square of the scale factor.

$x = 40(4)$ or 160 Evaluate the power.

The back porch will have an area of 160 square feet.

Got It? Do this problem to find out.

c. _____

c. Malia is painting a mural on her bedroom wall. The image she is reproducing is 4.8 inches by 7.2 inches. If the dimensions of the mural are 10 times the dimensions of the image, find the area of the mural in square inches.

Guided Practice

Check ✓

For each pair of similar figures, find the perimeter of the second figure. (Example 1)

1.

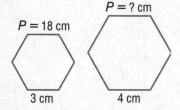

$P = 18$ cm $P = ?$ cm

3 cm   4 cm

2.

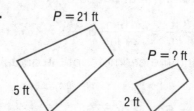

$P = 21$ ft $P = ?$ ft

5 ft   2 ft

Show your work.

3. Julie is enlarging a digital photograph on her computer. The original photograph is 5 inches by 7 inches. If she enlarges the dimensions 1.5 times, what will be the perimeter and area of the new image? (Examples 2 and 3)

_____

4. Logan is flying a kite that is made up of three similar rectangles. The sides of the three rectangles are in the ratio 1:2:3. If the area of the smallest rectangle is 72 square inches, what are the areas of the other two rectangles? (Example 3) _____

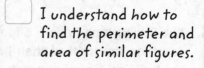

Rate Yourself!

☐ I understand how to find the perimeter and area of similar figures.

▶▶ Great! You're ready to move on!

5. **Building on the Essential Question** If you know two figures are similar and you are given the area of both figures, how can you determine the scale factor of the similarity?

_____

_____

☐ I still have some questions about the perimeter and area of similar figures.

 No Problem! Go online to access a Personal Tutor.

Independent Practice

 Go online for Step-by-Step Solutions

For each pair of similar figures, find the perimeter of the second figure.
(Example 1)

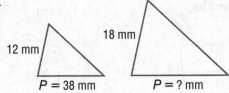

12 mm   18 mm

$P = 38$ mm $P = ?$ mm

2.

8.4 in.   6.3 in.

$P = 19.4$ in. $P = ?$ in.

 Show your work.

3. The city of Brice is planning to build a skate park. An architect designed the area shown at the right. In the plan, the perimeter of the park is 80 inches. If the actual length of $\overline{WX}$ is 50 feet, what will be the perimeter of the actual skate park? (Example 2) _____

_____

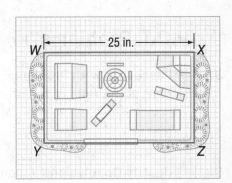

4. A child's desk is made so that the dimensions are two-thirds the dimensions of a full-size adult desk. Suppose the top of the full-size desk measures 54 inches long by 36 inches wide. What is the perimeter and area of the top of the child's desk? (Examples 2 and 3)

_____

_____

5. Theo is constructing a miniature putting green in his backyard. He wants it to be similar to a putting green at the local golf course, but one third the dimensions. The area of the putting green at the golf course is 1,134 square feet. What will be the area of the putting green Theo constructs?

6. Craig is making a model version of his neighborhood that uses model trains. The ratio of the model train to the actual train is 1:64. His neighborhood covers an area of 200,704 square feet. What will be the area of the model neighborhood?

_____

7. **CCGPS** **Identify Structure** Complete the graphic organizer to compare how the scale factor affects the side lengths, perimeter, and area of similar rectangles.

If the scale factor is...	Multiply the ...			
	Length by	Width by	Perimeter by	Area by
2				
4				
0.5				
$\frac{2}{3}$				
k				

H.O.T. Problems Higher Order Thinking

8. **CCGPS** **Persevere with Problems** Two circles have circumferences of π and 3π. What is the ratio of the area of the circles? the diameters? the radii?

_____

9. **CCGPS** **Justify Conclusions** A company wants to reduce the dimensions of its logo from 6 inches by 4 inches to 3 inches by 2 inches to use on business cards. Robert thinks that the new logo is $\frac{1}{4}$ the size of the original logo. Denise thinks that is $\frac{1}{2}$ of the original size. Explain their thinking to a classmate. _____

_____

_____

Georgia Test Practice

10. Two rectangular pieces of wood are similar. The ratio of the perimeters of the two pieces is 2:3. If the area of the smaller piece is 12 square inches, what is the area of the larger piece?

  Ⓐ 8 in^2

  Ⓑ 18 in^2

  Ⓒ 27 in^2

  Ⓓ 36 in^2

Extra Practice

For each pair of similar figures, find the unknown perimeter.

11.

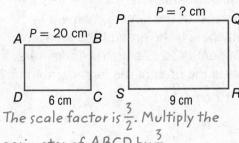

Homework Help →

The scale factor is $\frac{3}{2}$. Multiply the

perimeter of ABCD by $\frac{3}{2}$.

$P = 20 \cdot \frac{3}{2}$ or 30

__30 cm_____

12.

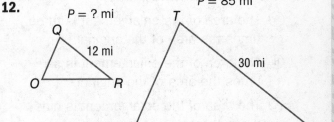

_____

13. For your birthday party, you make a map to your house on a 3-inch-wide by 5-inch-long index card. What will be the perimeter and area of your map if you use a copier to enlarge it so it is 8 inches long?

_____

14. A company wants to reduce the dimensions of its logo by one fourth to use on business cards. If the area of the original logo is 4 square inches, what is the area of the logo that will be used on the business cards?

_____

15. Two picture frames are similar. The ratio of the perimeters of the two pieces is 3:5. If the area of the smaller frame is 108 square inches, what

is the area of the larger frame? _____

16. **CCCPS** **Persevere with Problems** Mr. James is enlarging a logo for printing on the back of a T-shirt. He wants to enlarge a logo that is 3 inches by 5 inches so that the dimensions are 3 times larger than the original. How many times as large as the original logo will the area of the printing be?

_____

Georgia Test Practice

17. A photograph is enlarged to three times the size of the original. Which of the following statements is true?

Ⓐ The area of the enlargement is three times the area of the original.

Ⓑ The area of the enlargement is six times the area of the original.

Ⓒ The area of the enlargement is nine times the area of the original.

Ⓓ The area of the enlargement is twelve times the area of the original.

18. Kaitlyn made two ornaments in the shape of similar triangles. The perimeter of the smaller ornament is 9 inches and the perimeter of the larger ornament is 12 inches. If the area of the smaller ornament is 22.5 square centimeters, what is the area of the larger ornament?

Ⓕ 12 cm²

Ⓖ 16 cm²

Ⓗ 30 cm²

Ⓘ 40 cm²

19. Short Response A smaller copy of the 3-foot by 5-foot school flag at Brook Park Middle School is being made to appear on the front of the students' homework agenda books. The dimensions of the copy are to be $\frac{1}{6}$ of the school flag. How many times larger is the area of the flag than the area of the copy? _____

 Common Core Review

Graph each figure with the given vertices and its image after the indicated transformation. MCC8.G.3

20. $\overline{XY}$: $X(1, 1)$, $Y(-2, -3)$
translation of 1 unit right and 3 units up

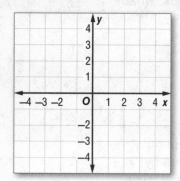

21. $\triangle ABC$: $A(0, -1)$, $B(0, 3)$, $C(3, 3)$
90° clockwise rotation about the origin

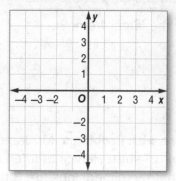

22. Omaha, Nebraska, and Sioux City, Iowa, are 90 miles apart.

If the distance on the map is $1\frac{1}{2}$ inches, find the scale of the map. MCC7.G.1

21ST CENTURY CAREER
in Car Design

Car Designer

Do you like drawing? Are you technical and precise in your drawings? You should consider a career as a car designer. Car designers use Computer Aided Design to create technical drawings that are used in manufacturing and construction. Information from architects and engineers is used to create highly specialized drawings that show how to construct everything from a nightstand to the space shuttle.

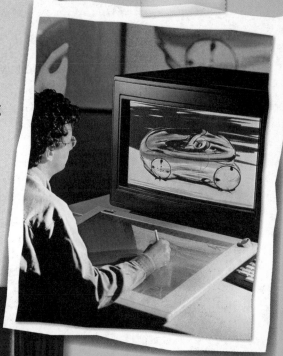

College & Career READINESS

Explore college and careers at ccr.mcgraw-hill.com

Is This the Career for You?

Are you interested in a career as a car designer? Take some of the following courses in high school.

◆ Geometry
◆ Mechanical Drawing
◆ Computer Graphics
◆ Design

Turn the page to find out how math relates to a career in Car Design.

Drive Yourself to Success

Use the information on the drawing to solve each problem.

1. What transformation maps the drawing to the actual car? _____

2. Are the views of the drawing of the car similar to views of the actual car? Explain.

   _____

   _____

3. If the scale factor is $\frac{1}{25}$, find the following:

   a. the length of the actual car _____

   b. the distance from the front wheel to the rear wheel of the actual car _____

4. If the actual height of the car is 60 inches, what is y? _____

5. If $x = 2\frac{4}{5}$ inches, what is the actual distance between the tires on the car?

   _____

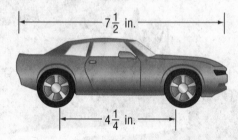

$7\frac{1}{2}$ in.

$4\frac{1}{4}$ in.

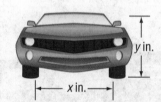

y in.

x in.

Career Project

It's time to update your career portfolio! Describe the features that you, as a car designer, would include in a new car design. Determine whether these features already exist in cars today.

_____

_____

_____

_____

_____

_____

_____

List several challenges associated with this career.

• _____

• _____

• _____

• _____

• _____

Vocabulary Check

Reconstruct the vocabulary word and definition from the letters under the grid. The letters for each column are scrambled directly under that column.

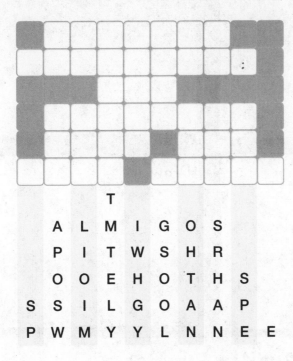

```
                  T
         A  L  M  I  G  O  S
         P  I  T  W  S  H  R
         O  O  E  H  O  T  H  S
         S  S  I  L  G  O  A  A  P
         P  W  M  Y  Y  L  N  N  E  E
```

Complete each sentence using vocabulary from the chapter.

1. Two figures are _____ if one can be obtained from the other by a series of rotations, reflections, or translations.

2. _____ uses properties of similar polygons to find distances or lengths that are difficult to measure directly.

3. The parts of congruent figures that match are called

   _____.

4. Two figures are _____ if one can be obtained from the other by a series of transformations and dilations.

5. When a transformation is applied to a figure and then another transformation is applied to the image, the result is called

   a _____.

Use Your FOLDABLES

Use your Foldable to help review the chapter.

Tab 1	Congruent Figures
Draw	Draw
Draw	Draw
Tab 2	Similar Figures

Got it?

Triangle *ABC* has vertices *A*(0, 0), *B*(2, 4), *C*(6, 0). Match each image with the description of its transformation.

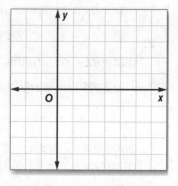

1. *A*'(0, 0), *B*'(2, −4), *C*'(6, 0)

2. *A*'(0, 0), *B*'(1, 2), *C*'(3, 0)

3. *A*'(0, 0), *B*'(4, −2), *C*'(0, −6)

4. *A*'(2, −6), *B*'(6, 2), *C*'(14, −6)

a. similar; a dilation with a scale factor of $\frac{1}{2}$

b. congruent; a 90° clockwise rotation about the origin

c. congruent; a reflection over the *x*-axis

d. similar; a translation of (*x* + 1, *y* − 3) followed by a dilation with a scale factor of 2

Problem Solving

1. Caryn found an old video game manual that showed characters that looked like the figures shown at the right. Are the two figures congruent? If so, describe the transformations that will map figure A onto figure B. If not, explain why not. (Lesson 1)

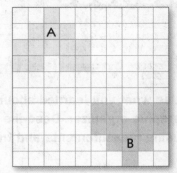

_____

_____

2. In the art design shown, △BGY ≅ △MGK. (Lessons 1 and 2)

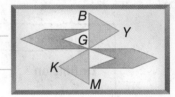

a. Determine which transformation(s) maps △MGK onto △BGY.

_____

b. If m∠B = 55°, find m∠M. _____

3. A 36-foot tree casts a 9-foot shadow at the same time a building casts a 15-foot shadow. How tall is the building? (Lesson 5) _____

4. A building casts an 18.6-foot shadow. How tall is the building if a 10-foot tall sculpture nearby casts a 6-foot shadow? (Lesson 5) _____

5. You have a digital print of your vacation that is 4 inches by 6 inches. You want to enlarge the dimensions by a scale factor of 2 to give to your grandparents. Your grandmother reduces the dimensions of her photo by a scale factor of 0.375 to put into her wallet. What will be the perimeter and area of the final image? (Lesson 6)

_____

Reflect

Use what you learned about congruence and similarity to complete the graphic organizer. Describe how you would show congruence or similarity using measurements and transformations.

Essential Question

HOW can you determine congruence and similarity?

Congruence	Similarity
Definition	**Definition**

Measurements	Transformations	Measurements	Transformations

Answer the Essential Question. HOW can you determine congruence and similarity?

UNIT 2

CCGPS **Exponents**

Essential Question

HOW can mathematical ideas be represented?

Chapter 3
Real Numbers

Rational numbers can be used to approximate the value of irrational numbers. In this chapter, you will perform operations on monomials and numbers written in scientific notation. You will then use rational approximations to estimate roots and to compare real numbers.

Chapter 4
Equations in One Variable

Linear equations in one variable can have one solution, infinitely many solutions, or no solutions. In this chapter, you will write and solve two-step equations and solve equations with variables on both sides.

Chapter 3
Real Numbers

Essential Question

WHY is it helpful to write numbers in different ways?

Common Core GPS

Content Standards
MCC8.NS.1, MCC8.NS.2, MCC8.EE.1, MCC8.EE.2, MCC8.EE.3, MCC8.EE.4

Mathematical Practices
1. 3, 4, 5, 6, 7, 8

Math in the Real World

Space The average distance from Earth to the Moon is about 384,403 kilometers. The Sun is the closest star to Earth and is about 150 million kilometers away. The next closest star is Proxima Centauri which is about 4.22 light years away from Earth.

A light year is defined as 9,461 billion kilometers. Find and label the distance in kilometers from Earth to Proxima Centauri.

FOLDABLES® Study Organizer

1 Cut out the correct Foldable from the FL pages in the back of this book.

2 Place your Foldable on the Key Concept page toward the end of this chapter.

3 Use the Foldable throughout this chapter to help you learn about real numbers.

Vocabulary

base	perfect cube	repeating decimal
cube root	perfect square	scientific notation
exponent	power	square root
irrational number	radical sign	terminating decimal
monomial	rational number	

Use a Mnemonic Device

When a mathematical expression has a combination of operations, the order of operations tells you which operation to perform first. How can you remember the orders easily? A mnemonic device is a verse or phrase to help you remember something.

In this case, it is *Please Excuse My Dear Aunt Sally*. On each rung of the ladder, fill in the operation that the mnemonic device represents. Then evaluate the numerical expression step-by-step.

$$3(5 - 15)^2 - 7 \cdot 3 + 24 \div 6$$

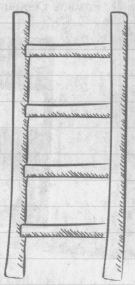

Please _____

Excuse _____

My Dear _____

Aunt Sally _____

 **Are You Ready?**

Try the Quick Check below.
Or, take the Online Readiness Quiz.

Quick Review CCGPS

Common Core Review MCC7.NS.2

Example 1

Find 5 • 4 • 5 • 4 • 5.

$5 \cdot 4 \cdot 5 \cdot 4 \cdot 5 = 4 \cdot 4 \cdot 5 \cdot 5 \cdot 5$
$= (4 \cdot 4) \cdot (5 \cdot 5 \cdot 5)$
$= 16 \cdot 125$
$= 2,000$

Example 2

Find the prime factorization of 60.

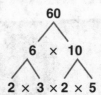

The prime factorization of 60 is
$2 \times 2 \times 3 \times 5$.

Quick Check

Simplify Expressions Find each product.

1. $2 \cdot 2 \cdot 4 \cdot 4 \cdot 4 =$ _____

 Show your work.

2. $(-8)(-8)(5)(5)(-8) =$ _____

3. The students at Hampton Middle School raised 8 • 8 • 2 • 8 • 2 dollars to help build a new community center. How much money did they raise?

_____

Prime Factorization Find the prime factorization of each number.

4. 36 _____

5. 24 _____

6. 18 _____

7. 100 _____

8. 121 _____

9. −42 _____

How Did You Do? Which problems did you answer correctly in the Quick Check? Shade those exercise numbers below.

① ② ③ ④ ⑤ ⑥ ⑦ ⑧ ⑨

Rational Numbers

What You'll Learn

Scan the lesson. Write the definitions of terminating decimal and repeating decimal.

- _____
  _____

- _____
  _____

Vocabulary Start-Up

Numbers that can be written as a comparison of two integers, expressed as a fraction, are called **rational numbers**.

Complete the graphic organizer.

Examples

Percent

Decimal

Rational Number

Define in your own words

_____

_____

Examples

Fraction

Mixed Numbers

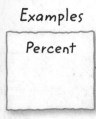

The root of the word *rational* is *ratio*. Describe the relationship between rational numbers and ratios. _____

_____

_____

 ## Real-World Link

During a recent regular season, a Texas Ranger baseball player had 126 hits and was at bat 399 times. Write a fraction in simplest form to represent the ratio of the number of hits to the number of at bats.

Essential Question

WHY is it helpful to write numbers in different ways?

Vocabulary

rational number
repeating decimal
terminating decimal

Common Core GPS

Content Standards
MCC8.NS.1
Mathematical Practices
1, 3, 4, 6, 7, 8

Rational Numbers

Words	A rational number is a number that can be written as the ratio of two integers in which the denominator is not zero.
Symbols	$\frac{a}{b}$, where a and b are integers and $b \neq 0$
Model	

Work Zone

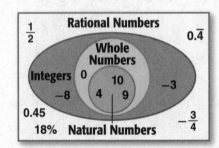

Rational Numbers

$\frac{1}{2}$ $0.\overline{4}$

Whole Numbers

Integers   0   10   −3

−8   4   9

0.45

18%   **Natural Numbers**   −$\frac{3}{4}$

Bar Notation

Bar notation is often used to indicate that a digit or group of digits repeats. The bar is placed above the repeating part. To write 8.636363... in bar notation, write 8.$\overline{63}$, not 8.$\overline{6}$ or 8.$\overline{636}$. To write 0.3444... in bar notation, write 0.3$\overline{4}$, not 0.$\overline{34}$.

Every rational number can be expressed as a decimal by dividing the numerator by the denominator. The decimal form of a rational number is called a **repeating decimal**. If the repeating digit is zero, then the decimal is a **terminating decimal**.

Rational Number	Repeating Decimal	Terminating Decimal
$\frac{1}{2}$	0.5000...	0.5
$\frac{2}{5}$	0.400...	0.4
$\frac{5}{6}$	0.833...	does not terminate

Examples

 Tutor

Write each fraction or mixed number as a decimal.

1. $\frac{5}{8}$

$\frac{5}{8}$ means $5 \div 8$.

$$
\begin{array}{r}
0.625 \\
8\overline{)5.000} \\
-48 \\
\hline
20 \\
-16 \\
\hline
40 \\
-40 \\
\hline
0
\end{array}
$$

Divide 5 by 8.

2. $-1\frac{2}{3}$

$-1\frac{2}{3}$ can be rewritten as $\frac{-5}{3}$.

Divide 5 by 3 and add a negative sign.

The mixed number $-1\frac{2}{3}$ can be written as $-1.\overline{6}$.

$$
\begin{array}{r}
1.6... \\
3\overline{)5.0} \\
-3 \\
\hline
20 \\
-18 \\
\hline
2
\end{array}
$$

Show your work.

a. _____

b. _____

c. _____

d. _____

Got It? Do these problems to find out.

a. $\frac{3}{4}$

b. $-\frac{2}{9}$

c. $4\frac{13}{25}$

d. $3\frac{1}{11}$

Example Tutor

3. **In a recent season, St. Louis Cardinals first baseman Albert Pujols had 175 hits in 530 at bats. To the nearest thousandth, find his batting average.**

To find his batting average, divide the number of hits, 175, by the number of at bats, 530.

175 ÷ 530 [ENTER] 0.3301886792

Look at the digit to the right of the thousandths place. Since 1 < 5, round down.

Albert Pujols's batting average was 0.330.

Got It? Do this problem to find out.

e. In a recent season, NASCAR driver Jimmie Johnson won 6 of the 36 total races held. To the nearest thousandth, find the part of races he won.

e. _____

Examples Tutor

4. **Write 0.45 as a fraction.**

$0.45 = \dfrac{45}{100}$ 0.45 is 45 hundredths.

$\quad\ \ = \dfrac{9}{20}$ Simplify.

5. **Write $0.\overline{5}$ as a fraction in simplest form.**

Assign a variable to the value $0.\overline{5}$. Let $N = 0.555...$. Then perform operations on N to determine its fractional value.

$N = 0.555...$

$10(N) = 10(0.555...)$ Multiply each side by 10 because 1 digit repeats.

$10N = 5.555...$ Multiplying by 10 moves the decimal point 1 place to the right.

$-N = 0.555...$ Subtract $N = 0.555...$ to eliminate the repeating part.

$\overline{9N = 5}$ Simplify.

$N = \dfrac{5}{9}$ Divide each side by 9.

The decimal $0.\overline{5}$ can be written as $\dfrac{5}{9}$.

6. Write $2.\overline{18}$ as a mixed number in simplest form.

Assign a variable to the value $2.\overline{18}$. Let $N = 2.181818...$. Then perform operations on N to determine its fractional value.

$$N = 2.181818...$$

$$100(N) = 100(2.181818...)$$

Multiply each side by 100 because 2 digits repeat.

$$100N = 218.181818$$

Multiplying by 100 moves the decimal point 2 places to the right.

$$-N = 2.181818...$$

Subtract $N = 2.181818...$ to eliminate the repeating part.

$$99N = 216$$

Simplify.

$$N = \frac{216}{99} \text{ or } 2\frac{2}{11}$$

Divide each side by 99. Simplify.

The decimal $2.\overline{18}$ can be written as $2\frac{2}{11}$.

 Show your work.

Got It? Do these problems to find out.

Write each decimal as a fraction or mixed number in simplest form.

f. _____

g. _____

    f. -0.14 **g.** $0.\overline{27}$

Guided Practice

 Check ✓

Write each fraction or mixed number as a decimal. (Examples 1 and 2)

1. $\frac{9}{16} =$ _____   **2.** $-1\frac{29}{40} =$ _____   **3.** $4\frac{5}{6} =$ _____

4. Monica won 7 of the 16 science competitions she entered. To the nearest thousandth, find her winning average. (Example 3) _____

Write each decimal as a fraction or mixed number in simplest form. (Examples 4–6)

5. $0.32 =$ _____   **6.** $-0.\overline{7} =$ _____

Rate Yourself!

I understand how to write a repeating decimal as a fraction.

7. **Building on the Essential Question** How can you determine if a number is a rational number?

_____

_____

For more help, go online to access a Personal Tutor.

 Tutor

Extra Practice

20. Write $\frac{5}{9}$ as a decimal. $0.\overline{5}$

$$
\begin{array}{r}
0.55 \\
9\overline{)5.00} \\
-45 \\
\overline{50} \\
-45 \\
\overline{5...}
\end{array}
$$

Homework Help →

21. Write $7.\overline{15}$ as a mixed number in simplest form. $7\frac{5}{33}$

$$N = 7.151515...$$
$$100(N) = 100(7.151515...)$$
$$100N = 715.151515...$$
$$\underline{-N = 7.151515...}$$
$$99N = 708$$
$$N = \frac{708}{99} \text{ or } 7\frac{5}{33}$$

CCGPS Identify Repeated Reasoning Write each fraction or mixed number as a decimal.

22. $\frac{4}{5} =$ _____

23. $5\frac{5}{16} =$ _____

24. $-6\frac{13}{15} =$ _____

Write each decimal as a fraction or mixed number in simplest form.

25. $-1.55 =$ _____

26. $3.\overline{8} =$ _____

27. $-0.\overline{09} =$ _____

Write the rainfall amount for each day as a fraction or mixed number.

28. Friday _____

29. Saturday _____

30. Sunday _____

Day	Rainfall (in.)
Friday	0.08
Saturday	2.4
Sunday	0.035

31. The table shows three popular flavors according to the results of a survey. What is the decimal value of those who liked vanilla, chocolate, or strawberry? Round to the nearest hundredth. _____

Flavor	Fraction
Vanilla	$\frac{3}{10}$
Chocolate	$\frac{1}{11}$
Strawberry	$\frac{1}{18}$

Georgia Test Practice

32. Short Response The table shows the number of free throws each player made during the last basketball season.

Player	Free Throws Made	Free Throws Attempted
Felisa	18	20
Morgan	13	24
Yasmine	15	22
Gail	10	14

Write the fraction of free throws made in simplest form for each player.

_____

_____

33. Short Response Write each fraction from Exercise 32 as a decimal. Round to the nearest thousandth if necessary.

_____

_____

34. While shopping for a new pair of jeans, Janet notices the sign below.

SALE!

All jeans on this rack are $\frac{1}{3}$ off the original price! (Regularly priced $29.99)

Which of the following expressions can be used to estimate the total discount on a pair of jeans?

Ⓐ 0.033 × $30

Ⓑ 0.33 × $30

Ⓒ 1.3 × $30

Ⓓ 33.3 × $30

35. Which of the following is *not* an example of a rational number?

Ⓕ $\frac{-6}{11}$ Ⓗ 18%

Ⓖ 15   Ⓘ 4.23242526. . .

Common Core Review

Fill in each ◯ with >, <, or = to make a true statement. MCC6.NS.7

36. $2\frac{7}{8}$ ◯ 2.75

37. $\frac{-1}{3}$ ◯ $\frac{-7}{3}$

38. $\frac{5}{7}$ ◯ $\frac{4}{5}$

39. $3\frac{6}{11}$ ◯ $3.\overline{54}$

40. At the grocery store, Karen was comparing the unit price for two different packages of laundry detergent. One package was $0.0733 per ounce. The other package was $3.64 for 52 ounces. Which package had the lower unit price? Explain. MCC6.RP.2 _____

_____

Powers and Exponents

What You'll Learn

Scan the lesson. Write the definitions of power, base, and exponent.

- _____
  _____

- _____
  _____

 Real-World Link

Savings Yogi decided to start saving money by putting a penny in his piggy bank, then doubling the amount he saves each week. Use the questions below to find how much money Yogi will save in 8 weeks.

1. Complete the table below to find the amount Yogi saved each week and the total amount in his piggy bank.

Week	0	1	2	3	4	5	6
Weekly Savings	1¢	2¢					
Total Savings	1¢	3¢					

2. How many 2s are multiplied to find his savings in Week 4? ☐

   Week 5? ☐

3. How much money will Yogi save in Week 8? _____

4. Continue the table to find when he will have enough to buy a pair of shoes for $80. _____

Week	7	8	9	10	11	12
Weekly Savings						
Total Savings						

 Essential Question

WHY is it helpful to write numbers in different ways?

Vocab **Vocabulary**

power
base
exponent

CCGPS **Common Core GPS**

Content Standards
MCC8.EE.1
Mathematical Practices
1, 3, 4, 8

Write and Evaluate Powers

A product of repeated factors can be expressed as a **power**, that is, using an exponent and a base.

IKR

The **base** is the common factor.

$$\overbrace{2 \cdot 2 \cdot 2 \cdot 2}^{4 \text{ factors}} = 2^4$$

The **exponent** tells how many times the base is used as a factor.

Powers are read in a certain way.

	Read and Write Powers	
Power	**Words**	**Factors**
3^1	3 to the first power	3
3^2	3 to the second power or 3 squared	$3 \cdot 3$
3^3	3 to the third power or 3 cubed	$3 \cdot 3 \cdot 3$
3^4	3 to the fourth power or 3 to the fourth	$3 \cdot 3 \cdot 3 \cdot 3$
$\vdots$	$\vdots$	$\vdots$
3^n	3 to the nth power or 3 to the nth	$\underbrace{3 \cdot 3 \cdot 3 \cdot \ldots \cdot 3}_{n \text{ factors}}$

Examples

Tutor

Write each expression using exponents.

1. $(-2) \cdot (-2) \cdot (-2) \cdot 3 \cdot 3 \cdot 3 \cdot 3$

The base -2 is a factor 3 times, and the base 3 is a factor 4 times.

$(-2) \cdot (-2) \cdot (-2) \cdot 3 \cdot 3 \cdot 3 \cdot 3 = (-2)^3 \cdot 3^4$

2. $a \cdot b \cdot b \cdot a \cdot b$

Use the properties of operations to rewrite and group like bases together. The base a is a factor 2 times, and the base b is a factor 3 times.

$a \cdot b \cdot b \cdot a \cdot b = a \cdot a \cdot b \cdot b \cdot b$
$= a^2 \cdot b^3$

Got It? Do these problems to find out.

a. $\frac{1}{2} \cdot \frac{1}{2} \cdot \frac{1}{2} \cdot \frac{1}{2}$ **b.** $4 \cdot 4 \cdot 4 \cdot 5 \cdot 5$ **c.** $m \cdot m \cdot n \cdot n \cdot m$

Show your work.

a. _____

b. _____ $4^3 \cdot 3^2$

c. _____ $n^3 \cdot n^2$

Example

Tutor

3. Evaluate $\left(-\frac{2}{3}\right)^4$.

$$\left(-\frac{2}{3}\right)^4 = \left(-\frac{2}{3}\right) \cdot \left(-\frac{2}{3}\right) \cdot \left(-\frac{2}{3}\right) \cdot \left(-\frac{2}{3}\right) \quad \text{Write the power as a product.}$$

$$= \frac{16}{81} \quad \text{Multiply.}$$

Got It? Do these problems to find out.

d. 4^4 **e.** $(-2)^6$ **f.** $\left(\frac{1}{5}\right)^3$

Tutor

Example

4. The deck of a skateboard has an area of about $2^5 \cdot 7$ square inches. What is the area of the skateboard deck?

$$2^5 \cdot 7 = 2 \cdot 2 \cdot 2 \cdot 2 \cdot 2 \cdot 7 \quad \text{Write the power as a product.}$$

$$= (2 \cdot 2 \cdot 2 \cdot 2 \cdot 2) \cdot 7 \quad \text{Associative Property}$$

$$= 32 \cdot 7 \text{ or } 224 \quad \text{Multiply.}$$

The area of the skateboard deck is about 224 square inches.

Got It? Do this problem to find out.

g. A school basketball court has an area of $2^3 \cdot 3 \cdot 5^2 \cdot 7$ square feet. What is the area of a school basketball court?

Tutor

Examples

Evaluate each expression if $a = 3$ and $b = 5$.

5. $a^2 + b^4$

$$a^2 + b^4 = 3^2 + 5^4 \quad \text{Replace } a \text{ with 3 and } b \text{ with 5.}$$

$$= (3 \cdot 3) + (5 \cdot 5 \cdot 5 \cdot 5) \quad \text{Write the powers as products.}$$

$$= 9 + 625 \text{ or } 634 \quad \text{Add.}$$

6. $(a - b)^2$

$$(a - b)^2 = (3 - 5)^2 \quad \text{Replace } a \text{ with 3 and } b \text{ with 5.}$$

$$= (-2)^2 \quad \text{Perform operations in the parentheses first.}$$

$$= (-2) \cdot (-2) \text{ or } 4 \quad \text{Write the powers as products. Then simplify.}$$

Evaluate
Remember that to evaluate an expression means to find its value.

Show your work.

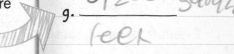

d. $4^4 = 4 \cdot 4 \cdot 4 \cdot 4$

e. $(-2)^6 = -2 \cdot -2 \cdot -2 \cdot -2 \cdot -2$

f. $\left(\frac{1}{5}\right)^3 = \frac{1}{5} \cdot \frac{1}{5} \cdot \frac{1}{5}$

g. 4200 square feet

h. _____

i. _____

Show your Work.

j. _____

Got It? Do these problems to find out.

Evaluate each expression if $c = -4$ and $d = 9$.

h. $c^3 + d^2$ **i.** $(c + d)^3$ **j.** $d^3 - (c^2 - 2)$

Guided Practice

Check

Write each expression using exponents. (Examples 1 and 2)

1. $(-11)(-11)(-11) =$ _____

2. $2 \cdot 2 \cdot 2 \cdot 3 \cdot 3 \cdot 3 =$ _____

3. $r \cdot s \cdot r \cdot r \cdot s \cdot s \cdot r \cdot r =$ _____

Evaluate each expression. (Example 3)

4. $2^6 =$ _____

5. $(-4)^4 =$ _____

6. $\left(\frac{1}{7}\right)^3 =$ _____

7. The table shows the average weights of some endangered mammals. What is the weight of each animal? (Example 4)

_____

Animal	Weight (lb)
Black bear	$2 \cdot 5^2 \cdot 7$
Key deer	$3 \cdot 5^2$
Panther	$2^3 \cdot 3 \cdot 5$

Evaluate each expression if $x = 2$ and $y = 10$. (Examples 5 and 6)

8. $x^2 + y^4 =$ _____

9. $(x^2 + y)^3 =$ _____

10. **Q** **Building on the Essential Question** How can I write repeated multiplication using powers? _____

_____

_____

_____

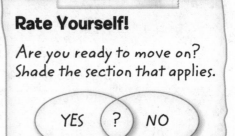
Rate Yourself!

Are you ready to move on? Shade the section that applies.

YES   ?   NO

For more help, go online to access a Personal Tutor.

Tutor

Extra Practice

17. Write $3 \cdot p \cdot p \cdot p \cdot 3 \cdot 3$ using exponents.

$\underline{3^3 \cdot p^3}$

$3 \cdot p \cdot p \cdot p \cdot 3 \cdot 3 = 3 \cdot 3 \cdot 3 \cdot p \cdot p \cdot p$
$\qquad\qquad\qquad\quad = 3^3 \cdot p^3$

18. Evaluate $x^3 + y^4$ if $x = -3$ and $y = 4$.

$\underline{229}$

$x^3 + y^4 = (-3)^3 + 4^4$
$\qquad = (-3) \cdot (-3) \cdot (-3) + 4 \cdot 4 \cdot 4 \cdot 4$
$\qquad = (-27) + 256$
$\qquad = 229$

Write each expression using exponents.

19. $\left(-\dfrac{5}{6}\right)\left(-\dfrac{5}{6}\right)\left(-\dfrac{5}{6}\right) =$ _____

20. $s \cdot (7) \cdot s \cdot (7) \cdot (7) =$ _____

21. $4 \cdot b \cdot b \cdot 4 \cdot b \cdot b =$

Evaluate each expression.

22. $k^4 \cdot m$, if $k = 3$ and $m = \dfrac{5}{6}$

23. $(c^3 + d^4)^2 - (c + d)^3$, if $c = -1$ and $d = 2$

Fill in each ◯ with <, >, or = to make a true statement.

24. $(6 - 2)^2 + 3 \cdot 4$ ◯ 5^2

25. $5 + 7^2 + 3^3$ ◯ 3^4

26. $\left(\dfrac{1}{2}\right)^4$ ◯ $\left(\dfrac{1}{4}\right)^2$

27. CCGPS **Multiple Representations** A square has a side length of s inches.

a. **Tables** Copy and complete the table showing the side length, perimeter, and area of the square on a separate piece of paper.

b. **Graphs** On a separate piece of grid paper, graph the ordered pairs (side length, perimeter) and (side length, area) on the same coordinate plane. Then connect the points for each set.

c. **Words** On a separate sheet of paper, compare and contrast the graphs of the perimeter and area of the square. Which graph is a line?

Side Length (in.)	Perimeter (in.)	Area (in²)
1	4	1
2		
3		
4		
5		
⋮		
10		

28. To find the volume of a cube, multiply its base, its height, and its width.

6 in.

What is the volume of the cube expressed as a power?

Ⓐ 6^2 in^3 Ⓒ 6^4 in^3

Ⓑ 6^3 in^3 Ⓓ 6^6 in^3

29. Short Response The volume of an ice cube in cubic millimeters is represented by the term 11^3. What is 11^3 in standard form? _____

30. What is the value of $x^2 - y^4$ if $x = -3$ and $y = -2$?

Ⓕ -7 Ⓗ 2

Ⓖ -2 Ⓘ 7

CCGPS Common Core Review

31. The table below shows the number of ants in an ant farm on different days. The number of ants doubles every ten days. MCC7.EE.3

Day	51	61	71
Number of Ants	320	640	1,280

a. How many ants were in the farm on Day 1? _____

b. How many ants will be in the farm on Day 91? _____

32. Nieves and her three friends are playing a video game. The table shows their scores at the end of the first round. MCC7.NS.1

a. What is the difference between the highest and lowest scores?

_____

b. By how many points is Nieves losing to Polly? _____

Player	Score
Nieves	−189
Polly	−142
Saul	230
Harry	−48

Add. MCC7.NS.1

33. $-12 + (-1$

35. $-5 + 6 =$ _____

Multiply and Divide Monomials

What You'll Learn

Scan the lesson. List two headings you would use to make an outline of the lesson.

- _____
  _____

- _____
  _____

Essential Question

WHY is it helpful to write numbers in different ways?

Vocabulary

monomial

Common Core GPS

Content Standards
MCC8.EE.1

Mathematical Practices
1, 3, 4, 7

Real-World Link

Arachnids Spiders in North America can range in size from 1 millimeter in length to 7.6 centimeters in length. Use the table to see how other metric measurements of length are related to the millimeter.

Unit of Length	Times Longer than a Millimeter	Written Using Powers
Millimeter	1	10^0
Centimeter	$1 \times 10 = \boxed{}$	10^1
Decimeter	$10 \times 10 = \boxed{}$	$10^1 \times 10^1 = 10^2$
Meter	$100 \times 10 = 1{,}000$	$10^2 \times 10^1 = 10^{\boxed{}}$
Dekameter	$1{,}000 \times 10 = 10{,}000$	$10^3 \times 10^1 = 10^{\boxed{}}$
Hectometer	$10{,}000 \times 10 = \boxed{}$	$10^4 \times 10^1 = 10^5$
Kilometer	$100{,}000 \times 10 = \boxed{}$	$10^5 \times 10^1 = 10^{\boxed{}}$

1. Look at the entries in the last column. What do you observe about the exponents of the factors and the exponent of the product for each entry? _____

_____

2. A *megameter* is $100{,}000{,}000 \times 10$ or $1{,}000{,}000{,}000$ times longer than a millimeter. Extend the pattern to write this number using powers. _____

_____

Product of Powers

Words To multiply powers with the same base, add their exponents.

Examples Numbers
$$2^4 \cdot 2^3 = 2^{4+3} \text{ or } 2^7$$

Algebra
$$a^m \cdot a^n = a^{m+n}$$

A **monomial** is a number, a variable, or a product of a number and one or more variables. You can use the Laws of Exponents to simplify monomials.

$$\underbrace{3^2}_{\text{2 factors}} \cdot \underbrace{3^4}_{\text{4 factors}} = \underbrace{(3 \cdot 3) \cdot (3 \cdot 3 \cdot 3 \cdot 3 \cdot)}_{\text{6 factors}} \text{ or } 3^6$$

Notice that the sum of the original exponents is the exponent in the final product.

Examples

Simplify using the Laws of Exponents.

1. $5^2 \cdot 5$

$5^2 \cdot 5 = 5^2 \cdot 5^1$ $5 = 5^1$

$= 5^{2+1}$ The common base is 5.

$= 5^3 \text{ or } 125$ Add the exponents. Simplify.

Check $5^2 \cdot 5 = (5 \cdot 5) \cdot 5$

$= 5 \cdot 5 \cdot 5$

$= 5^3 ✓$

2. $c^3 \cdot c^5$

$c^3 \cdot c^5 = c^{3+5}$ The common base is c.

$= c^8$ Add the exponents.

3. $-3x^2 \cdot 4x^5$

$-3x^2 \cdot 4x^5 = (-3 \cdot 4)(x^2 \cdot x^5)$ Commutative and Associative Properties

$= (-12)(x^{2+5})$ The common base is x.

$= -12x^7$ Add the exponents.

Got It? Do these problems to find out.

a. $9^3 \cdot 9^2$ **b.** $a^3 \cdot a^2$ **c.** $-2m(-8m^5)$

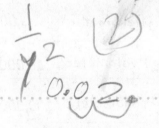

Show your work.

a. _____

b. _____

c. _____

Quotient of Powers

Words To divide powers with the same base, subtract their exponents.

Examples

Numbers
$$\frac{3^7}{3^3} = 3^{7-3} \text{ or } 3^4$$

Algebra
$$\frac{a^m}{a^n} = a^{m-n}, \text{ where } a \neq 0$$

Quiotiner of powers
Sure base Cosa,
Sub tract exponents

STOP and Reflect

Explain below why the Quotient of Powers rule cannot be used to simplify the expression $\frac{x^5}{y^3}$.

$Ex, \dfrac{a^7}{a^3} = a^{7-3}$

There is also a Law of Exponents for dividing powers with the same base.

$$\frac{5^7}{5^4} = \frac{\overbrace{5 \cdot 5 \cdot 5 \cdot \cancel{5} \cdot \cancel{5} \cdot \cancel{5} \cdot \cancel{5}}^{7 \text{ factors}}}{\underbrace{\cancel{5} \cdot \cancel{5} \cdot \cancel{5} \cdot \cancel{5}}_{4 \text{ factors}}} \text{ or } 5^3$$

Notice that the difference of the original exponents is the exponent in the final quotient.

Examples

Tutor

Simplify using the Laws of Exponents.

4. $\dfrac{4^8}{4^2}$

$\dfrac{4^8}{4^2} = 4^{8-2}$ The common base is 4.

$= 4^6$ or 4,096   Simplify.

5. $\dfrac{n^9}{n^4}$

$\dfrac{n^9}{n^4} = n^{9-4}$ The common base is n.

$= n^5$ Simplify.

6. $\dfrac{2^5 \cdot 3^5 \cdot 5^2}{2^2 \cdot 3^4 \cdot 5}$

$\dfrac{2^5 \cdot 3^5 \cdot 5^2}{2^2 \cdot 3^4 \cdot 5} = \left(\dfrac{2^5}{2^2}\right)\left(\dfrac{3^5}{3^4}\right)\left(\dfrac{5^2}{5}\right)$ Group by common base.

$= 2^3 \cdot 3^1 \cdot 5^1$ Subtract the exponents.

$= 8 \cdot 3 \cdot 5$ $2^3 = 8$

$= 120$ Simplify.

Got It? Do these problems to find out.

d. $\dfrac{5^7}{5^4}$

e. $\dfrac{x^{10}}{x^3}$

f. $\dfrac{12w^5}{2w}$

g. $\dfrac{3^4 \cdot 5^2 \cdot 7^5}{3^2 \cdot 5 \cdot 7^3}$

h. $\dfrac{5^6 \cdot 7^4 \cdot 8^3}{5^4 \cdot 7^2 \cdot 8^2}$

i. $\dfrac{(-2)^5 \cdot 3^4 \cdot 5^7}{(-2)^2 \cdot 3 \cdot 5^4}$

$3^2 \cdot 5 \cdot 7^2$
$9 \cdot 5 \cdot 49$

$5^2 \cdot 7^2 \cdot 8$

Show your work.

d. 5^3

e. x^7

f. $6w^4$

g. 22

h. 9800

i. $-27,000$

Example

Tutor

7. Hawaii's total shoreline is about 2^{10} miles long. New Hampshire's shoreline is about 2^7 miles long. About how many times longer is Hawaii's shoreline than New Hampshire's?

To find how many times longer, divide 2^{10} by 2^7.

$$\frac{2^{10}}{2^7} = 2^{10-7} \text{ or } 2^3 \qquad \text{Quotient of Powers}$$

Hawaii's shoreline is about 2^3 or 8 times longer.

Guided Practice

Check

Simplify using the Laws of Exponents. (Examples 1–6)

1. $4^5 \cdot 4^3 =$ _____

Show your work.

2. $-2a(3a^4) =$ _____

3. $\dfrac{y^8}{y^5} =$ _____

4. $\dfrac{24k^9}{6k^6} =$ _____

5. $\dfrac{2^2 \cdot 3^3 \cdot 4^5}{2 \cdot 3 \cdot 4^4} =$ _____

6. $\dfrac{(-3)^4 \cdot (-4)^3 \cdot 5^2}{(-3)^2 \cdot (-4) \cdot 5} =$ _____

7. The table shows the number of people worldwide that speak certain languages. How many times as many people speak French than Sicilian?

(Example 7) _____

Language	Total (millions)
French	2^6
Sicilian	2^2

8. 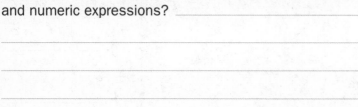 **Building on the Essential Question** How can I use the properties of integer exponents to simplify algebraic and numeric expressions? _____

_____

_____

_____

Rate Yourself!

Are you ready to move on?
Shade the section that applies.

YES ? NO

For more help, go online to access a Personal Tutor.

Tutor

FOLDABLES *Time to update your Foldable!*

Extra Practice

Simplify using the Laws of Exponents.

24. $(3x^8)(5x) =$ _15x⁹_

$$(3x^8)(5x) = 3 \cdot 5 \cdot x^8 \cdot x$$

> Homework Help →

$$= 15 \cdot x^{8+1}$$

$$= 15x^9$$

25. $\dfrac{h^7}{h^6} =$ h^1 or h

$$\dfrac{h^7}{h^6} = h^{7-6}$$

$$= h^1 \text{ or } h$$

26. $2g^2 \cdot 7g^6 =$ _____

27. $(8w^4)(-w^7) =$ _____

28. $(-p)(-9p^2) =$ _____

29. $\dfrac{2^9}{2} =$ _____

30. $\dfrac{36d^{10}}{6d^5} =$ _____

31. $\dfrac{5^3 \cdot 7^4 \cdot 10}{5 \cdot 7^4} =$ _____

32. $\dfrac{(-3)^2 \cdot 4^3 \cdot (-1)^8}{4 \cdot (-1)^5} =$ _____

33. **CCGPS** **Persevere with Problems** The figure at the right is composed of a circle and a square. The circle touches the square at the midpoints of the four sides.

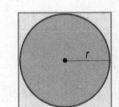

a. What is the length of one side of the square? _____

b. The formula $A = \pi r^2$ is used to find the area of a circle. The formula $A = 4r^2$ can be used to find the area of the square. Write the ratio of the area of the circle to the area of the square in simplest form.

_____

c. Complete the table.

Radius (units)	2	3	4	2r
Area of Circle (units²)	$\pi(2)^2$ or 4π			
Length of 1 Side of the Square	4			
Area of Square (units²)	4^2 or 16			
Ratio $\dfrac{\text{(Area of circle}}{\text{Area of square)}}$				

d. What can you conclude about the relationship between the areas of the circle and the square? _____

34. One meter is 10^3 times longer than one millimeter. One kilometer is 10^6 times longer than one millimeter. How many times longer is one kilometer than one meter?

Ⓐ 10^9 Ⓒ 10^3

Ⓑ 10^6 Ⓓ 10

35. Which of the following is equivalent to $\left(-\dfrac{2}{3}\right)^3$?

Ⓕ $-\dfrac{6}{9}$ Ⓗ $\dfrac{8}{27}$

Ⓖ $-\dfrac{8}{27}$ Ⓘ $\dfrac{6}{9}$

36. Short Response What is the area of the rectangle below?

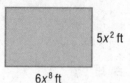

$5x^2$ ft

$6x^8$ ft

Common Core Review

Multiply or divide. MCC7.NS.2

37. $14(-2) = $ _____

38. $-20(-3) = $ _____

39. $-5(7) = $ _____

40. $-12 \div (-4) = $ _____

41. $63 \div (-7) = $ _____

42. $250 \div (-50) = $ _____

43. Three-fourths of a pan of lasagna is to be divided equally among 6 people. What part of the lasagna will each person receive? MCC6.NS.1

_____

44. The tallest mountain in the United States is Mount McKinley in Alaska. The elevation is about $2^2 \cdot 5 \cdot 10^3$ feet above sea level. What is the height of Mount McKinley? MCC6.EE.1

_____

Powers of Monomials

What You'll Learn

Scan the lesson. Predict two things you will learn about the Laws of Exponents.

- _____
  _____
  _____

- _____
  _____

 Essential Question

WHY is it helpful to write numbers in different ways?

 Common Core GPS

Content Standards
MCC8.EE.1

Mathematical Practices
1, 3, 4, 7

 ## Real-World Link

Aquariums The Marine Club at Westview Middle School purchased an aquarium. The aquarium is in the shape of a cube with a side length of 2^4 inches. Use the questions to find the amount of water the aquarium willl hold.

1. Write a multiplication expression to represent the volume of the aquarium. _____

2. Simplify the expression. Write as a single power of 2. ☐

3. Using 2^4 as the base, write the multiplication expression $2^4 \cdot 2^4 \cdot 2^4$ using an exponent. ☐

4. Explain why $(2^4)^3 = 2^{12}$. _____
   _____

5. Use a calculator to find the volume of the tank.
   ☐ cubic inches

6. One gallon of water is equal to 231 cubic inches. Write an expression to find how many gallons of water the tank will hold if it is filled to the top. $\dfrac{\boxed{}}{\boxed{}}$

7. How many gallons of water will the aquarium hold? Round your answer to the nearest gallon. ☐ gallons

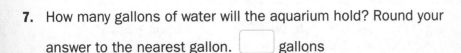

Power of a Power

Words To find the power of a power, multiply the exponents.

Examples

Numbers

$(5^2)^3 = 5^{2 \cdot 3}$ or 5^6

Algebra

$(a^m)^n = a^{m \cdot n}$

Work Zone

Power of a Power

one base, multiply

exponents

Ex. $(a^9)^7 = a^{35}$

ex. $(2^1 a^5 b^3)^2$

$2^{1 \cdot 2} \cdot a^{5 \cdot 2} \cdot b^{3 \cdot 2}$

$4 b^{11} b^6$

You can use the rule for finding the *product* of powers to discover another Law of Exponents for finding the *power* of a power.

$$\overbrace{(6^4)^5 = (6^4)(6^4)(6^4)(6^4)(6^4)}^{\text{5 factors}}$$

$$= 6^{4 + 4 + 4 + 4 + 4}$$ Apply the rule for the product of powers.

$$= 6^{20}$$

Notice that the product of the original exponents, 4 and 5, is the final power 20.

Examples

Simplify using the Laws of Exponents.

1. $(8^4)^3$

$(8^4)^3 = 8^{4 \cdot 3}$ Power of a Power

$\quad\quad = 8^{12}$ Simplify.

Show your work.

a. *2^{10}*

2. $(k^7)^5$

$(k^7)^5 = k^{7 \cdot 5}$ Power of a Power

$\quad\quad = k^{35}$ Simplify.

b. *w^{24}*

Got It? Do these problems to find out.

c. *3^{12}*

a. $(2^5)^2$ **b.** $(w^4)^6$ **c.** $[(3^2)^3]^2$

$2^{5 \cdot 2}$ *$w^{4 \cdot 6}$*   *$3^{2 \cdot 3 \cdot 2}$*

Power of a Product

Words   To find the power of a product, find the power of each factor and multiply.

Examples   Numbers

$(6x^2)^3 = (6)^3 \cdot (x^2)^3$ or $216x^6$

Algebra

$(ab)^m = a^m b^m$

Extend the power of a *power* rule to find the Laws of Exponents for the power of a *product*.

$$\overbrace{(3a^2)^5 = (3a^2)(3a^2)(3a^2)(3a^2)(3a^2)}^{\text{5 factors}}$$

$$= 3 \cdot 3 \cdot 3 \cdot 3 \cdot 3 \cdot a^2 \cdot a^2 \cdot a^2 \cdot a^2 \cdot a^2$$

$$= 3^5 \cdot (a^2)^5 \qquad \text{Write using powers.}$$

$$= 243 \cdot a^{10} \text{ or } 243a^{10} \qquad \text{Power of a Power}$$

> **Common Error**
> When finding the power of a power, do not add the exponents.
> $(8^4)^3 = 8^{12}$, not 8^7.

Examples

Tutor

Simplify using the Laws of Exponents.

3. $(4p^3)^4$

$$(4p^3)^4 = 4^4 \cdot p^{3 \cdot 4} \qquad \text{Power of a Product}$$

$$= 256p^{12} \qquad \text{Simplify.}$$

4. $(-2m^7 n^6)^5$

$$(-2m^7 n^6)^5 = (-2)^5 m^{7 \cdot 5} n^{6 \cdot 5} \qquad \text{Power of a Product}$$

$$= -32m^{35} n^{30} \qquad \text{Simplify.}$$

Got It?   Do these problems to find out.

d. $(8b^9)^2$

$8^2 b^{18}$

e. $(6x^5 y^{11})^4$

$6^4 x^{20} y^{44}$

f. $(-5w^2 z^8)^3$

$-5^3 w^6 z^{24}$

Show your work.

d. $64 b^{18}$

e. $1296 x^{20} y^{44}$

f. $-125 w^6 z^{24}$

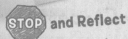

 Example

5. A magazine offers a special service to its subscribers. If they scan the square logo shown on a smartphone, they can receive special offers from the magazine. Find the area of the logo.

$A = s^2$	Area of a square
$A = (7a^4b)^2$	Replace s with $7a^4b$.
$A = 7^2(a^4)^2(b^1)^2$	Power of a Product
$A = 49a^8b^2$	Simplify.

 $7a^4b$

The area of the logo is $49a^8b^2$ square units.

Guided Practice

Check ✓

Simplify using the Laws of Exponents. (Examples 1–4)

1. $(3^2)^5 =$ _____

   Show your work.

2. $(h^6)^4 =$ _____

3. $[(2^3)^2]^3 =$ _____

4. $(7w^7)^3 =$ _____

5. $(5g^8k^{12})^4 =$ _____

6. $(-6r^5s^9)^2 =$ _____

7. The floor of the commons room at King Middle School is in the shape of a square with side lengths of x^2y^3 feet. New tile is going to be put on the floor of the room. Find the area of the floor. (Example 5)

_____

8. @ **Building on the Essential Question** How does the Product of Powers law apply to finding the power of a power?

_____

_____

Extra Practice

Simplify using the Laws of Exponents.

23. $(2^2)^7 = \underline{2^{14}}$

$(2^2)^7 = 2^{2 \cdot 7}$

$= 2^{14}$

[Homework Help →]

24. $(8v^9)^5 = \underline{32,768v^{45}}$

$(8v^9)^5 = 8^5 \cdot v^{9 \cdot 5}$

$= 32,768v^{45}$

25. $(3^4)^2 = \underline{\hspace{1.5cm}}$

26. $(m^8)^5 = \underline{\hspace{1.5cm}}$

27. $(z^{11})^5 = \underline{\hspace{1.5cm}}$

28. $[(4^3)^2]^2 = \underline{\hspace{1.5cm}}$

29. $[(2^3)^3]^2 = \underline{\hspace{1.5cm}}$

30. $(14y)^4 = \underline{\hspace{1.5cm}}$

Express the area of each square as a monomial.

31. _____

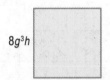

$8g^3h$

32. _____

$12d^6e^7$

Express the volume of each cube as a monomial.

33. _____

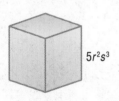

$5r^2s^3$

34. _____

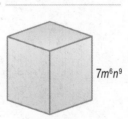

$7m^6n^9$

Simplify.

35. $(0.5k^5)^2 = \underline{\hspace{1.5cm}}$

36. $(0.3p^7)^3 = \underline{\hspace{1.5cm}}$

37. $\left(\frac{1}{4}w^5z^3\right)^2 = \underline{\hspace{1.5cm}}$

38. **CCGPS** **Persevere with Problems** A ball is dropped from the top of a building. The expression $4.9x^2$ gives the distance in meters the ball has fallen after x seconds. Write and simplify an expression that gives the distance in meters the ball has fallen after x^2 seconds. after x^3 seconds.

Georgia Test Practice

39. What is the volume of the cube shown below?

$8m^3$

Ⓐ $8m^3$ Ⓒ $64m^9$

Ⓑ $16m^5$ Ⓓ $512m^9$

40. Which expression has the same value as $81h^8k^6$?

Ⓕ $(9h^6k^4)^2$ Ⓗ $(6h^5k^3)^3$

Ⓖ $(9h^4k^3)^2$ Ⓘ $(3h^2k)^6$

41. Which expression is equivalent to $(2x^2)^4(5x^6)$?

Ⓐ $10x^{12}$ Ⓒ $10x^{14}$

Ⓑ $80x^{12}$ Ⓓ $80x^{14}$

42. Short Response Manny has four pieces of carpet in the shape of a square like the one shown. He wants to use them together to carpet a portion of his basement. What is the area of the space he can cover with the carpet? _____

$2x^2$ yards

 Common Core Review

Simplify using the Laws of Exponents. MCC8.EE.1

43. $6^4 \cdot 6^7 =$ _____

44. $18^3 \cdot 18^5 =$ _____

5. $(-3x^{11})(-6x^3) =$ _____

46. $(-9a^4)(2a^7) =$ _____

47. The table shows the heights of some United States waterfalls. What is the height of each waterfall? MCC6.EE.1

_____

_____

Waterfall	Height (ft)
Bridalveil (California)	$2^2 \cdot 5 \cdot 31$
Fall Creek (Tennessee)	2^8
Shoshone (Idaho)	$2^2 \cdot 53$

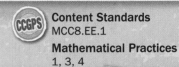

CCGPS Content Standards
MCC8.EE.1
Mathematical Practices
1, 3, 4

Case #1 Texting Trail

Lillian received a text about a concert. She forwarded the text to two of her friends. They each forwarded it to two more friends, and so on.

How many texts were sent at the 4th stage?

Understand *What are the facts?*

You know that each person at each stage sends a text to two people. You can use counters to represent the trail of texts sent.

Plan *What is your strategy to solve this problem?*

Use red counters to represent the texts in the first stage. Use yellow counters to show the texts sent at the second stage. Continue the pattern. Draw the counters representing the number of texts sent in the 4th stage.

Solve *How can you apply the strategy?*

1st stage
2nd stage
3rd stage
4th stage

There are ☐ counters in the 4th row. So, ☐ texts were sent during the 4th stage.

Check *Does the answer make sense?*

The number of texts at each stage is a power of 2. So, find 2^4.
Since $2^4 = 16$, the answer is correct. ✓

Analyze the Strategy

CCGPS Justify Conclusions At what stage would there be more than 1,000 texts sent? Explain.

_____

_____

Case #2 Green Mileage

A test of a hybrid car resulted in 4,840 miles driven using 88 gallons of gas.

At this rate, how many gallons of gas will this vehicle need to travel 1,155 miles?

Understand

Read the problem. What are you being asked to find?

I need to find _____.

Underline key words and values in the problem. What information do you know?

The hybrid car can travel _____ miles using _____ gallons of gas.

Is there any information that you do *not* need to know?

I do not need to know _____.

Plan

How do the facts relate to one another?

_____

Solve

Write and solve a proportion comparing miles to gallons. Let *g* represent the amount of gas needed to travel 1,155 miles.

$$\frac{\text{miles}}{\text{gallons}} \quad \frac{\boxed{}}{\boxed{}} = \frac{\boxed{}}{\boxed{}}$$

How many gallons of gas will the car use to travel 1,155 miles? $\boxed{}$

Check

Use information from the problem to check your answer.

_____

_____

Collaborate Work with a small group to solve the following cases. Show your work on a separate piece of paper.

Case #3 Class Trip

All of Mr. Bassett's science classes are going to the Natural History Museum. A tour guide is needed for each group of eight students. His classes have 28 students, 35 students, 22 students, 33 students, and 22 students.

How many tour guides are needed?

_____

Case #4 Gardening

Mrs. Lopez is designing her garden in the shape of a rectangle. The area of her garden is 2 times greater than the area of the rectangle shown.

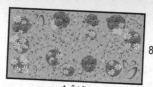

$8s^2$ ft

$4s^3t$ ft

Write the area of Mrs. Lopez's garden in simplest form.

_____

Case #5 Toothpicks

The figures to the right are made from toothpicks.

Figure 1   Figure 2   Figure 3   Figure 4

How many toothpicks would be needed to make the tenth figure?

_____

Circle a strategy below to solve the problem.
• Look for a pattern.
• Act it out.
• Determine reasonable answers.
• Make a table.

Case #6 Number Sense

Study the following sequence:

$1 - \frac{1}{2}, 1 - \frac{1}{2}, 1 - \frac{1}{3}, 1 - \frac{1}{4}, ..., 1 - \frac{1}{48}, 1 - \frac{1}{49}$, and $1 - \frac{1}{50}$

What is the product of all of the terms?

Mid-Chapter Check

Vocabulary Check

1. **CCGPS** **Be Precise** Define *power* using the words *base* and *exponent*. Give an example of a power and label the base and exponent. (Lesson 2)

   _____

   _____

   _____

2. Describe the Product of Powers rule. Give an example. (Lesson 3)

   _____

Skills Check and Problem Solving

3. Write $1\frac{7}{16}$ as a decimal. (Lesson 1) _____

Show your work.

4. Write $0.\overline{15}$ as a fraction in simplest form.

   (Lesson 1) _____

5. The mass of a baseball glove is $5 \cdot 5 \cdot 5 \cdot 5$ grams. Write the mass using exponents. Then find the value of the expression. (Lesson 2) _____

Simplify using the Laws of Exponents. (Lessons 3 and 4)

6. $2^3 a^7 \cdot 2a^3 =$ _____

7. $\dfrac{24y^4}{4y^2} =$ _____

8. $(2p^3 r^2)^3 =$ _____

9. **Georgia Test Practice** Which expression below has the same value as $5m^2$? (Lesson 2)

   Ⓐ $5m$

   Ⓑ $5 \cdot m \cdot m$

   Ⓒ $5 \cdot 5 \cdot m \cdot m$

   Ⓓ $5 \cdot m \cdot m \cdot m$

Negative Exponents

What You'll Learn

Scan the lesson. Predict two things you will learn about exponents that are not positive.

- _____
  _____

- _____
  _____

 Essential Question

WHY is it helpful to write numbers in different ways?

 Common Core GPS

Content Standards
MCC8.EE.1

Mathematical Practices
1, 3, 4, 7

 ## Real-World Link

Insects The table shows the approximate wing beats per minute for certain insects.

Insect	Wing Beats per Minute
house fly	10,000
small butterfly	100

1. Write a ratio in simplest form that compares the number of wing beats for a butterfly to a housefly. $\dfrac{\boxed{}}{\boxed{}}$

2. Write the ratio as a fraction with an exponent in the denominator and as a decimal. $\dfrac{\boxed{}}{\boxed{}}$; $\boxed{}$

3. Complete the 1ˢᵗ 4 rows of the table showing the exponential and standard forms of power of 10.

4. What operation is performed when you move down the table?

_____

5. What happens to the exponent?

_____

6. Extend the table to include the next three entries.

Exponential Form	Standard Form
10^3	
$10^{\boxed{}}$	100
10^1	
10^0	

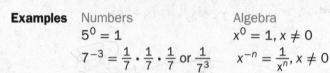

Key Concept → Zero and Negative Exponents

Words   Any nonzero number to the zero power is 1. Any nonzero number to the negative n power is the multiplicative inverse of its nth power.

Examples Numbers   Algebra

$$5^0 = 1 \qquad\qquad x^0 = 1, x \neq 0$$

$$7^{-3} = \frac{1}{7} \cdot \frac{1}{7} \cdot \frac{1}{7} \text{ or } \frac{1}{7^3} \qquad x^{-n} = \frac{1}{x^n}, x \neq 0$$

Work Zone

> **Negative Exponents**
> Remember that 6^{-3} is equal to $\frac{1}{6^3}$, not -216 or -18.

You can use exponents to represent very small numbers.

Negative powers are the result of repeated division.

Examples

 Show your work.

Write each expression using a positive exponent.

1. 6^{-3}

$6^{-3} = \dfrac{1}{6^3}$ Definition of negative exponent

2. a^{-5}

$a^{-5} = \dfrac{1}{a^5}$ Definition of negative exponent

a. _____

b. _____

> **Got It?** Do these problems to find out.

c. _____

a. 7^{-2}

b. b^{-4}

c. 5^0

d. m^{-3}

d. _____

Examples

Write each fraction as an expression using a negative exponent other than -1.

3. $\dfrac{1}{5^2}$

$\dfrac{1}{5^2} = 5^{-2}$ Definition of negative exponent

4. $\dfrac{1}{36}$

$\dfrac{1}{36} = \dfrac{1}{6^2}$ Definition of exponent

$= 6^{-2}$ Definition of negative exponent

e. _____

f. _____

> **Got It?** Do these problems to find out.

g. _____

e. $\dfrac{1}{8^3}$

g. $\dfrac{1}{c^5}$

f. $\dfrac{1}{4}$

h. $\dfrac{1}{27}$

h. _____

Example

 Tutor

5. **STEM** One human hair is about 0.001 inch in diameter. Write the decimal as a power of 10.

$0.001 = \dfrac{1}{1,000}$ Write the decimal as a fraction.

$ = \dfrac{1}{10^3}$ $1,000 = 10^3$

$ = 10^{-3}$ Definition of negative exponent

A human hair is 10^{-3} inch thick.

Got It? Do this problem to find out.

i. **STEM** A water molecule is about 0.0000000001 meter long. Write the decimal as a power of 10.

 STOP and Reflect

Explain below the difference between the expressions $(-4)^2$ and 4^{-2}.

i. _____

Multiply and Divide with Negative Exponents

 The Product of Powers and the Quotient of Powers rules can be used to multiply and divide powers with negative exponents.

Examples

 Tutor

Simplify each expression.

6. $5^3 \cdot 5^{-5}$

$5^3 \cdot 5^{-5} = 5^{3 + (-5)}$ Product of Powers

$\phantom{5^3 \cdot 5^{-5}} = 5^{-2}$ Simplify.

$\phantom{5^3 \cdot 5^{-5}} = \dfrac{1}{5^2}$ or $\dfrac{1}{25}$ Write using positive exponents. Simplify.

Show your work.

7. $\dfrac{w^{-1}}{w^{-4}}$

$\dfrac{w^{-1}}{w^{-4}} = w^{-1 - (-4)}$ Quotient of Powers

$\phantom{\dfrac{w^{-1}}{w^{-4}}} = w^{(-1) + 4}$ or w^3 Subtract the exponents.

Got It? Do these problems to find out.

j. $3^{-8} \cdot 3^2$ **k.** $\dfrac{11^2}{11^4}$

l. $n^9 \cdot n^{-4}$ **m.** $\dfrac{b^{-4}}{b^{-7}}$

j. _____

k. _____

l. _____

 m. _____

Write each expression using a positive exponent. (Examples 1 and 2)

1. $2^{-4} =$ _____

2. $4^{-3} =$ _____

3. $a^{-4} =$ _____

4. $g^{-7} =$ _____

Show your work.

Write each fraction as an expression using a negative exponent other than −1.
(Examples 3 and 4)

5. $\dfrac{1}{3^4} =$ _____

6. $\dfrac{1}{m^5} =$ _____

7. $\dfrac{1}{16} =$ _____

8. $\dfrac{1}{49} =$ _____

9. An American green tree frog tadpole is about 0.00001 kilometer in length when it hatches. Write this decimal as a power of 10.

(Example 5) _____

Simplify. (Examples 6 and 7)

10. $3^{-3} \cdot 3^{-2} =$ _____

11. $r^{-7} \cdot r^3 =$ _____

12. $\dfrac{p^{-2}}{p^{-12}} =$ _____

13. 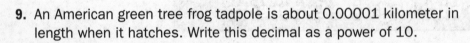 **Building on the Essential Question** How are negative exponents and positive exponents related?

_____

_____

_____

_____

_____

Rate Yourself!

How well do you understand understand negative exponents? Circle the image that applies.

Clear

Somewhat Clear

Not So Clear

For more help, go online to access a Personal Tutor.

Tutor

Extra Practice

25. Write 3^{-5} using positive exponents. $\dfrac{1}{3^5}$

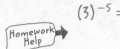

$$(3)^{-5} = \dfrac{1}{3^5}$$

26. Simplify $(4^{-4})(4^2)$. $\dfrac{1}{16}$

$$(4^{-4})(4^2) = 4^{-4+2}$$
$$= 4^{-2}$$
$$= \dfrac{1}{4^2} \text{ or } \dfrac{1}{16}$$

Write each expression using a positive exponent.

27. $6^{-8} =$ _____

28. $(-3)^{-5} =$ _____

29. $s^{-9} =$ _____

30. $t^{-11} =$ _____

Simplify.

31. $z^2 \cdot z^{-3} =$ _____

32. $n^{-1} \cdot n^3 =$ _____

33. $\dfrac{b^{-7}}{b^5} =$ _____

34. $\dfrac{x^4}{x^{-2}} =$ _____

35. $2^{-4} =$ _____

36. $(-5)^{-4} =$ _____

37. $(-10)^{-4} =$ _____

38. $(0.5)^{-4} =$ _____

Persevere with Problems Find the missing exponent.

39. $\dfrac{17^\bullet}{17^4} = 17^8$ _____

40. $\dfrac{k^6}{k^\bullet} = k^2$ _____

41. $\dfrac{p^{-1}}{p^\bullet} = p^{10}$ _____

42. A blood cell has a diameter of about 5^{-5} inches.

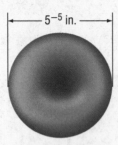

←— 5^{-5} in. —→

Write 5^{-5} using positive exponents.

Ⓐ 5^5

Ⓑ $\dfrac{1}{5^{-5}}$

Ⓒ $\dfrac{5^5}{1}$

Ⓓ $\dfrac{1}{5^5}$

43. When written without exponents, 10^{-5} is equal to which of the following?

Ⓕ 0.00001

Ⓖ 0.000001

Ⓗ −0.00001

Ⓘ −0.000001

44. Short Response Evaluate 3^{-4}. Write your answer using a positive exponent and as a fraction. _____

Common Core Review

Evaluate. MCC6.EE.1

45. $10^2 =$ _____

46. $10^3 =$ _____

47. $10^6 =$ _____

48. $10^5 =$ _____

Find each missing value. MCC6.NS.3

49. $0.003 \times$ _____ $= 3$

50. $0.079 \times$ _____ $= 7.9$

51. $0.00041 \times$ _____ $= 4.1$

[5]7 ÷ _____ $= 9.87$

53. $3,400 \div$ _____ $= 3.4$

54. $7,450 \div$ _____ $= 745$

Scientific Notation

What You'll Learn

Scan the lesson. List two real-world scenarios in which you would use scientific notation.

- _____
  _____
- _____
  _____

Essential Question

WHY is it helpful to write numbers in different ways?

Vocabulary

scientific notation

Common Core GPS

Content Standards
MCC8.EE.4

Mathematical Practices
1, 3, 4, 7

Real-World Link

Electronics A single sided, single layer DVD has a storage capacity of 4.7 gigabytes. One gigabyte is equal to 10^9 bytes.

1. Write a multiplication expression that represents how many bytes can be stored on the DVD. _____

2. Complete the table below.

Expression	Product	Expression	Product
$4.7 \times 10^1 = 4.7 \times 10$	47	$4.7 \times 10^{-1} = 4.7 \times \frac{1}{10}$	0.47
$4.7 \times 10^2 = 4.7 \times 100$		$4.7 \times 10^{-2} = 4.7 \times \frac{1}{100}$	
$4.7 \times 10^3 = 4.7 \times 1{,}000$		$4.7 \times 10^{-3} = 4.7 \times \frac{1}{1000}$	
$4.7 \times 10^4 = 4.7 \times \underline{\hspace{1cm}}$		$4.7 \times 10^{-4} = 4.7 \times \underline{\hspace{1cm}}$	

3. If 4.7 is multiplied by a positive power of 10, what relationship exists between the decimal point's new position and the exponent?

_____

_____

4. When 4.7 is multiplied by a negative power of 10, how does the new position of the decimal point relate to the negative exponent? _____

Key Concept ▸ Scientific Notation

Words   **Scientific notation** is when a number is written as the product of a factor and an integer power of 10. The factor must be greater than or equal to 1 and less than 10.

Symbols $a \times 10^n$, where $1 \le a < 10$ and n is an integer

[handwritten: $\cdot$ lllb $\times 10^{-3}$]

Example $425,000,000 = 4.25 \times 10^8$

Work Zone
order of magnitude

Powers of Ten
Multiplying a factor by a positive power of 10 moves the decimal point right. Multiplying a factor by a negative power of 10 moves the decimal point left.

a. _742000_

b. _0.061_

c. _371.4_

Use these rules to express a number in scientific notation.

- If the number is greater than or equal to 1, the power of ten is positive.
- If the number is between 0 and 1, the power of ten is negative.

Examples

Write each number in standard form.

1. 5.34×10^4

$5.34 \times 10^4 = 53,400.$

2. 3.27×10^{-3}

$3.27 \times 10^{-3} = 0.00327$

Got It?   Do these problems to find out.

Show your work.

a. 7.42×10^5 **b.** 6.1×10^{-2} **c.** 3.714×10^2

[handwritten: 742 000]

Examples

Write each number in scientific notation.

3. 3,725,000

$3,725,000 = 3.725 \times 1,000,000$ The decimal point moves 6 places.

$\quad\quad\quad\quad = 3.725 \times 10^6$ Since $3,725,000 > 1$, the exponent is positive.

4. 0.000316

$0.000316 = 3.16 \times 0.0001$ The decimal point moves 4 places.

$\quad\quad\quad = 3.16 \times 10^{-4}$ Since $0 < 0.000316 < 1$, the exponent is negative.

212   **Chapter 3** Real Numbers

Copyright © The McGraw-Hill Companies, Inc.

Got It? Do these problems to find out.

d. 14,140,000   e. 0.00876   f. 0.114

Show your work.

d. $14,140,000 \times 10^7$

e. 0.00876×10^3

f. 01.14×10^1

Example

Watch ▶ Tutor 💬

5. Refer to the table at the right. Order the countries according to the amount of money visitors spent in the United States from greatest to least.

Dollars Spent by International Visitors in the U.S	
Country	Dollars Spent
Canada	1.03×10^7
India	1.83×10^6
Mexico	7.15×10^6
United Kingdom	1.06×10^7

Canada and United Kingdom   Mexico and India

Step 1 $\begin{Bmatrix} 1.06 \times 10^7 \\ 1.03 \times 10^7 \end{Bmatrix} > \begin{Bmatrix} 7.15 \times 10^6 \\ 1.83 \times 10^6 \end{Bmatrix}$ ← Group the numbers by their power of 10.

Step 2 $1.06 > 1.03$ $7.15 > 1.83$ ← Order the decimals.

United Kingdom Canada   Mexico India

Got It? Do this problem to find out.

g. Some of the top U.S. cities visited by overseas travelers are shown in the table. Order the cities according to the number of visitors from least to greates

U.S. City	Number of Visitors
Boston	7.21×10^5
Las Vegas	1.3×10^6
Los Angeles	2.2×10^6
Metro D.C. area	9.01×10^5

1. Los angeles
2. Las vegas
3. Metro D.C area
4. Boston

g. _____

721 000
1 360000
2 200 000
901 000

Example

Tutor 💬

6. **STEM** If you could walk at a rate of 2 meters per second, it would take you 1.92×10^8 seconds to walk to the moon. Is it more appropriate to report this time as 1.92×10^8 seconds or 6.09 years? Explain your reasoning.

The measure 6.09 years is more appropriate. The number 1.92×10^8 seconds is very large so choosing a larger unit of measure is more meaningful.

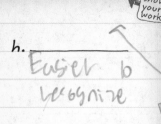

h. _____

Easier b
recognize

Got It? Do this problem to find out.

h. **STEM** In an ocean, the sea floor moved 475 kilometers over 65 million years. Is it more appropriate to report this rate as 7.31×10^{-5} kilometer per year or 7.31 centimeters per year? Explain your reasoning.

Guided Practice

Write each number in standard form. (Examples 1 and 2)

1. $9.931 \times 10^5 =$ _____

2. $6.02 \times 10^{-4} =$ _____

Write each number in scientific notation. (Examples 3 and 4)

3. $8,785,000,000 =$ _____

4. $0.524 =$ _____

5. The table lists the total value of music shipments for four years. List the years from least to greatest dollar amount.
(Example 5)

_____

_____

Year	Music Shipments($)
1	1.22×10^{10}
2	1.12×10^{10}
3	7.15×10^{6}
4	1.06×10^{7}

6. **STEM** A plant cell has a diameter of 1.3×10^{-8} kilometer. Is it more appropriate to report the diameter of a plant cell as 1.3×10^{-8} kilometer or 1.3×10^{-2} millimeter? Explain your reasoning. (Example 6)

_____

_____

7. Ⓔ **Building on the Essential Question** How is scientific notation useful in the real world?

_____

_____

_____

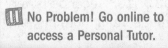

Extra Practice

16. Write 7.113×10^7 in standard form.
71,130,000
_____

$7.113 \times 10^7 = \underset{\sim\sim\sim\sim\sim\sim}{71130000.}$ The decimal point moves 7 places right.

 Homework Help →

17. Write 0.00000707 in scientific notation.
7.07×10^{-6}
_____

$0.\underset{\sim\sim\sim\sim\sim\sim}{00000707} = 7.07 \times 0.000001$
$= 7.07 \times 10^{-6}$

The decimal point moves 6 places. Since $0 < 0.00000707 < 1$, the exponent is negative.

Write each number in standard form.

18. $2.08 \times 10^2 =$ _____

19. $7.8 \times 10^{-3} =$ _____

20. $8.73 \times 10^{-4} =$ _____

Write each number in scientific notation.

21. $6,700 =$ _____

22. $52,300,000 =$ _____

23. $0.037 =$ _____

24. **STEM** The table shows the mass in grams of one atom of each of several elements. List the elements in order from the least mass to greatest mass per atom.

_____

Element	Mass per Atom
Carbon	1.995×10^{-23} g
Gold	3.272×10^{-22} g
Hydrogen	1.674×10^{-24} g
Oxygen	2.658×10^{-23} g
Silver	1.792×10^{-22} g

 Identify Structure **Arrange each set of numbers in increasing order.**

25. $216,000,000, 2.2 \times 10^3, 3.1 \times 10^7, 310,000$

_____

26. $4.56 \times 10^{-2}, 4.56 \times 10^3, 4.56 \times 10^2, 4.56 \times 10^{-3}$

_____

27. Short Response By the year 2050, the world population is expected to reach 10 billion people. When 10 billion is written in scientific notation, what is the exponent of the power of ten?

_____

28. The thermosphere layer of the atmosphere is between 90 thousand and 110 thousand meters above sea level. What is 110 thousand written in scientific notation?

Ⓐ 1.1×10^5

Ⓑ 1.1×10^4

Ⓒ 1.1×10^{-4}

Ⓓ 1.1×10^{-5}

29. The attendance records for four Major League baseball teams for a recent year are shown below.

Team	Attendance
Florida Marlins	6.76×10^5
Los Angeles Angels	1.87×10^6
Pittsburgh Pirates	9.68×10^5
St. Louis Cardinals	1.98×10^6

Which team had the greatest attendance?

Ⓕ Florida Marlins

Ⓖ Los Angeles Angels

Ⓗ Pittsburgh Pirates

Ⓘ St. Louis Cardinals

Common Core Review

Find each sum or difference. MCC6.NS.3

30. $9.7 + 0.532 =$ _____

31. $4.39 - 0.035 =$ _____

32. $679 - 1.4 =$ _____

Find each product or quotient. MCC6.NS.3

33. $(3.7)(1.2) =$ _____

34. $9.72 \div 1.8 =$ _____

35. $4.64 \div 2.9 =$ _____

Simplify. Express using exponents. MCC8.EE.1

36. $3a^4 \cdot 12a^2 =$ _____

37. $(5x)^2 \cdot 2x^5 =$ _____

38. $\dfrac{3^9}{3^2} =$ _____

Compute with Scientific Notation

What You'll Learn

Scan the lesson. List two real-world scenarios in which you would compute using scientific notation.

- _____
  _____
- _____
  _____

 Essential Question

WHY is it helpful to write numbers in different ways?

 Common Core GPS

Content Standards
MCC8.EE.3, MCC8.EE.4

Mathematical Practices
1, 3, 4

 Real-World Link

E-mail Every day, nearly 130 billion spam E-mails are sent worldwide! Use the steps below to find out how many are sent each year. The numbers are too large even for your calculator.

1. Express 130 billion in scientific notation.

_____

2. Round 365 to the nearest hundred and express it in scientific notation.

_____

3. Write a multiplication expression using the number in Exercises 1 and 2 to represent the total number of spam E-mails sent each year.

_____

4. If you use the Commutative Property of Multiplication, you can rewrite the expression in Exercise 3 as $(1.3 \times 4)(10^{11} \times 10^2)$. Evaluate this expression to find the number of spam E-mails sent in a year. Express the result in both scientific notation and standard form.

_____

Multiplication and Division with Scientific Notation

You can use the Product of Powers and Quotient of Powers properties to multiply and divide numbers written in scientific notation.

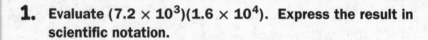

Example

Tutor

1. Evaluate $(7.2 \times 10^3)(1.6 \times 10^4)$. Express the result in scientific notation.

$$
\begin{aligned}
(7.2 \times 10^3)(1.6 \times 10^4) &= (7.2 \times 1.6)(10^3 \times 10^4) && \text{Commutative and Associative Properties} \\
&= (11.52)(10^3 \times 10^4) && \text{Multiply 7.2 by 1.6.} \\
&= 11.52 \times 10^{3+4} && \text{Product of Powers} \\
&= 11.52 \times 10^7 && \text{Add the exponents.} \\
&= 1.152 \times 10^8 && \text{Write in scientific notation.}
\end{aligned}
$$

Decimal Point

Since, 11.52×10^7 is not written in scientific notation, move the decimal point 1 place to the left and add 1 to the exponent.

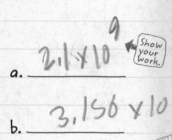

a. _____ 2.1×10^9

Show your work.

b. _____ 3.156×10

Got It? Do these problems to find out.

a. $(8.4 \times 10^2)(2.5 \times 10^6)$ b. $(2.63 \times 10^4)(1.2 \times 10^{-3})$

21×10^8

3.15

Example

Real World

Tutor

2. In 2010, the world population was about 6,860,000,000. The population of the United States was about 3×10^8. About how many times larger is the world population than the population of the United States?

Estimate the population of the world and write in scientific notation.

$6,860,000,000 \approx 7,000,000,000$ or 7×10^9

Find $\dfrac{7 \times 10^9}{3 \times 10^8}$.

$$
\begin{aligned}
\frac{7 \times 10^9}{3 \times 10^8} &= \left(\frac{7}{3}\right)\left(\frac{10^9}{10^8}\right) && \text{Associative Property} \\
&\approx 2.3 \times \left(\frac{10^9}{10^8}\right) && \text{Divide 7 by 3. Round to the nearest tenth.} \\
&\approx 2.3 \times 10^{9-8} && \text{Quotient of Powers} \\
&\approx 2.3 \times 10^1 && \text{Subtract the exponents.}
\end{aligned}
$$

So, the population of the world is about 23 times larger than the population of the United States.

Got It? Do this problem to find out.

c. The surface area of Lake Superior, the largest of the Great Lakes, is 8×10^4 square kilometers. The surface area of the smallest Great Lake, Ontario, is 18,160 square kilometers. About how many times as great is the area covered by Lake Superior than Lake Ontario?

18000

$\dfrac{8 \times 10^4}{1.8 \times 10^4}$ 4.4×10^0

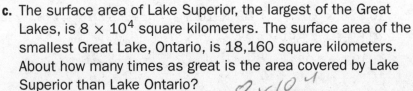 *Show your work.*

c. $\dfrac{4.4}{4.4 \times 10^0}$

Addition and Subtraction with Scientific Notation

When adding or subtracting decimals in standard form, it is necessary to line up the place values. In scientific notation, the place value is represented by the exponent. Before adding or subtracting, both numbers must be expressed in the same form.

Examples

 Tutor

Evaluate each expression. Express the result in scientific notation.

3. $(6.89 \times 10^4) + (9.24 \times 10^5)$

$(6.89 \times 10^4) + (9.24 \times 10^5)$

$= (6.89 \times 10^4) + (92.4 \times 10^4)$ Write 9.24×10^5 as 92.4×10^4.

$= (6.89 + 92.4) \times 10^4$ Distributive Property

$= 99.29 \times 10^4$ Add 6.89 and 92.4.

$= 9.929 \times 10^5$ Rewrite in scientific notation.

4. $(7.83 \times 10^8) - 11,610,000$

$(7.83 \times 10^8) - (1.161 \times 10^7)$ Rewrite 11,610,000 in scientific notation.

$(7.83 \times 10^8) - (1.161 \times 10^7)$

$= (78.3 \times 10^7) - (1.161 \times 10^7)$ Write 7.83×10^8 as 78.3×10^7.

$= (78.3 - 1.161) \times 10^7$ Distributive Property

$= 77.139 \times 10^7$ Subtract 1.161 from 78.3.

$= 7.7139 \times 10^8$ Rewrite in scientific notation.

 **STOP and Reflect**

Explain below how to estimate the sum of (4.215×10^{-2}) and (3.2×10^{-4}). Then find the estimate.

d. _1.0551 × 10⁷_

e. _1.24775 × 10⁹_

f. _3.33 × 10⁶_

5. $593{,}000 + (7.89 \times 10^6)$

$593{,}000 + (7.89 \times 10^6)$

$= (5.93 \times 10^5) + (7.89 \times 10^6)$ Rewrite 593,000 in scientific notation.

$= (0.593 \times 10^6) + (7.89 \times 10^6)$ Write 5.93×10^5 as 0.593×10^6

$= (0.593 + 7.89) \times 10^6$ Distributive Property

$= 8.483 \times 10^6$ Add 0.593 and 7.89.

Got It? Do these problems to find out.

d. $(8.41 \times 10^3) + (9.71 \times 10^4)$

e. $(1.263 \times 10^9) - (1.525 \times 10^7)$

f. $(6.3 \times 10^5) + 2{,}700{,}000$ _+ 27_

Guided Practice

Evaluate each expression. Express the result in scientific notation. (Examples 1 and 2)

1. $(2.6 \times 10^5)(1.9 \times 10^2) = $ _____

2. $\dfrac{8.37 \times 10^8}{2.7 \times 10^3} = $ _____

3. In 2005, 8.1×10^{10} text messages were sent in the United States. In 2010, the number of annual text messages had risen to 1,810,000,000,000. About how many times as great was the number of text messages in 2010 than 2005? (Example 2)

_____

Evaluate each expression. Express the result in scientific notation. (Examples 3–5)

4. $(8.9 \times 10^9) + (4.2 \times 10^6) = $ _____

5. $(9.64 \times 10^8) - (5.29 \times 10^6) = $ _____

6. $(1.35 \times 10^6) - (117{,}000) = $ _____

7. $5{,}400 + (6.8 \times 10^5) = $ _____

8. **Building on the Essential Question** How does scientific notation make it easier to perform computations with very large or very small numbers? _____

_____

_____

Rate Yourself!

Are you ready to move on? Shade the section that applies.

YES   ?   NO

For more help, go online to access a Personal Tutor.

Extra Practice

Evaluate each expression. Express the result in scientific notation.

17. $(3.7 \times 10^{-2})(1.2 \times 10^3) =$ _4.44×10^1_

$(3.7 \times 10^{-2})(1.2 \times 10^3) = (3.7 \times 1.2) \times$
$(10^{-2} \times 10^3)$

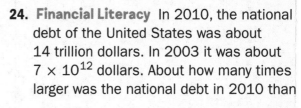
Homework Help

$= 4.44 \times 10^{-2+3}$
$= 4.44 \times 10^1$

18. $\dfrac{4.64 \times 10^{-4}}{2.9 \times 10^{-6}} =$ _1.6×10^2_

$\dfrac{4.64 \times 10^{-4}}{2.9 \times 10^{-6}} = \dfrac{4.64}{2.9} \times \dfrac{10^{-4}}{10^{-6}}$

$= 1.6 \times 10^{-4-(-6)}$
$= 1.6 \times 10^2$

19. $\dfrac{3.24 \times 10^{-4}}{8.1 \times 10^{-7}} =$ _____

20. $(7.3 \times 10^5) + 2{,}400{,}000 =$ _____

21. $(8.64 \times 10^6) + (1.334 \times 10^{10}) =$

_____

22. $(1.21 \times 10^5) - 9{,}500 =$

_____

23. CCGPS **Persevere with Problems** A circular swimming pool holds 1.22×10^6 cubic inches of water. It is being filled at a rate of 1.5×10^3 cubic inches per minute. How many hours will it take to fill the swimming

pool? _____

_____

24. **Financial Literacy** In 2010, the national debt of the United States was about 14 trillion dollars. In 2003 it was about 7×10^{12} dollars. About how many times larger was the national debt in 2010 than in 2003? _____

25. The rectangle has an area of 9.14×10^{-7} square kilometers.

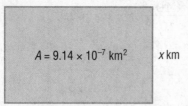

$A = 9.14 \times 10^{-7}$ km^2 x km

1.656×10^{-3} km

What is the approximate length of the missing side?

Ⓐ 2.74×10^{-6}

Ⓑ 5.52×10^{-4}

Ⓒ 1.656×10^{-3}

Ⓓ 1.51×10^{11}

26. There are approximately 45 hundred species of mammals on Earth and 2.8×10^{4} species of fish. What is the difference in the number of species?

Ⓕ 6.2×10^{0}

Ⓖ 2.35×10^{4}

Ⓗ 1.6×10^{-1}

Ⓘ 3.25×10^{4}

27. Alaska is the largest state in the United States with an area of about 1.5×10^{6} square kilometers. Rhode Island is the smallest state with an area of about 2,700 square kilometers. About how many times larger is Alaska than Rhode Island?

Ⓐ 5   Ⓒ 500

Ⓑ 50   Ⓓ 5,000

CCGPS Common Core Review

28. A cube measures 6.6 inches on each side. MCC6.G.2

　a. Find the area of one face of the cube. _____

　b. Find the volume of the cube. _____

29. Complete the table shown. MCC6.EE.1

x	x^2	x^3	x	x^2	x^3
1			7		
2			8		
3			9		
4			10		
5			11		
6			12		

Inquiry **WHAT** are the similarities and differences between a number written in scientific notation and the calculator notation of the number shown on a screen?

CCGPS Content Standards
MCC8.EE.3,
MCC8.EE.4
Mathematical Practices
1, 3, 5

Solar System The table shows the mass of some planets in our solar system. What is the mass of Earth written in scientific notation?

Planet	Mass (kg)
Earth	5,973,700,000,000,000,000,000,000
Mars	641,850,000,000,000,000,000,000
Saturn	568,510,000,000,000,000,000,000,000

What do you know? _____

_____

What do you need to find? _____

_____

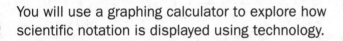
Investigation 1

You will use a graphing calculator to explore how scientific notation is displayed using technology.

Step 1 Press CLEAR to clear the home screen.

Step 2 Enter the value in standard form for Earth's mass. Press ENTER.

Copy your calculator screen on the blank screen shown.

Step 3 Write the value for Earth's mass using scientific notation.

_____

Collaborate

CCGPS **Use Math Tools** **Work with a partner. Repeat Steps 1 and 2 for each of the following.**

1. mass of Mars

2. mass of Saturn

Show your work. →

3. What does the E symbol represent on the calculator screen?

_____

_____

What does the value after the E symbol represent? _____

_____

4. Based on your answer for Exercise 1, what is the mass of Mars in scientific notation? _____

5. Based on your answer for Exercise 2, what is the mass of Saturn in scientific notation? _____

Analyze

Work with a partner to complete the table.

	Calculator Notation	Scientific Notation	Standard Form
6.	3.1E7		
7.		6.39×10^{10}	
8.			0.02357
9.	1.7E−11		

10. CCGPS **Reason Inductively** The Moon has a mass of about 73,600,000,000,000,000,000,000 kilograms. Without entering the value in your calculator, predict how the mass of the Moon will be displayed on the calculator screen. _____

Investigation 2

Measurement A human blood cell is about 1×10^{-6} meter in diameter. The Moon is about 3.476×10^{6} meters in diameter. How many times greater is the diameter of the Moon than the diameter of a blood cell?

Step 1 Press CLEAR to clear the home screen.

Step 2 Perform the following keystrokes:

3.476 [2nd] [EE] **6** [÷] **1** [2nd] [EE] **−6** [ENTER]

Copy your calculator screen on the blank screen shown.

Step 3 Write the value in standard form.

_____

So, the Moon is _____ times greater than a human blood cell.

Investigation 3

When in "Normal" mode, a calculator will show answers in scientific notation only if they are very large numbers or very small numbers. You can set your calculator to show scientific notation for all numbers by using the "Sci" mode.

Step 1 Press CLEAR to clear the home screen. Put your calculator in scientific mode by pressing MODE ▶ ENTER. Then press CLEAR to return to the home screen.

Step 2 Complete the table by entering the numbers in the first column into your calculator.

Enter	Calculator Notation	Standard Form
$14 \div 100$		
$60 - 950$		
$360 \cdot 15$		
$1 + 1$		

Collaborate

CCGPS **Use Math Tools** Work with a partner. Write down the keystrokes and fill in the calculator screen to find each of the following using a calculator in "Sci" mode. Write your final answer in standard form.

11. $(6.2 \times 10^5)(2.3 \times 10^7)$

Show your work.

Keystrokes: _____

_____

Answer in standard form: _____

12. $(8.5 \times 10^{-3}) - (4.8 \times 10^{-5})$

Keystrokes: _____

_____

Answer in standard form: _____

 **Analyze**

13. **CCGPS** **Use Math Tools** A *micrometer* is 0.000001 meter. Use your calculator to determine how many micrometers are in each of the following. Write your answer in both calculator and scientific notation.

	Calculator Notation	Scientific Notation
5,000 meters		
4.08 E14 meters		
2.9 E-10 meter		

 Reflect

14. **Inquiry** WHAT are the similarities and differences between a number written in scientific notation and the calculator notation of the number

shown on a screen? _____

_____

_____

What You'll Learn

Scan the lesson. Predict two things you will learn about square roots and cube roots.

- _____
  _____

- _____
  _____
  _____

Essential Question

WHY is it helpful to write numbers in different ways?

Vocabulary

square root
perfect square
radical sign
cube root
perfect cube

Common Core GPS

Content Standards
MCC8.EE.2
Mathematical Practices
1, 3, 4

Vocabulary Start-Up

A **square root** of a number is one of its two equal factors. Numbers such as 1, 4, 9, 16, and 25 are called **perfect squares** because they are squares of integers.

Complete the graphic organizer.

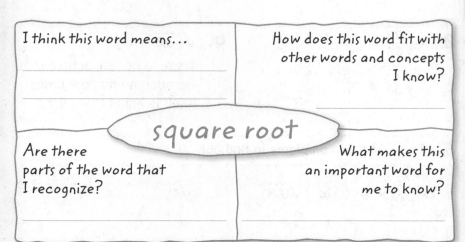

| I think this word means... | How does this word fit with other words and concepts I know? |
| Are there parts of the word that I recognize? | What makes this an important word for me to know? |

square root

What is the relationship between squaring a number

and finding the square root? _____

Real-World Link

The square base of the Great Pyramid of Giza covers almost 562,500 square feet. How could you determine the length of each side of the base?

_____

Square Root

Words   A square root of a number is one of its two equal factors.

Symbols   If $x^2 = y$, then x is a square root of y.

Example $5^2 = 25$ so 5 is a square root of 25.

Work Zone

Every positive number has *both* a positive and negative square root. In most real-world situations, only the positive or *principal* square root is considered. A **radical sign**, $\sqrt{}$, is used to indicate the principal square root. If $n^2 = a$, then $n = \pm\sqrt{a}$.

Examples

Tutor

Find each square root.

1. $\sqrt{64}$

$\sqrt{64} = 8$ Find the positive square root of 64; $8^2 = 64$.

2. $\pm\sqrt{1.21}$

$\pm\sqrt{1.21} = \pm1.1$ Find both square roots of 1.21; $1.1^2 = 1.21$.

Show your work.

a. $\dfrac{3}{4}$

3. $-\sqrt{\dfrac{25}{36}}$

$-\sqrt{\dfrac{25}{36}} = -\dfrac{5}{6}$ Find the negative square root of $\dfrac{25}{36}$; $\left(\dfrac{5}{6}\right)^2 = \dfrac{25}{36}$.

4. $\sqrt{-16}$

There is no real square root because no number times itself is equal to -16.

b. ± 0.9

c. -7

Got It?   Do these problems to find out.

a. $\sqrt{\dfrac{9}{16}}$ b. $\pm\sqrt{0.81}$ c. $-\sqrt{49}$ d. $\sqrt{-100}$

d. $10i$

Example

Tutor

5. Solve $t^2 = 169$. Check your solution(s).

$t^2 = 169$ Write the equation.

$t = \pm\sqrt{169}$ Definition of square root

$t = 13$ and -13 Check $13 \cdot 13 = 169$ and $(-13)(-13) = 169$ ✓

e. $a = 17$ and -17

f. $m = 0.3$ and -0.3

Got It?   Do these problems to find out.

e. $289 = a^2$ f. $m^2 = 0.09$ g. $y^2 = \dfrac{4}{25}$

g. $y = \dfrac{2}{5}$ and $-\dfrac{2}{5}$

$a = 17$

Cube Roots

Words   A **cube root** of a number is one of its three equal factors.

Symbols   If $x^3 = y$, then x is the cube root of y.

Numbers such as 8, 27, and 64 are **perfect cubes** because they are the cubes of integers.

$8 = 2 \cdot 2 \cdot 2$ or 2^3 $27 = 3 \cdot 3 \cdot 3$ or 3^3 $64 = 4 \cdot 4 \cdot 4$ or 4^3

The symbol $\sqrt[3]{}$ is used to indicate a cube root of a number.

If $n^3 = a$, then $n = \sqrt[3]{a}$. You can use this relationship to solve equations that involve cubes.

Examples

Find each cube root.

6. $\sqrt[3]{125}$

$\sqrt[3]{125} = 5$ $5^3 = 5 \cdot 5 \cdot 5$ or 125

7. $\sqrt[3]{-27}$

$\sqrt[3]{-27} = -3$ $(-3)^3 = (-3) \cdot (-3) \cdot (-3)$ or -27

Cube Roots
While $\sqrt{-16}$ is not a real number, $\sqrt[3]{-27}$ is a real number. $-3 \cdot -3 \cdot -3 = -27$

> **Got It?**   Do these problems to find out.
>
> **h.** $\sqrt[3]{729}$ **i.** $\sqrt[3]{-64}$ **j.** $\sqrt[3]{1,000}$

Show your work.

h. _____9_____

i. _____−4_____

j. _____10_____

Real World Example

8. **Dylan has a planter in the shape of a cube that holds 8 cubic feet of potting soil. Solve the equation $8 = s^3$ to find the side length s of the container.**

$8 = s^3$ Write the equation.

$\sqrt[3]{8} = s$ Take the cube root of each side.

$2 = s$ Definition of cube root

So, each side of the container is 2 feet.

Check $(2)^3 = 8$ ✓

k. _1.5 feet_

Got It? Do this problem to find out.

k. An aquarium in the shape of a cube that will hold 25 gallons of water has a volume of 3.375 cubic feet. Solve $s^3 = 3.375$ to find the length of one side of the aquarium.

Guided Practice

Check ✓

Find each square root. (Examples 1–4)

1. $-\sqrt{1.69} =$ _____

2. $\pm\sqrt{\dfrac{49}{144}} =$ _____

3. $\sqrt{-1.44} =$ _____

Solve each equation. Check your solution(s). (Example 5)

4. $p^2 = 36$ _____

5. $t^2 = \dfrac{1}{9}$ _____

6. $6.25 = r^2$ _____

Find each cube root. (Examples 6 and 7)

7. $\sqrt[3]{216} =$ _____

8. $\sqrt[3]{-125} =$ _____

9. $\sqrt[3]{-8} =$ _____

10. A cube-shaped packing box can hold 729 cubic inches of packing material. Solve $729 = s^3$ to find the length of one side of the box. (Example 8) _____

11. ⓔ **Building on the Essential Question** Why would I need to use square roots and cube roots?

_____
_____
_____
_____

Rate Yourself!

☐ I understand how to find square roots and cube roots.

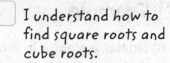 Great! You're ready to move on!

☐ I still have some questions about finding square roots and cube roots.

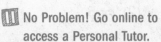 No Problem! Go online to access a Personal Tutor. Tutor

Extra Practice

Find each square root.

24. $-\sqrt{81} =$ ___-9___

Homework Help ➡ $9 \cdot 9 = 81$

So, $-\sqrt{81} = -9$.

25. $-\sqrt{\dfrac{64}{225}} =$ _____

26. $-\sqrt{\dfrac{16}{25}} =$ _____

27. $\pm\sqrt{1.44} =$ _____

Find each cube root.

28. $\sqrt[3]{-216} =$ _____

29. $\sqrt[3]{-512} =$ _____

30. $\sqrt[3]{-1,000} =$ _____

31. $\sqrt[3]{-343} =$ _____

Solve each equation. Check your solution(s).

32. $b^2 = 100$

33. $\dfrac{9}{64} = c^2$

34. $a^2 = 1.21$

35. $\dfrac{1}{8} = z^3$

36. $1.331 = c^3$

37. $m^3 = 8,000$

38. $\sqrt{x} = 5$

39. $\sqrt{y} = 20$

40. $\sqrt{z} = 10.5$

41. **CCGPS Persevere with Problems** A concert crew needs to set up some chairs on the floor level. The chairs are to be placed in a square pattern consisting of four square sections. If one of the square sections holds 900 chairs, how many chairs will there be along each length of the larger square? _____

42. A marching band wants to form a square in the middle of the field. If there are 100 members in the band, how many should be in each row?

   Ⓐ 4   Ⓒ 25

   Ⓑ 10   Ⓓ 50

43. Mr. Freeman's farm has a square cornfield. Find the area of the cornfield if the sides are measured in whole numbers.

   Ⓕ 164,000 ft^2

   Ⓖ 170,150 ft^2

   Ⓗ 170,586 ft^2

   Ⓘ 174,724 ft^2

44. Short Response A puzzle cube is shown. The volume of the cube is 512 cubic centimeters. What is the length of one side of the puzzle cube?

Evaluate each expression. MCC8.EE.2

45. $13^3 =$ _____

46. $25^2 =$ _____

47. $15^3 =$ _____

48. $34^2 =$ _____

49. $5 \cdot \sqrt{121} =$ _____

50. $-6 \cdot \sqrt{36} =$ _____

51. $10 \cdot \sqrt[3]{8} =$ _____

52. $-4 \cdot \sqrt{144} =$ _____

Express the volume of each cube as a monomial. MCC8.EE.1

53. _____

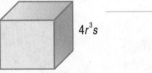

$4r^3s$

54. _____

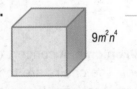

$9m^2n^4$

Inquiry HOW can you estimate the square root of a non-perfect square number?

CCGPS Content Standards
MCC8.NS.2, MCC8.EE.2

Mathematical Practices
1, 3, 4, 5

Crafts Mindi is making a quilting piece from a square pattern as shown. Each of the dotted lines is 6 inches. What is the approximate length of one side of the square?

What do you know? _____

What do you need to find? _____

Investigation

Tools

Step 1 The outline of the square on dot paper is shown. Draw dotted lines connecting opposite vertices.

When you draw the lines, four triangles that are the same shape and size are formed. What are the dimensions of the triangles?

base = ☐ units   height = ☐ units

The area of one triangle is ☐ square units.

The area of the square is ☐ square units.

Step 2 Copy and cut out the square in Step 1 on another sheet of paper.

Step 3 Place one side of your square on the number line. Between what two consecutive whole numbers is $\sqrt{18}$, the side length of the square,

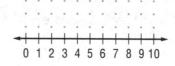
0 1 2 3 4 5 6 7 8 9 10

located? _____

The side of the square is closer to which one of the two whole

numbers? _____   Estimate $\sqrt{18}$. _____

So, one side of the square is about ☐ units long.

Collaborate

CCGPS Use Math Tools Work with a partner. Determine the two consecutive whole numbers the side length of each square is located between using the method shown in the Investigation.

Show your work.

1. _____

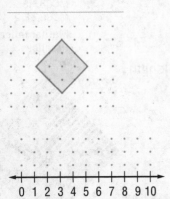

0 1 2 3 4 5 6 7 8 9 10

2. _____

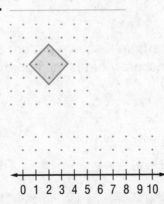

0 1 2 3 4 5 6 7 8 9 10

3. _____

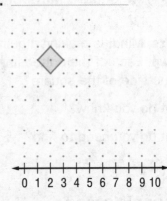

0 1 2 3 4 5 6 7 8 9 10

CCGPS Use Math Tools Estimate the side length of each square in Exercises 1–3. Verify your estimate by using a calculator.

4. Exercise 1

Estimate _____

Calculator _____

5. Exercise 2

Estimate _____

Calculator _____

6. Exercise 3

Estimate _____

Calculator _____

7. CCGPS Reason Inductively How does the area of a square relate to the square of a number? _____

_____

Reflect

8. CCGPS Model with Mathematics How does using a square model help you find the square root of a non-perfect square? _____

_____

_____

9. Inquiry HOW can you estimate the square root of a non-perfect square?

_____

_____

_____

Estimate Roots

What You'll Learn

Scan the lesson. List two headings you would use to make an outline of the lesson.

- _____
- _____

Essential Question

WHY is it helpful to write numbers in different ways?

Common Core GPS

Content Standards
MCC8.NS.2, MCC8.EE.2

Mathematical Practices
1, 3, 4

Real-World Link

Watch ▶

Gravity Legend states that while sitting in his garden one day, Sir Isaac Newton was struck on the head by an apple. Suppose the apple was 25 feet above his head. Use the following steps to find how long it took the apple to fall.

1. What is the square root of 25? 5

2. The formula $t = \dfrac{\sqrt{h}}{4}$ can be used to find the time t in seconds it will take an object to fall from a certain height h in feet. How long did it take the apple to fall?

   _____ 1.25_s _____

3. Suppose another apple was 13 feet above the ground. Use the formula to write an equation representing the time it would have taken for the apple to hit the ground.

   _____ $t = \dfrac{\sqrt{13}}{4}$ _____

4. Can you write $\dfrac{\sqrt{13}}{4}$ without a radical sign? Explain.

   No it is not a
   perfect square

Estimate Square and Cube Roots

You know that $\sqrt{8}$ is not a whole number because 8 is not a perfect square.

The number line below shows that $\sqrt{8}$ is between 2 and 3. Since 8 is closer to 9 than 4, the best whole number estimate for $\sqrt{8}$ is 3.

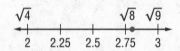

Examples

Tutor

1. **Estimate $\sqrt{83}$ to the nearest integer.**

- The largest perfect square less than 83 is 81. $\sqrt{81} = 9$
- The smallest perfect square greater than 83 is 100. $\sqrt{100} = 10$

Plot each square root on a number line. Then estimate $\sqrt{83}$.

$$81 < \quad 83 < 100 \qquad \text{Write an inequality.}$$
$$9^2 < \quad 83 < 10^2 \qquad 81 = 9^2 \text{ and } 100 = 10^2$$
$$\sqrt{9^2} < \sqrt{83} < \sqrt{10^2} \qquad \text{Find the square root of each number.}$$
$$9 < \sqrt{83} < 10 \qquad \text{Simplify.}$$

So, $\sqrt{83}$ is between 9 and 10. Since $\sqrt{83}$ is closer to $\sqrt{81}$ than $\sqrt{100}$, the best integer estimate for $\sqrt{83}$ is 9.

> **Inequalities**
> $81 < 83 < 100$ is read 81 is less than 83 which is less than 100, or 83 is between 81 and 100.

2. **Estimate $\sqrt[3]{320}$ to the nearest integer.**

- The largest perfect cube less than 320 is 216. $\sqrt[3]{216} = 6$
- The smallest perfect cube greater than 320 is 343. $\sqrt[3]{343} = 7$

$$216 < \quad 320 < 343 \qquad \text{Write an inequality.}$$
$$6^3 < \quad 320 < 7^3 \qquad 216 = 6^3 \text{ and } 343 = 7^3$$
$$\sqrt[3]{6^3} < \sqrt[3]{320} < \sqrt[3]{7^3} \qquad \text{Find the cube root of each number.}$$
$$6 < \sqrt[3]{320} < 7 \qquad \text{Simplify.}$$

So, $\sqrt[3]{320}$ is between 6 and 7. Since 320 is closer to 343 than 216, the best integer estimate for $\sqrt[3]{320}$ is 7.

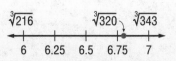

Got It? Do these problems to find out.

a. $\sqrt{35}$ b. $\sqrt{170}$ c. $\sqrt{44.8}$

d. $\sqrt[3]{62}$ e. $\sqrt[3]{25}$ f. $\sqrt[3]{129.6}$

a. _____ 6 __

b. _____ 13 0

c. _____ 7

d. _____ 4

e. _____ 3

f. _____ 5

 Example

 Tutor

3. Wyatt wants to fence in a square portion of the yard to make a play area for his new puppy. The area covered is 2 square meters. How much fencing should Wyatt buy?

√2 m

2 m² √2 m

Wyatt will need $4 \cdot \sqrt{2}$ meters of fencing. The square root of 2 is between 1 and 2 so $4 \cdot \sqrt{2}$ is between 4 and 8. Is this the best approximation? You can truncate the decimal expansion of $\sqrt{2}$ to find better approximations.

Estimate $\sqrt{2}$ by truncating, or dropping, the digits after the first decimal place, then after the second decimal place, and so on until an appropriate approximation is reached.

$\sqrt{2} \approx 1.414213562$ Use a calculator.

$\sqrt{2} \approx 1.41~4213562$ Truncate, or drop, the digits after the first decimal place. $\sqrt{2}$ is between 1.4 and 1.5.

$5.6 < 4\sqrt{2} < 6.0$ $4 \cdot 1.4 = 5.6$ and $4 \cdot 1.5 = 6.0$

To find a closer approximation, expand $\sqrt{2}$ then truncate the decimal expansion after the first two decimal places.

$\sqrt{2} \approx 1.41~4213562$ $\sqrt{2}$ is between 1.41 and 1.42.

$5.64 < 4\sqrt{2} < 5.68$ $4 \cdot 1.41 = 5.64$ and $4 \cdot 1.42 = 5.68$

The approximations indicate that Wyatt should buy 6 meters of fencing.

STOP and Reflect

What is the difference between an exact value and an approximate value when finding square roots of numbers that are not perfect squares? Explain below.

Got It? Do this problem to find out.

g. Kelly needs to put trim around a circular tablecloth with a diameter of 36 inches. Use the equation $C = \pi d$ to find three sets of approximations for the amount of trim she will need. Truncate the value of π to the ones, tenths, and hundredths place. Then determine how much trim she should buy.

g. _____

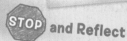

Example

4. The *golden rectangle* is found frequently in the nautilus shell. The length of the longer side divided by the length of the shorter side is equal to $\dfrac{1 + \sqrt{5}}{2}$. Estimate this value.

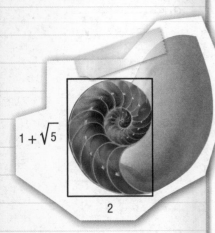

$1 + \sqrt{5}$

2

First estimate the value of $\sqrt{5}$.

$4 < 5 < 9$	4 and 9 are the closest perfect squares.
$2^2 < 5 < 3^2$	$4 = 2^2$ and $9 = 3^2$
$\sqrt{2^2} < \sqrt{5} < \sqrt{3^2}$	Find the square root of each number.
$2 < \sqrt{5} < 3$	Simplify.

Since 5 is closer to 4 than 9, the best integer estimate for $\sqrt{5}$ is 2. Use this value to evaluate the expression.

$$\frac{1 + \sqrt{5}}{2} \approx \frac{1 + 2}{2} \text{ or } 1.5$$

Guided Practice

 Check

Estimate to the nearest integer. (Examples 1 and 2)

Show your work.

1. $\sqrt{28} \approx$ _____

2. $\sqrt{135} \approx$ _____

3. $\sqrt{38.7} \approx$ _____

4. $\sqrt[3]{51} \approx$ _____

5. $\sqrt[3]{200} \approx$ _____

6. $\sqrt[3]{95} \approx$ _____

7. STEM Tobias dropped a tennis ball from a height of 60 meters. The time in seconds it takes for the ball to fall 60 feet is $0.25(\sqrt{60})$. Find three sets of approximations for the amount of time it will take. Then determine how long it will take for the ball to hit the ground. (Example 3)

_____

_____

8. The number of swings back and forth of a pendulum of length L in inches each minute is $\dfrac{375}{\sqrt{L}}$. About how many swings will a 40-inch pendulum make each minute? (Example 4)

_____

9. (e) **Building on the Essential Question** How can I estimate the square root of a non-perfect square?

_____

_____

Rate Yourself!

How confident are you about finding the square root of a non-perfect square? Mark an X in the section that applies.

I'm on target.

I need help.

For more help, go online to access a Personal Tutor.

Tutor

Extra Practice

Estimate to the nearest integer.

20. $\sqrt{44} \approx$ ___7___

> **Homework Help** →
> $36 \ < \ 44 \ < 49$
> $6^2 \ < \ 44 \ < 7^2$
> $\sqrt{6^2} < \sqrt{44} < \sqrt{7^2}$
> $\sqrt{44}$ is closer to $\sqrt{49}$ or 7.

21. $\sqrt[3]{199} \approx$ ___6___

> $125 \ < \ 199 < 216$
> $5^3 \ < \sqrt[3]{199} < 6^3$
> $\sqrt{5^3} < \sqrt[3]{199} < \sqrt{6^3}$
> $\sqrt[3]{199}$ is closer to $\sqrt{216}$ or 6.

22. $\sqrt{125} \approx$ _____

23. $\sqrt{23.5} \approx$ _____

24. $\sqrt[3]{59} \approx$ _____

25. $\sqrt[3]{430} \approx$ _____

Estimate the solution of each equation to the nearest integer.

26. $y^2 = 55$

27. $d^2 = 95$

28. $p^2 = 6.8$

The volume of each cube is given. Estimate the side length of the cube to the nearest integer. Use the formula $V = s^3$.

29. _____

210 in³

30. _____

520 cm³

31. **CCGPS** **Use Math Tools** Jacob is buying a bag of grass seed. The two-pound bag will cover 1,000 square feet of lawn. Estimate the side length of the largest square Jacob could seed if he purchases 5 bags.

_____

32. The radius of a circle with area A is approximately $\sqrt{\frac{A}{3}}$. If a pizza has an area of 78 square inches, which of the following is the best approximation of the radius of the pizza?

(A) 3 inches   (C) 8 inches

(B) 5 inches   (D) 26 inches

33. The new library at Walnut Hills Middle School has a carpeted floor in the shape of a square. If the area of the floor is 52,000 square feet, what is the approximate length in feet of one side of the square floor?

(F) 26,000   (H) 1,500

(G) 3,000   (I) 225

34. Short Response After an accident, officials use the formula below to estimate the speed the car was traveling based on the length of the car's skid marks.

$$s = \sqrt{24m}$$

In the formula, s represents the speed in miles per hour and m is the length of the skid marks in feet. If a car leaves a skid mark of 50 feet, what was its approximate speed? Show all work necessary to justify your answer.

CCGPS Common Core Review

Write each of the following as a fraction in simplest form. MCC7.NS.2.d

35. $-36 =$ _____

36. $1.7 =$ _____

37. $-0.048 =$ _____

38. $98\% =$ _____

Order each set of numbers from least to greatest. MCC6.NS.7

39. $\{4(8), 3^3, 5^2\}$

40. $\{3^4, 5^2, 2^5\}$

41. $\{25^2 \cdot 3, 10^3, 12^2 + 4\}$

42. Of the 150 students in Mr. Bacon's classes, 16% play soccer, $\frac{9}{25}$ play basketball, 3^3 play football and 14 do not play a sport at all. Write the number of students in order from least to greatest. MCC6.NS.7

Compare Real Numbers

What You'll Learn

Scan the lesson. Write the definitions of irrational number and real number.

- _____

  _____

- _____

  _____

Essential Question

WHY is it helpful to write numbers in different ways?

Vocabulary

irrational number
real number

Common Core GPS

Content Standards
MCC8.NS.1, MCC8.NS.2, MCC8.EE.2

Mathematical Practices
1, 3, 4, 6

Real-World Link

Sports Major League baseball has rules for the dimensions of the baseball diamond. A model of the diamond is shown.

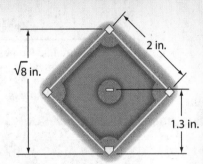

2 in.

$\sqrt{8}$ in.

1.3 in.

1. On the model, the distance from the pitching mound to home plate is 1.3 inches. Is 1.3 a rational number? Explain.

   _____

2. On the model, the distance from first base to second base is 2 inches. Is 2 a rational number? Explain.

   _____

3. The distance from home plate to second base is $\sqrt{8}$ inches. Using a calculator, find $\sqrt{8}$. Does it appear to terminate or repeat?

   _____

   _____

4. To determine if the number terminates, on your calculator, multiply your answer to $\sqrt{8}$ by itself. Do not use the x^2 button.

   Is the answer 8? _____

5. Based on your results, can you classify $\sqrt{8}$ as a rational number? Explain.

   _____

   _____

Real Numbers

Work Zone

STOP and Reflect

Explain below how you know that $\sqrt{2}$ is an irrational number.

Words

Rational Number

A rational number is a number that can be expressed as the ratio $\frac{a}{b}$, where a and b are integers and $b \neq 0$.

Irrational Number

An **irrational number** is a number that *cannot* be expressed as the ratio $\frac{a}{b}$, where a and b are integers and $b \neq 0$.

Examples $-2, 5, 3.\overline{76}, -12\frac{7}{8}$ $\sqrt{2} \approx 1.414213562...$

Numbers that are not rational are called irrational numbers. The square root of any number that is not a perfect square number is irrational. The set of rational numbers and the set of irrational numbers together make up the set of **real numbers**. Study the Venn diagram below.

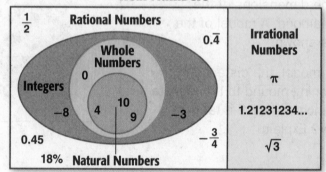

Real Numbers

Examples

Tutor

Name all sets of numbers to which each real number belongs.

1. **0.2525...**   The decimal ends in a repeating pattern. It is a rational number because it is equivalent to $\frac{25}{99}$.

2. **$\sqrt{36}$**   Since $\sqrt{36} = 6$, it is a natural number, a whole number, an integer, and a rational number.

Show your work.

3. **$-\sqrt{7}$** $-\sqrt{7} \approx -2.645751311...$ The decimal does not terminate nor repeat, so it is an irrational number.

Got It?   Do these problems to find out.

   a. $\sqrt{10}$ **b.** $-2\frac{2}{5}$ **c.** $\sqrt{100}$

[handwritten notes in margin:]

irRational

3.16

a. _____

b. Rational

c. Natural

Compare and Order Real Numbers

You can compare and order real numbers by writing them in the same notation. Write the numbers in decimal notation before comparing or ordering them.

Examples

Fill in each ◯ with <, >, or = to make a true statement.

4. $\sqrt{7}$ ◯ $2\frac{2}{3}$

$\sqrt{7} \approx 2.645751311...$

$2\frac{2}{3} = 2.666666666...$

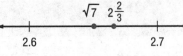

Since 2.645751311... is less than 2.66666666..., $\sqrt{7} < 2\frac{2}{3}$.

---

5. **15.7%** ◯ $\sqrt{0.02}$

$15.7\% = 0.157$

$\sqrt{0.02} \approx 0.141$

Since 0.157 is greater than 0.141, $15.7\% > \sqrt{0.02}$.

---

6. Order the set $\left\{\sqrt{30}, 6, 5\frac{4}{5}, 5.3\overline{6}\right\}$ from least to greatest. Verify your answer by graphing on a number line.

Write each number as a decimal. Then order the decimals.

$\sqrt{30} \approx 5.48$

$6 = 6.00$

$5\frac{4}{5} = 5.80$

$5.3\overline{6} \approx 5.37$

From least to greatest, the order is $5.3\overline{6}$, $\sqrt{30}$, $5\frac{4}{5}$, and 6.

Got It? Do these problems to find out.

d. $\sqrt{11}$ ◯ $3\frac{1}{3}$ **e.** $\sqrt{17}$ ◯> 4.03   **f.** $\sqrt{6.25}$ ◯ 250%

g. Order the set $\left\{-7, -\sqrt{60}, -7\frac{7}{10}, -\frac{66}{9}\right\}$ from least to greatest. Verify your answer by graphing on the number line below.

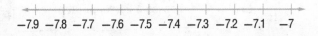

Show your work.

$-\sqrt{60}, -7\frac{7}{10}, -\frac{66}{9}$

g. -7

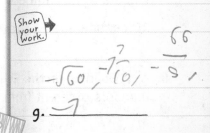

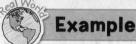

Example

Watch | Tutor

7. On a clear day, the number of miles a person can see to the horizon is about 1.23 times the square root of his or her distance from the ground in feet. Suppose Frida is at the Empire Building observation deck at 1,250 feet and Kia is at the Freedom Tower observation deck at 1,362 feet. How much farther can Kia see than Frida?

Use a calculator to approximate the distance each person can see.

Frida: $1.23 \cdot \sqrt{1{,}250} \approx 43.49$ Kia: $1.23 \cdot \sqrt{1{,}362} \approx 45.39$

Kia can see $45.39 - 43.49$ or 1.90 miles farther than Frida.

Guided Practice

Check

Name all sets of numbers to which each real number belongs. (Examples 1–3)

Show your work.

1. 0.050505… _____

2. $-\sqrt{64}$ _____

3. $\sqrt{17}$ _____

Fill in each ◯ **with <, >, or = to make a true statement.** (Examples 4 and 5)

4. $\sqrt{15}$ ◯ 3.5

5. $\sqrt{2.25}$ ◯ 150%

6. $\sqrt{6.2}$ ◯ $2.\overline{4}$

7. Order the set $\left\{ \sqrt{5}, 220\%, 2.25, 2.\overline{2} \right\}$ from least to greatest. Verify your answer by graphing on a number line. (Example 6)

2.19 2.2 2.21 2.22 2.23 2.24 2.25 2.26 2.27 2.28 2.29 2.3

_____

8. The formula $A = \sqrt{s(s-a)(s-b)(s-c)}$ can be used to find the area A of a triangle. The variables a, b, and c are the side measures and s is one half the perimeter. Use the formula to find the area of a triangle with side lengths of 7 centimeters, 9 centimeters, and

10 centimeters. (Example 7) _____

9. ⓔ **Building on the Essential Question** How are real numbers different from irrational numbers?

_____

_____

Rate Yourself!

How well do you understand real numbers? Circle the image that applies.

Clear

Somewhat Clear

Not So Clear

For more help, go online to access a Personal Tutor.

Tutor

Extra Practice

21. Name all sets of real numbers to which
$\sqrt{10}$ belongs. _irrational_

$\sqrt{10} \approx 3.16227766...$ Since the decimal
does not terminate nor repeat, it is an
irrational number.

22. Fill in ◯ with <, >, or = to make
5.1$\overline{5}$ ⊙ $\sqrt{26}$ a true statement.

Write each number as a decimal.
5.1$\overline{5}$ = 5.155555...
$\sqrt{26} \approx 5.099019...$
Since 5.155555... is greater than 5.099019...,
5.1$\overline{5}$ > $\sqrt{26}$.

Name all sets of numbers to which each real number belongs.

23. 14

_____

24. $-\sqrt{16}$

_____

25. $-\sqrt[3]{90}$

_____

Fill in each ◯ with <, >, or = to make a true statement.

26. $\sqrt{12}$ ◯ 3.5

27. $6\frac{1}{3}$ ◯ $\sqrt[3]{240}$

28. 240% ◯ $\sqrt{5.76}$

29. About how much greater is the perimeter of a square with area
250 square meters than a square with an area of 125 square meters?

_____

30. **CCGPS** **Persevere with Problems** In the sequence 4, 12, ■, 108, 324, the
missing number can be found by simplifying $\sqrt{ab}$ where a and b are the
numbers on either side of the missing number. Find the missing number.

_____

Fill in each ◯ with <, >, or = to make a true statement.

31. $3 + \sqrt{7}$ ◯ 6

32. $4 - \sqrt{10}$ ◯ $\sqrt{2}$

33. 13 ◯ $8 + \sqrt{20}$

34. Anna wants to plant circular garden in her back yard like the one shown.

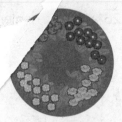

$A = 150 \text{ ft}^2$

The formula $r = \sqrt{\dfrac{A}{\pi}}$ gives the value of the radius r given the area A. What is the best approximation for the radius of Anna's garden?

Ⓐ 4 feet   Ⓒ 8 feet

Ⓑ 7 feet   Ⓓ 14 feet

35. Which number represents the point graphed on the number line?

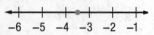

-6   -5   -4   -3   -2   -1

Ⓕ $-\sqrt{12}$

Ⓖ $-\sqrt{10}$

Ⓗ $-\sqrt{15}$

Ⓘ $-\sqrt{8}$

36. Short Response Which of the two real numbers below is greater?

$$\sqrt{3} \qquad \frac{1}{3}$$

Common Core Review

37. Order the set $\{7, \sqrt{53}, \sqrt{32}, 6\}$ from least to greatest. MCC8.EE.2

Solve each equation. MCC8.EE.2

38. $t^2 = 25$ _____

39. $y^2 = \dfrac{1}{49}$ _____

40. $0.64 = a^2$ _____

Evaluate each expression. Express the result in scientific notation. MCC8.EE.4

41. $(7.2 \times 10^4)(1.1 \times 10^{-6}) =$ _____

42. $(3.6 \times 10^3) + (5.7 \times 10^5) =$ _____

43. The table shows the approximate population of several countries. Order the countries from the greatest population to the least population. MCC8.EE.4

Country	Population
China	1.3×10^9
India	1.2×10^9
Indonesia	2.3×10^8
United States	3.1×10^8

Robotics Engineer

Are you mechanically inclined? Do you like to find new ways to solve problems? If so, a career as a robotics engineer is something you should consider. Robotics engineers design and build robots to perform tasks that are difficult, dangerous, or tedious for humans. For example, a robotic insect was developed based on a real insect. Its purpose was to travel over water surfaces, take measurements, and monitor water quality.

College & Career
READINESS

Explore college and careers at ccr.mcgraw-hill.com

Is This the Career for You?

Are you interested in a career as a robotics engineer? Take some of the following courses in high school.

- Calculus
- Electro-Mechanical Systems
- Fundamentals of Robotics
- Physics

Turn the page to find out how math relates to a career in Engineering.

Relying on Robots

Use the information in the table to solve each problem.

1. Write the mass of the robot in standard form. _____

2. Write the length of the robot in scientific notation. _____

3. Write the leg diameter of the robot in scientific notation. _____

4. What is the mass in milligrams? Write in standard form. _____

5. Real insects called water striders can travel 8.3 times faster than the robot. Write the speed of water striders in scientific notation. _____

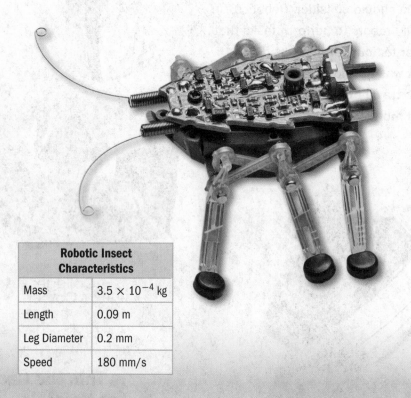

Robotic Insect Characteristics	
Mass	3.5×10^{-4} kg
Length	0.09 m
Leg Diameter	0.2 mm
Speed	180 mm/s

Career Project

It's time to update your career portfolio! Investigate the education and training requirements for a career in robotics engineering.

_____
_____
_____
_____
_____
_____

What skills would you need to improve to succeed in this career?
- _____
- _____
- _____
- _____
- _____

Vocabulary Check

Complete the crossword puzzle using the vocabulary list at the beginning of the chapter.

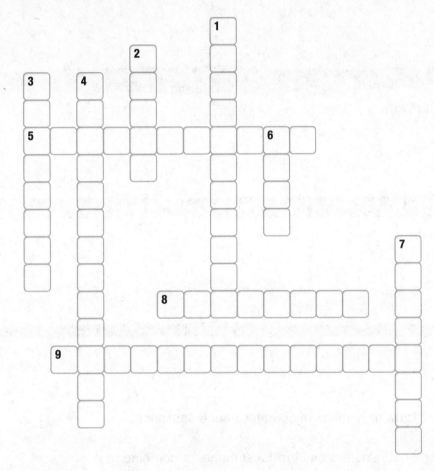

Across

5. a rational number whose cube root is a whole number

8. a number, a variable, or a product of a number and one or more variables

9. numbers that can be written as a comparison of two integers, expressed as a fraction

Down

1. the symbol used to indicate a positive square root

2. a product of repeated factors using a base and exponent

3. this tells how many times a number is used as a factor

4. a rational number whose square root is a whole number

6. in a power, the number that is the common factor

7. one of a number's three equal factors

Use Your FOLDABLES®

Use your Foldable to help review the chapter.

Tape here

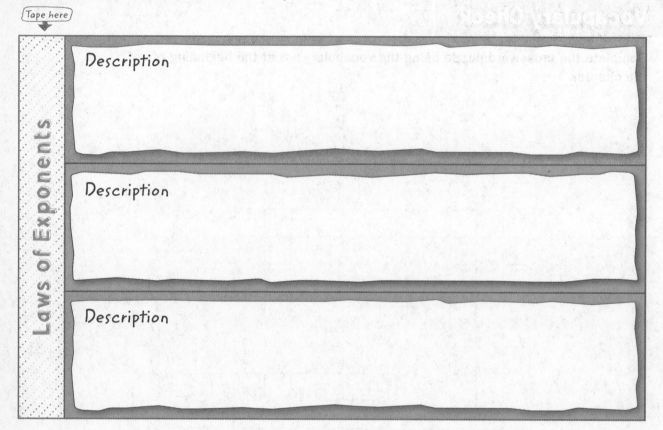

Laws of Exponents

Description

Description

Description

Got it?

Circle the correct term or number to complete each sentence.

1. The sets of rational numbers and irrational numbers combine to make the (whole, real) numbers.

2. The product of $3a^2b$ and $-3a^2b$ is ($-9a^4b^2$, a^4b).

3. You would use the (Power of a Product rule, Product of Powers rule) to simplify the expression $(p^2r)^4$.

4. The expression $\dfrac{6^2 \cdot 2^6 \cdot 8^4}{6 \cdot 2^3 \cdot 8^3}$ is equal to (384, 288).

5. Another way to write $(9^4)^7$ is (9^{11}, 9^{28}).

6. 3^{-4} is equal to $\left(-81, \dfrac{1}{81}\right)$.

7. Scientific notation is when a number is written as a product of a power of 10 and a factor greater than or equal to 1 and (less than, less than or equal to) 10.

Problem Solving

1. To close school, the principal calls six teachers, who in turn call six more. If each of those teachers call six more, how many calls will be made by the teachers in this last group? (Lesson 3) _____

Show your work.

2. In a house, the area of the den is 3^4 square feet. The area of the kitchen is 3^3 square feet. How many times larger is the den than the kitchen?

(Lesson 3) _____

3. The smallest mammal is Kitti's hog-nosed bat weighing about 4.375×10^{-3} pound. Write this weight in standard form. (Lesson 6)

_____

4. The Guadalupe River is 2.56×10^2 miles long. The Amazon River is 4.096×10^3 miles long. How many times longer is the Amazon River

than the Guadalupe River? (Lesson 7) _____

5. Jodie took the measurements of her favorite jewelry box. Order the set of measurements $\left\{2.\overline{2}, 2\frac{1}{5}, 2.25, \sqrt{5}\right\}$ from least to greatest. (Lesson 10)

_____

6. A quilter made 256 small squares for a large quilt. If the quilt is shaped like a square, how many small squares will she use on each side? (Lesson 8)

_____

Reflect

 Answering the Essential Question

Use what you learned about numbers to complete the graphic organizer. For each category, describe why you would use that form for the number $35{,}036\frac{1}{3}$. Then write the number in that form. If you would not use the number in that form, explain why.

Decimal

Power

Fraction

Scientific Notation

WHY is it helpful to write numbers in different ways?

Answer the Essential Question. WHY is it helpful to write numbers in different ways?

Chapter 4
Equations in One Variable

Essential Question
WHAT is equivalence?

Common Core GPS

Content Standards
MCC8.EE.7, MCC8.EE.7a, MCC8.EE.7b

Mathematical Practices
1, 2, 3, 4, 5, 7

Math in the Real World

Tips Maria and her family had salads and dinner at a local restaurant. Her mother wants to leave an 18% tip. The proportion $\frac{p}{\$35.60} = \frac{18}{100}$ can be used to find the amount of tip she should leave.

Use the proportion to find the amount of tip Maria's mother should leave. Then find the total amount.

Pizzeria
Date:
Card Type:
Acct. No.:
Exp. Date:
Check:
Table:
Subtotal: **$35.60**
Tip: _ _ _ _ _ _
Total: _ _ _ _ _ _

FOLDABLES® Study Organizer

1 Cut out the correct Foldable from the FL pages in the back of this book.

2 Place your Foldable on the Key Concept page toward the end of this chapter.

3 Use the Foldable throughout this chapter to help you learn about solving equations.

What Tools Do You Need?

Vocabulary

coefficient	multiplicative inverse	properties
identity	null set	two-step equation

Study Skill: Writing Math

Justify Your Answer When you justify your answer, you give *reasons* why your answer is correct.

The different plans an online movie rental company offers are shown. Mariah wants to purchase the 2 DVDs at-a-time plan. This month, the plans are advertised at $\frac{1}{4}$ off. If she has $10.00 to spend, does she have enough?
Justify your answer.

Online DVD Rental	
Plan	**Monthly Price ($)**
3 DVDs at-a-time	14.50
2 DVDs at-a-time	12.00
1 DVD at-a-time	8.00

Step 1 **Solve the problem.**	Find the discount. $\frac{1}{4}$ of 12 = 3 The discount is $3.00. Find the discounted price. $12 − $3 = $9
Step 2 **Answer the question.**	Mariah does have enough money.
Step 3 **Justify your answer.** Always write complete sentences.	Mariah has enough money because $9.00 is less than $10.00.

You can buy 3 used CDs at The Music Shoppe for $12.99, or you can buy 5 for $19.99 at Quality Sounds. Which is the better buy? Justify your answer.

Step 1 **Solve the problem.**	
Step 2 **Answer the question.**	
Step 3 **Justify your answer.** Always write complete sentences.	

 **Are You Ready?**

Try the Quick Check below.
Or, take the Online Readiness Quiz. Check ✓

CCGPS Quick Review Common Core Review MCC7.EE.4

Example 1

Solve $44 = k - 7$.

$$44 = k - 7 \qquad \text{Write the equation.}$$
$$\underline{+\,7 = +\,7} \qquad \text{Addition Property of Equality}$$
$$51 = k$$

Example 2

Solve $18m = -360$.

$$18m = -360 \qquad \text{Write the equation.}$$
$$\frac{18m}{18} = \frac{-360}{18} \qquad \text{Division Property of Equality}$$
$$m = -20 \qquad \text{Simplify.}$$

Quick Check

One-Step Equations Solve each equation. Check your solution.

1. $n + 8 = -9$

2. $4 = p + 19$

3. $-4 + a = 15$

 Show your work.

4. $3c = -18$

5. $-42 = -6b$

6. $\frac{w}{4} = -8$

7. Barry has 18 more marbles than Heidi. If Barry has 92 marbles, write and solve an equation to determine the number of marbles Heidi has.

_____

 How Did You Do?

Which problems did you answer correctly in the Quick Check?
Shade those exercise numbers below.

①　②　③　④　⑤　⑥　⑦

Solve Equations with Rational Coefficients

What You'll Learn

Scan the lesson. List two headings you would use to make an outline of the lesson.

- _____
- _____

Vocabulary Start-Up

Two numbers with a product of 1, such as $\frac{3}{4}$ and $\frac{4}{3}$, are called reciprocals or **multiplicative inverses**.

Complete the graphic organizer.

Define It	Describe It
List Some Examples	List Some Nonexamples

(multiplicative inverse)

Describe how a multiplicative inverse is used in division of fractions.

_____

 Real-World Link

How can the action of the motorcyclist in the photo help you

remember what the multiplicative inverse is? _____

_____

Essential Question

WHAT is equivalence?

Vocabulary

multiplicative inverse
coefficient

Common Core GPS

Content Standards
MCC8.EE.7, MCC8.EE.7a,
MCC8.EE.7b

Mathematical Practices
1, 3, 4, 7

Yikes!

Inverse Property of Multiplication

Words	The product of a number and its multiplicative inverse is 1.
Numbers	$\frac{7}{8} \times \frac{8}{7} = 1 \qquad\qquad -\frac{3}{2} \times -\frac{2}{3} = 1$
Symbols	$\frac{a}{b} \cdot \frac{b}{a} = 1$, where a and $b \neq 0$

Work Zone

STOP and Reflect

What is the multiplicative inverse of $-\frac{3}{2}$?

The numerical factor of a term that contains a variable is called the **coefficient** of the variable.

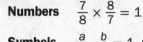

coefficient $\cdots\!\rightarrow$ **3x** $\leftarrow\!\cdots$ variable

In the equation $\frac{3}{4}c = 18$, the coefficient of c is a rational number. To solve an equation when the coefficient is a fraction, multiply each side by the multiplicative inverse of the fraction.

Example

Tutor

1. Solve $\frac{3}{4}c = 18$. Check your solution.

$\frac{3}{4}c = 18$ — Write the equation.

$\left(\frac{4}{3}\right) \cdot \frac{3}{4}c = \left(\frac{4}{3}\right) \cdot 18$ — Multiply each side by the multiplicative inverse of $\frac{3}{4}$, $\frac{4}{3}$.

$\overset{1}{\underset{1}{\frac{4}{3}}} \cdot \overset{1}{\underset{1}{\frac{3}{4}}}c = \frac{4}{3} \cdot \overset{6}{\underset{1}{\frac{18}{1}}}$ — Write 18 as $\frac{18}{1}$. Divide by common factors.

$c = 24$ — Simplify.

Check $\frac{3}{4}c = 18$ — Write the original equation.

$\frac{3}{4}(24) \overset{?}{=} 18$ — Replace c with 24.

$\frac{3}{4} \cdot \overset{6}{\underset{1}{\frac{24}{1}}} \overset{?}{=} 18$ — Write 24 as $\frac{24}{1}$. Divide by common factors.

$18 = 18$ ✓ — This sentence is true.

Got It? Do these problems to find out.

Show your work.

a. _$x = 60$_

b. _$d = -18$_

c. _$9 = N$_

d. _$\frac{168}{6} = P$_

$\overset{5}{\underset{1}{}}$ **a.** $\frac{1}{5}x = 12$ ×$\frac{5}{}$ $= 60\overset{9}{\underset{2}{}}$ **b.** $-\frac{2}{9}d = 4$ $-\frac{9}{2}$

$x = 60$ $d = 18$

$\overset{3}{\underset{5}{}}$× **c.** $15 = \frac{5}{3}n$ $\frac{3}{5}$ **d.** $-24 = -\frac{6}{7}p$× $-\frac{7}{6}$

$-\frac{3}{6}$× $\overset{}{\underset{1}{}}$

$9 = N$ $\frac{168}{6} = P$

Example

2. Solve $1\frac{1}{2}s = 16\frac{1}{2}$. Check your solution.

$$1\frac{1}{2}s = 16\frac{1}{2}$$ Write the equation.

$$\frac{3}{2}s = \frac{33}{2}$$ Rename $1\frac{1}{2}$ as $\frac{3}{2}$ and $16\frac{1}{2}$ as $\frac{33}{2}$.

$$\left(\frac{2}{3}\right) \cdot \frac{3}{2}s = \left(\frac{2}{3}\right) \cdot \frac{33}{2}$$ Multiply each side by the multiplicative inverse of $\frac{3}{2}$, $\frac{2}{3}$.

$$\frac{\overset{1}{\cancel{2}}}{\underset{1}{\cancel{3}}} \cdot \frac{\overset{1}{\cancel{3}}}{\underset{1}{\cancel{2}}}s = \frac{\overset{1}{\cancel{2}}}{\underset{1}{\cancel{3}}} \cdot \frac{\overset{11}{\cancel{33}}}{\underset{1}{\cancel{2}}}$$ Divide by common factors.

$$s = 11$$ Simplify.

Got It? Do these problems to find out.

d. $4\frac{1}{6} = 3\frac{1}{3}c$ **e.** $-9\frac{5}{8}w = 108$ **f.** $1\frac{7}{8}y = 4\frac{1}{2}$

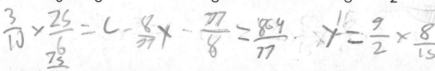

d. $1\frac{1}{4}$

e. $-\frac{864}{77}$

f. $2\frac{12}{5}$

Solve Equations with Decimal Coefficients

In the equation $3.15 = 0.45n$ the coefficient of n is a decimal. To solve an equation with a decimal coefficient, divide each side of the equation by the coefficient.

Quick Review

Division

$$0.45\overline{)3.15}$$
$$\underline{-315}$$
$$0$$
(quotient 7)

Example

3. Solve $3.15 = 0.45n$. Check your solution.

$$3.15 = 0.45n$$ Write the equation.

$$\frac{3.15}{0.45} = \frac{0.45n}{0.45}$$ Division Property of Equality

$$7 = n$$ Simplify.

Check $3.15 = 0.45n$ Write the original equation.

$$3.15 = 0.45(7)$$ Replace n with 7.

$$3.15 = 3.15 ✓$$ The sentence is true.

Got It? Do these problems to find out.

g. $\dfrac{4.9}{0.7} = \dfrac{0.7t}{0.7}$ **h.** $\dfrac{-1.4m}{-7} = \dfrac{2.1}{-7}$ **i.** $\dfrac{-5.6k}{-5.6} = \dfrac{-12.88}{-5.6}$

$7 = t$

$\dfrac{-2m = -3}{2 \quad\quad 2}$

$m = -1.5$

g. $7 = t$

h. $m = -1.5$

i. $k = 2.3$

$5.6\overline{)12.88}$

3

Lesson 1 Solve Equations with Rational Coefficients **269**

4. Latoya's softball team won 75%, or 18, of its games. Define a variable. Then write and solve an equation to determine the number of games the team played.

Latoya's softball team won 18 games, which was 75% of the games played. Let n represent the number of games played. Write and solve an equation.

$0.75n = 18$ Write the equation. Write 75% as 0.75.

$$\frac{0.75n}{0.75} = \frac{18}{0.75}$$ Division Property of Equality

$n = 24$ Simplify.

Latoya's softball team played 24 games.

Guided Practice

 Check

Solve each equation. Check your solution. (Examples 1–3)

1. $60 = \frac{3}{4}p$

 Show your work.

2. $-\frac{27}{25}x = -\frac{9}{5}$

3. $-2.7t = 810$

4. Paula has read 70% of the total pages in a book she is reading for English class. Paula has read 84 pages. Define a variable. Then write and solve an equation to determine how many pages are in the book. (Example 4)

5. **Building on the Essential Question** How is the multiplicative inverse used to solve an equation that has a rational coefficient?

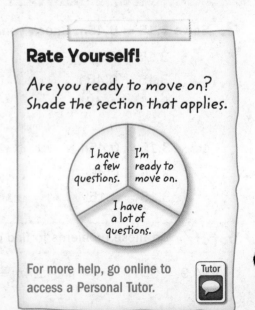

Extra Practice

Solve each equation. Check your solution.

19. $\frac{1}{2} = \frac{2}{5}z$

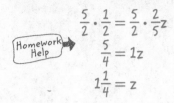

$$\frac{5}{2} \cdot \frac{1}{2} = \frac{5}{2} \cdot \frac{2}{5}z$$
$$\frac{5}{4} = 1z$$
$$1\frac{1}{4} = z$$

20. $-\frac{3}{4}t = 5$

21. $-\frac{2}{9}g = -\frac{7}{9}$

22. $0.6w = 0.48$

23. $-226.8 = 21.6y$

24. $-30 = 1.25c$

25. $1\frac{1}{2}x = 9\frac{9}{20}$

26. $-12\frac{2}{3} = -1\frac{1}{9}y$

27. $1\frac{5}{7} = 1\frac{13}{14}a$

28. One third of the bagels in a bakery are sesame bagels. There are 72 sesame bagels. Define a variable. Then write and solve an equation to find how many bagels there were in the bakery.

_____

_____

29. CCGPS **Find the Error** Sarah is solving the equation $-\frac{7}{8}x = 24$. Circle her mistake and correct it.

_____

_____

_____

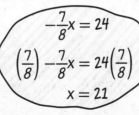

$$-\frac{7}{8}x = 24$$
$$\left(\frac{7}{8}\right) -\frac{7}{8}x = 24\left(\frac{7}{8}\right)$$
$$x = 21$$

Georgia Test Practice

30. What is the reciprocal of $-\frac{4}{3}$?

Ⓐ $-1\frac{1}{3}$

Ⓑ $-\frac{3}{4}$

Ⓒ $\frac{3}{4}$

Ⓓ $1\frac{1}{3}$

31. An airplane travels 100 miles in 0.4 hour. Which speed represents the rate of the airplane?

Ⓕ 50 miles per hour

Ⓖ 100 miles per hour

Ⓗ 250 miles per hour

Ⓘ 500 miles per hour

32. Short Response To train for a marathon, Uyen ran a total of 71 miles in one month. This distance is $2\frac{1}{2}$ times the distance that she ran in the first week. How many miles did Uyen run in the first week?

_____

_____

 ## Common Core Review

Solve each equation. Check your solution. MCC7.EE.4

33. $w + 5 = -20$

34. $x - 17 = -32$

35. $t + 7.2 = 1.65$

36. $-0.4 = g - 4.9$

37. $y - \frac{2}{5} = 1\frac{3}{5}$

38. $-5\frac{1}{6} = 2\frac{1}{3} + p$

39. Financial Literacy Simone saved \$65.35 more than her brother Dan and \$37.50 less than her sister Carly. Carly saved \$127.75. Write and solve equations to find how much money Simone and Dan saved. MCC6.EE.7

_____

40. A college basketball team won 72.5% of the games they played. If they played 80 games, how many did they win? MCC6.RP.3 _____

Inquiry HOW does a bar diagram help you solve a real-world problem involving a two-step equation?

 Content Standards
MCC8.EE.7,
MCC8.EE.7a
Mathematical Practices
1, 2, 3, 4

Postcards Miranda bought two large postcards and four small postcards at a souvenir shop. Each small postcard costs $0.50. If Miranda spent $5.00 on postcards, what is the cost of one large postcard?

What do you know? _____

_____

What do you need to find? _____

Investigation

Step 1 The bar diagram represents the total number of postcards and the total cost. Label the missing parts.

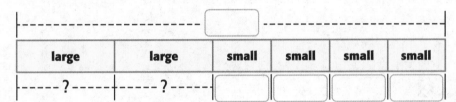

Step 2 Fill in the boxes to write an equation that represents the bar diagram. The cost of a large postcard is the unknown, so it is represented by the variable p.

$$2p + \boxed{} = \boxed{}$$

Step 3 Find the cost of the large postcards by working backward.

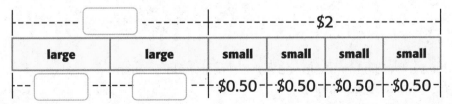

The cost of one large postcard is _____.

CCGPS **Reason Abstractly** Work with a partner. Use a bar diagram to write and solve an equation for each exercise.

1. Brooke and two friends went to the movies and spent a total of $42. The movie tickets were $5 each and they each bought a popcorn combo. What is the cost of one popcorn combo?

 Show your work.

2. Four medium postcards and 4 small postcards cost $5. What is the cost of one medium postcard?

medium	medium	medium	medium	small	small	small	small

$5

| | | | | 0.50 | 0.50 | 0.50 | 0.50 |

 Reflect

3. **CCGPS** **Model with Mathematics** Write and solve a word problem that could represent the bar diagram shown.

4. **Inquiry** HOW does a bar diagram help you solve a real-world problem involving a two-step equation?

Solve Two-Step Equations

What You'll Learn

Scan the lesson. List two real-world scenarios in which you would solve two-step equations.

- _____
  _____

- _____

Essential Question

WHAT is equivalence?

Vocabulary

properties
two-step equation

CCGPS Common Core GPS

Content Standards
MCC8.EE.7, MCC8.EE.7a,
MCC8.EE.7b

Mathematical Practices
1, 2, 3, 4

Vocabulary Start-Up

Recall that in mathematics, **properties** are statements that are true for any number.

Complete the graphic organizer by matching the Property of Equality with the correct example.

Addition Property of Equality	$\frac{1}{2}x = 10$ $2 \cdot \frac{1}{2}x = 10 \cdot 2$
Division Property of Equality	$3x = 9$ $\frac{3x}{3} = \frac{9}{3}$
Multiplication Property of Equality	$x + 3 = 1$ $x + 3 - 3 = 1 - 3$
Subtraction Property of Equality	$x - 5 = 6$ $x - 5 + 5 = 6 + 5$

Real-World Link

A property in science is a trait of matter that is always true under a given set of conditions. For example, pure water freezes at 0°C. How is the definition of *property* similar in science and math?

_____

Solve Two-Step Equations

A **two-step equation** contains two operations. In the equation $2x + 3 = 7$, x is multiplied by 2 and then 3 is added. To solve two-step equations, undo each operation in reverse order.

Example

1. Solve $2x + 3 = 7$.

Method 1   Use a model.

Remove three 1-tiles from each mat.

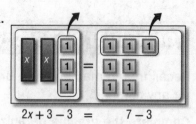

$$2x + 3 - 3 = 7 - 3$$

Separate the remaining tiles into 2 equal groups.

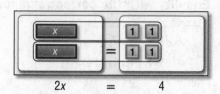

$$2x = 4$$

There are two 1-tiles in each group, so $x = 2$.

Method 2   Use symbols.

$2x + 3 = 7$	Write the equation.
$\dfrac{-3 = -3}{2x \quad = 4}$	Subtraction Property of Equality
$\dfrac{2x}{2} = \dfrac{4}{2}$	Division Property of Equality
$x = 2$	Simplify.

Using either method, the solution is 2.

Show your work.

a. $\underline{\quad x = 6 \quad}$

b. $\underline{\quad n = -3 \quad}$

Got It?   Do these problems to find out.

a. $3x + 2 = 20$

$\; -2 \;\; -2$

$\dfrac{3x = 18}{3 \qquad 3}$

$x = 6$

b. $5 + 2n = -1$

$-5 \qquad -5$

$\dfrac{2n}{2} = \dfrac{-6}{2}$

$n = -3$

Example

2. Solve $25 = \frac{1}{4}n - 3$.

$25 = \frac{1}{4}n - 3$ Write the equation.

$\underline{+3 = \quad + 3}$ Addition Property of Equality

$28 = \frac{1}{4}n$ Simplify.

$4 \cdot 28 = 4 \cdot \frac{1}{4}n$ Multiplication Property of Equality

$112 = n$

The solution is 112.

Got It?   Do these problems to find out.

c. $-1 = \frac{1}{2}a + 9$ **d.** $\frac{2}{5}r - 5 = 7$

handwritten:
$\begin{array}{l} -9 \qquad\qquad -9 \\ \frac{2}{1} \times -10 = \frac{1}{2}a \times \frac{2}{1} \\ -20 = a \end{array}$

$\begin{array}{l} +5 \quad +5 \\ \frac{5}{2} \times \frac{2}{5}r = 12 \times \frac{5}{2} = \frac{60}{2} \\ R = 30 \end{array}$

Example

3. Solve $6 - 3x = 21$.

$6 - 3x = 21$ Write the equation.

$6 + (-3x) = 21$ Rewrite the left side as addition.

$\underline{-6 \qquad\qquad = -6}$ Subtraction Property of Equality

$-3x = 15$ Simplify.

$\frac{-3x}{-3} = \frac{15}{-3}$ Division Property of Equality

$x = -5$ Simplify.

The solution is -5.

Check $6 - 3x = 21$ Write the equation.

$6 - 3(-5) \stackrel{?}{=} 21$ Replace x with -5.

$6 - (-15) \stackrel{?}{=} 21$ Multiply.

$6 + 15 \stackrel{?}{=} 21$ To subtract a negative number, add its opposite.

$21 = 21$ ✓   The sentence is true.

Got It?   Do these problems to find out.

e. $10 - \frac{2}{3}p = 52$ **f.** $-19 = -3x + 2$ **g.** $\frac{n}{-3} - 2 = -18$

handwritten:
$\begin{array}{l} -10 \qquad\qquad -10 \\ -\frac{3}{2} \times -\frac{2}{3}p = 42 \times \frac{3}{2} \\ p = \frac{126}{2} \end{array}$

$\begin{array}{l} -2 \qquad\qquad -2 \\ \frac{-21}{-3} = \frac{-3x}{-3} \\ 7 = x \end{array}$

$\begin{array}{l} +2 \quad +2 \\ \frac{N}{-3} = -16 \\ x-3 \quad x-3 \\ N = 48 \end{array}$

Show your work.

c. $-20 = A$

d. $R = 30$

e. $P = -63$

f. $x = 7$

g. $n = 48$

Common Error
A common mistake when solving the equation in Example 3 is to divide each side by 3 instead of -3. Since $6 - 3x = 6 + (-3x)$, the coefficient is -3.

Example

Watch   Tutor

4. **STEM** Chicago's lowest recorded temperature in degrees Fahrenheit is $-27°$. Solve the equation $-27 = 1.8C + 32$ to convert to degrees Celsius.

$-27 = 1.8C + 32$	Write the equation.
$\underline{-32 = \qquad -32}$	Subtraction Property of Equality
$-59 = 1.8C$	Simplify.
$\dfrac{-59}{1.8} = \dfrac{1.8C}{1.8}$	Division Property of Equality
$-32.8 \approx C$	Simplify. Check the solution.

So, Chicago's lowest recorded temperature is about -32.8 degrees Celsius.

Guided Practice

Check ✓

Solve each equation. Check your solution. (Examples 1–3)

 Show your work.

1. $6x + 5 = 29$

2. $3 - 5y = -37$

3. $\dfrac{2}{3}x - 5 = 7$

4. Cassidy went to the movies with some of her friends. The tickets cost $6.50 each, and they spent $17.50 on snacks. The total amount paid was $63.00. Solve the equation $63 = 6.50p + 17.50$ to determine how many people went to the movies. (Example 4)

5. **Ⓠ Building on the Essential Question** How can you use the *work backward* problem-solving strategy to solve a two-step equation?

Rate Yourself!

How confident are you about solving equations? Check the box square that applies.

For more help, go online to access a Personal Tutor.

Tutor

Extra Practice

Solve each equation. Check your solution.

17. $2h + 9 = 21$

$$2h + 9 = 21$$
$$\underline{-9 = -9}$$
$$\frac{2h}{2} = \frac{12}{2}$$
$$h = 6$$

Homework Help →

18. $12 - \frac{3}{5}p = -27$

$$12 - \frac{3}{5}p = -27$$
$$\underline{-12 \qquad = -12}$$
$$-\frac{3}{5}p = -39$$
$$\left(-\frac{5}{3}\right)\left(-\frac{3}{5}p\right) = -39\left(-\frac{5}{3}\right)$$
$$p = 65$$

19. $11 = 2b + 17$

20. $-17 = 6p - 5$

21. $2g - 3 = -19$

22. $13 = \frac{g}{3} + 4$

23. $13 - 3d = -8$

24. $-\frac{2}{3}m - 4 = 10$

25. $-5y - 25 = 25$

26. Some friends decide to go to the aquarium together. Each person pays $7.50 to get in. They spend a total of $40 for the shark exhibit. The total cost is $70. Solve $7.5x + 40 = 70$ to find how many people went to the aquarium. _____

27. **CCGPS** **Identify Structure** Brent had $26 when he went to the fair. After playing 7 games, he had $15.50 left. Solve $15.50 = 26 - 7p$ to find the price for each game. Then list the Properties of Equality you used to solve the equation.

_____

28. The width of the rectangle below can be found by solving the equation $6w + 6 = 36$.

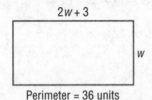

$2w + 3$

w

Perimeter = 36 units

What is the width of the rectangle?

Ⓐ 4 units   Ⓒ 6 units

Ⓑ 5 units   Ⓓ 7 units

29. Short Response What value of y makes the equation true? _____

$$\frac{y}{4} - 7 = 3$$

30. What is the vaue of x in the following equation?

$$40 = -11 + 3x$$

Ⓕ -17 Ⓗ $\frac{29}{3}$

Ⓖ $-\frac{29}{3}$ Ⓘ 17

Common Core Review

Solve each equation. Check your solution. MCC6.EE.7

31. $t - 17 = 5$

32. $a - 5 = 14$

33. $9 = 5 + x$

Write and solve an equation for each of the following. MCC6.EE.7

34. Solomon is 9 years younger than his brother. His brother is 21. How old is Solomon? _____

35. Kelly spent $45 more on boots than she did on a pair of jeans. She spent $79.50 on the boots. How much did she spend on the jeans?

_____

36. The product of two integers is 72. If one integer is 18, what is the other integer? _____

Write Two-Step Equations

What You'll Learn

Scan the lesson. List two headings you would use to make an outline of the lesson.

• _____

_____

• _____

_____

Essential Question

WHAT is equivalence?

Common Core GPS

Content Standards
MCC8.EE.7, MCC8.EE.7a, MCC8.EE.7b

Mathematical Practices
1, 2, 3, 4

Real-World Link

Robotics You want to attend a two-week robotic day camp that costs $700. Your parents will pay the deposit of $400 if you pay the rest in weekly payments of $15. Use the questions below to help you find the number of weeks you will need to make payments.

1. Complete the table below. How much is paid after 2, 3, and 4 weeks?

Payments	Amount Paid
0	$400 + 15(0) = 400$
1	$400 + 15(1) = 415$
2	
3	
4	

2. It will take a long time to solve the problem with a table. Instead, write and solve an equation to find the number of payments *p* you will need to make.

_____

3. How many payments will you make? _____

4. Suppose you received $75 in birthday money that you want to use towards the camp. Write and solve an equation to find the number of payments *p* you will need to make. _____

_____

Translate Sentences into Equations

There are three steps to writing a two-step equation.

Words	Describe the situation. Use only the most important words.
Variable	Define a variable to represent the unknown quantity.
Equation	Translate your verbal model into an algebraic equation.

You know how to write verbal sentences as one-step equations. Some verbal sentences translate into two-step equations.

Examples

Tutor

Translate each sentence into an equation.

1. **Eight less than three times a number is −23.**

Words	Eight less than three times a number is −23.
Variable	Let n represent the number.
Equation	$3n - 8 = -23$

2. **Thirteen is 7 more than one-fifth of a number.**

Words	Thirteen is 7 more than one-fifth of a number.
Variable	Let n represent the number.
Equation	$13 = \frac{1}{5}n + 7$

Show your work.

a. $N = 2$

Got It? Do these problems to find out.

b. $N = -30$

c. $N = 60$

a. Fifteen equals three more than six times a number.
$$6n + 3 = 15$$
b. Ten increased by the quotient of a number and 6 is 5.
$$10 = \frac{n}{6}$$
c. The difference between 12 and $\frac{2}{3}$ of a number is 18.
$$12 \times \frac{2}{3}n = 18$$

STOP and Reflect

Name 3 words that indicate an addition statement.

Examples

3. You buy 3 books that each cost the same amount and a magazine, all for \$55.99. You know that the magazine costs \$1.99. How much does each book cost?

Words	Three books and a magazine cost \$55.99.
Variable	Let b represent the cost of one book.
Equation	$3b + 1.99 = 55.99$

$$3b + 1.99 = 55.99$$ Write the equation.

$$-1.99 = -1.99$$ Subtraction Property of Equality

$$3b = 54.00$$ Simplify.

$$\frac{3b}{3} = \frac{54.00}{3}$$ Division Property of Equality

$$b = 18$$ Simplify.

So, the books each cost \$18.

4. A personal trainer buys a weight bench for \$500 and w weights for \$24.99 each. The total cost of the purchase is \$849.86. How many weights were purchased?

Words	Bench plus \$24.99 per weight equals \$849.86
Variable	Let w represent the number of weights.
Equation	$500 + 24.99 \cdot w = 849.86$

$$500 + 24.99w = 849.86$$ Write the equation.

$$-500 = -500$$ Subtraction Property of Equality

$$24.99w = 349.86$$ Simplify.

$$\frac{24.99w}{24.99} = \frac{349.86}{24.99}$$ Division Property of Equality

$$w = 14$$ Simplify.

So, 14 weights were purchased.

2 59
2 64
2 69
2 74
2 79
2 84

Got It? Do this problem to find out.

Show your work.

d. The current temperature is 54°F. It is expected to rise 2.5°F each hour. In how many hours will the temperature be 84°F?

d. 12

54+2.5x=84

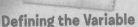

 Example

Watch ▶ | Tutor 💬

5. Your and your friend's lunch cost $19. Your lunch cost $3 more than your friend's. How much was your friend's lunch?

Words	Your friend's lunch plus your lunch equals $19.
Variable	Let f represent the cost of your friend's lunch.
Equation	$f + f + 3 = 19$

$f + f + 3 =$	19	Write the equation.
$2f + 3 =$	19	$f + f = 2f$
$-3 = -3$		Subtraction Property of Equality
$2f =$	16	Simplify.
$\dfrac{2f}{2} = \dfrac{16}{2}$		Division Property of Equality
$f = 8$		Simplify.

Your friend spent $8.

> **Defining the Variable**
> When the equation is solved, you can refer back to the definition of the variable to see if the question is answered or if additional steps are needed.

Guided Practice

 Check ✓

Translate each sentence into an equation. (Examples 1 and 2)

1. One more than three times a number is 7. _____

2. Seven less than one-fourth of a number is −1. _____

3. The quotient of a number and 5, less 10, is 3. _____

4. You already owe $4.32 in overdue rental fees and are returning a movie that is 4 days late. Now you owe $6.48. Define a variable. Then write and solve an equation to find the daily fine for an overdue movie. (Examples 3–5)

_____

5. ⓔ **Building on the Essential Question** Why is it important to define a variable before writing an equation? _____

_____

_____

> **Rate Yourself!**
>
> ☐ I understand how to write two-step equations.
>
> ▶▶ Great! You're ready to move on!
>
> ☐ I still have some questions about writing two-step equations.
>
> ⏸ No Problem! Go online to access a Personal Tutor. | Tutor 💬

Extra Practice

Translate each sentence into an equation.

14. Twenty-two less than three times a number is −70. $\underline{3n - 22 = -70}$

Words   *Twenty-two less than three times a number is −70.*

Variable   *Let n represent the number.*

Equation   *3n − 22 = −70*

15. The product of a number and 4 increased by 16 is −2. _____

16. Twelve less than the one-fifth of a number is −7. _____

17. Six more than nine times a number is 456. _____

Define a variable. Then write and solve an equation to solve each problem.

18. It costs $13 for admission to an amusement park, plus $1.50 for each ride. If you have a total of $35.50 to spend, what is the greatest number

of rides you can go on? _____

19. Trey went to the batting cages to practice hitting. He rented a helmet for $4 and paid $0.75 for each group of 20 pitches. If he spent a total of $7 at the batting cages, how many groups of pitches did he pay for?

_____

20. **CCGPS** **Make a Conjecture** Hunter and Amado are each trying to save $600 for a summer trip. Hunter started with $150 and earns $7.50 per hour working at a grocery store. Amado has nothing saved, but he earns $12 per hour painting houses.

a. Make a conjecture about who will take longer to save enough money for

the trip. Justify your reasoning. _____

_____

_____

b. Write and solve two equations to check your conjecture.

_____

21. A company employs 72 workers. It plans to increase the number of employees by 6 per month until it has twice its current workforce. Which equation can be used to determine m, the number of months it will take for the number of employees to double?

Ⓐ $6m + 72m = 144$

Ⓑ $2m + 72 = 144$

Ⓒ $2(6m + 72) = 144$

Ⓓ $6m + 72 = 144$

22. What is the value of x in the following equation?

$$-3x + 4 = -23$$

Ⓕ -9

Ⓖ $-6\frac{1}{3}$

Ⓗ $6\frac{1}{3}$

Ⓘ 9

23. Short Response The table shows the number of baseball cards in two baseball collections. If Marcus and James have 120 cards altogether, write and solve an equation that could be used to find the number of cards in Marcus' collection. _____

Person	Cards
Marcus	m
James	$2m + 6$

Solve each equation. Check your solution. MCC7.EE.4

24. $\frac{y}{7} = 22$

25. $\frac{a}{6} = -108$

26. $-6 = \frac{n}{8} + 1$

27. $-15 = -4p + 9$

28. In a recent NFL game, the Green Bay Packers scored 14 points less than the Tennessee Titans. Write and solve an equation to find the total points the Tennessee Titans scored. MCC6.EE.7 _____

Preseason Week 4	
Team	**Total Points**
Packers	17
Titans	p

Content Standards
MCC8.EE.7
Mathematical Practices
1, 4, 7

Case #1 Game Switcheroo!

Hector and Alex traded video games. Alex gave Hector one fourth of his video games in exchange for 6 video games. Then he sold 3 video games and gave 2 video games to his brother. Alex ended up with 16 video games.

How many video games did Alex have when he started?

1 Understand *What are the facts?*

· Alex now has 16 games.

· He gave some away, sold some, and traded some.

2 Plan *What is your strategy to solve this problem?*

Start with the ending number of video games, 16, and work backward.

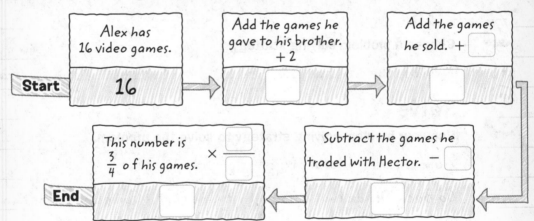

| Alex has 16 video games. | Add the games he gave to his brother. + 2 | Add the games he sold. + ☐ |

Start 16

| This number is $\frac{3}{4}$ of his games. × ☐/☐ | Subtract the games he traded with Hector. − ☐ |

End

3 Solve *How can you apply the strategy?*

So, Alex had ☐ video games at the beginning.

4 Check *Does the answer make sense?*

Start with 20. Perform operations in reverse order.

Analyze the Strategy Tutor

CCGPS **Identify Structure** How is working backward similar to solving an equation?

Case #2 Shoot the Rapids

Aurora raised money for a white water rafting trip. Jacy made the first donation. Guillermo's donation was twice Jacy's donation. Rosa's mother tripled what Aurora had raised so far. Now Aurora has $120.

How much did Jacy donate?

 Understand

Read the problem. What are you being asked to find?

I need to find _____.

Underline key words and values. What information do you know?

Jacy donated _____ . Guillermo _____ and

Rosa's mother _____ the whole amount collected.

Is there any information that you do _not_ need to know?

I do not need to know _____.

 Plan

Choose a problem-solving strategy.

I will use the _____ strategy.

 Solve

Use your problem-solving strategy to solve the problem.

Aurora raised a total of _____.

Go Back Divide that amount by 4. One part is Guillermo's donation and three parts is the amount donated by Rosa's mother. $120 ÷ 4 = _____

Go Back Divide that amount by 3. One part is for Jacy's donation and two parts is the amount that Guillermo donated. _____ ÷ 3 = _____

Jacy was the first to donate. So, Jacy donated _____.

 Check

Use information from the problem to check your answer.

Begin with $10 and perform operations in reverse. _____ × 2 = $20;

$20 + $10 = _____ ; _____ × 3 = $90; _____ + _____ = _____ .

Collaborate Work with a small group to solve the following cases. Show your work on a separate piece of paper.

Case #3 Shopping

Janelle has $75. She buys jeans that are on sale for half price and then uses an in-store coupon for $10 off. After paying $1.80 in sales tax, she receives $37.20 in change.

What was the original price of the jeans?

_____

Case #4 Schedule

Nyoko needs to be at school at 7:45 A.M. It takes her 25 minutes to walk to school, 25 minutes to eat breakfast, and 35 minutes to get dressed.

What time should Nyoko get up to be at school 5 minutes early?

_____

Case #5 Money

At the end of the month, Mr. Copley had $1,475 in his checking account. His checkbook showed the following transactions.

What was his balance at the beginning of the month?

_____

Chk No.	Date	Payment or Withdrawal	Deposit
			$150 00
132		$45 00	
		$100 00	
133		$18 50	
			$250 00

Case #6 Geometry

Study the pattern below.

Draw the next two figures in the pattern.

Circle the strategy below to solve the problem.
- Look for a pattern.
- Act it out.
- Use logical reasoning.
- Guess, check, and revise.

Mid-Chapter Check

Vocabulary Check

1. **CCGPS** **Be Precise** Define *multiplicative inverse*. Give an example of a number and its multiplicative inverse. (Lesson 1)

_____

_____

2. Fill in the blank in the sentence below with the correct term. (Lesson 2)

The first step in solving the equation $3x + 4 = 20$ is to _____

from each side. This is an example of the _____ Property of

_____.

Skills Check and Problem Solving

Solve each equation. Check your solution. (Lessons 1–2)

3. $\frac{2}{3}x = -8$

4. $-4.5 = -0.15p$

5. $2\frac{1}{3}c = 2\frac{1}{10}$

Show your work.

6. $3m + 5 = 14$

7. $-2k + 7 = -3$

8. $11 = \frac{1}{3}a + 2$

9. **Georgia Test Practice** A diagram of a room is shown. If the perimeter of the room is 78 feet, find w, the width of the room. (Lesson 3)

   Ⓐ 12 ft   Ⓒ 25 ft

   Ⓑ 15 ft   Ⓓ 27 ft

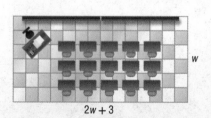

$2w + 3$

Inquiry HOW do you use the Properties of Equality when solving an equation using algebra tiles?

CCGPS Content Standards
MCC8.EE.7,
MCC8.EE.7a

Mathematical Practices
1, 3, 5

Shopping Leah bought 4 pens and a bottle of nail color. Her sister bought 2 of the same pens and 4 bottles of nail color, and spent the same amount as Leah. The nail color cost $2. Use algebra tiles to find the cost of each pen.

Investigation 1

The equation $4x + 2 = 2x + 8$ represents the situation above. Use algebra tiles to solve the equation.

Step 1 Model the equation.

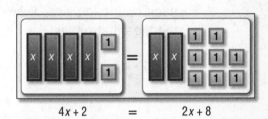

$4x + 2 \quad = \quad 2x + 8$

Step 2 Remove ☐ x-tiles from each side of the mat until there are x-tiles on only one side.

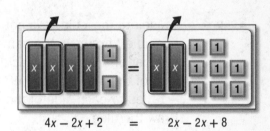

$4x - 2x + 2 \quad = \quad 2x - 2x + 8$

Step 3 Remove ☐ 1-tiles from each side of the mat until the x-tiles are by themselves on one side.

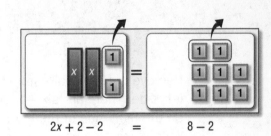

$2x + 2 - 2 \quad = \quad 8 - 2$

Step 4 Separate the tiles in ☐ equal groups.

Check $4 \cdot \boxed{} + 2 \stackrel{?}{=} 2 \cdot \boxed{} + 8$

$14 = 14 \checkmark$

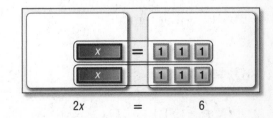

$2x \quad = \quad 6$

So, each pen costs $ ☐ .

Investigation 2

Use algebra tiles to solve $3x + 3 = 2x - 3$. Draw the tiles in the blank mats shown. The first one is done for you.

Step 1 Model the equation.

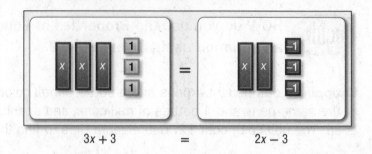

$$3x + 3 \qquad = \qquad 2x - 3$$

Step 2 Remove 2 x-tiles from each side of the mat in Step 1 so that there is an x-tile by itself on the left side. Draw the tiles that remain.

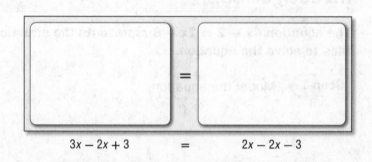

$$3x - 2x + 3 \qquad = \qquad 2x - 2x - 3$$

Step 3 To isolate the x-tile, it is not possible to remove the same number of 1-tiles from each side of the mat. Add three −1-tiles to each side of the mat. Draw the tiles.

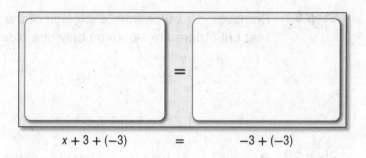

$$x + 3 + (-3) \qquad = \qquad -3 + (-3)$$

Step 4 Remove the zero pairs from the left side. There are six −1-tiles on the right side of the mat. The x-tile is isolated on the left side of the mat. Draw the tiles that remain.

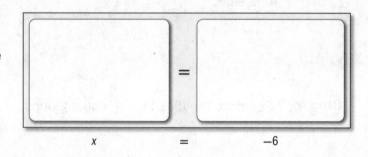

$$x \qquad = \qquad -6$$

So, $x = \boxed{}$.

Check $3\left(\boxed{}\right) + 3 \overset{?}{=} 2\left(\boxed{}\right) - 3$

$\qquad -15 = -15 \checkmark$ The solution is correct.

298 Chapter 4 Equations in One Variable

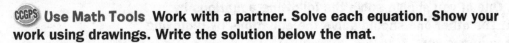 Use Math Tools Work with a partner. Solve each equation. Show your work using drawings. Write the solution below the mat.

1. $x + 2 = 2x + 1$

2. $2x + 7 = 3x + 4$

$x =$ _____

$x =$ _____

3. $2x - 5 = x - 7$

4. $x + 6 = 3x - 2$

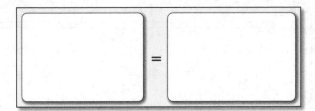

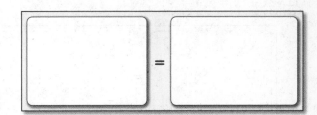

$x =$ _____

$x =$ _____

5. $8 + x = 3x$

6. $3x + 6 = 6x$

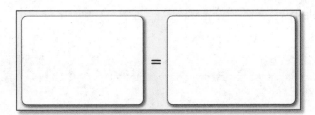

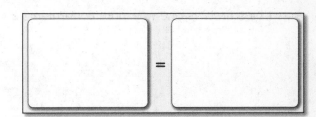

$x =$ _____

$x =$ _____

7. $3x + 3 = x - 5$

8. $2x + 5 = 4x - 1$

$x =$ _____

$x =$ _____

Work with a partner. One of you should solve the following equations by removing 1-tiles first. The other one should solve the equations by removing x-tiles first. Compare your answers.

9. $x + 4 = 3x - 4$

$x =$ _____

10. $x + 2 = 2x - 3$

$x =$ _____

11. $2x + 1 = x - 7$

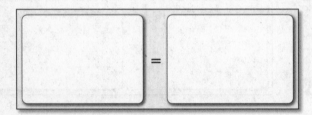

$x =$ _____

12. $4x + 2 = x - 4$

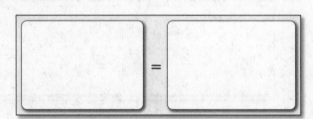

$x =$ _____

13. **CCGPS** **Reason Inductively** Does it matter whether you remove x-tiles or 1-tiles first? Is one way more convenient? Explain. _____

_____

_____

Reflect

14. **CCGPS** **Use Math Tools** Explain why you can remove an x-tile from each side of the mat. _____

_____

15. **Inquiry** HOW do you use the Properties of Equality to solve an equation using algebra tiles? _____

Solve Equations with Variables on Each Side

What You'll Learn

Scan the lesson. Predict two things you will learn about solving equations when the variable is on each side.

- _____
  _____
- _____
  _____

 Essential Question

WHAT is equivalence?

 Common Core GPS

Content Standards
MCC8.EE.7, MCC8.EE.7a, MCC8.EE.7b

Mathematical Practices
1, 3, 4

Real-World Link

Watch ▶

Cell Phones A wireless company offers two cell phone plans. Plan A charges $24.95 per month plus $0.10 per minute for calls. Plan B charges $19.95 per month plus $0.20 per minute. Use the questions to find when the two plans cost the same.

1. Complete the table.

Minutes (m)	Plan A $24.95 + 0.10m$	Plan B $19.95 + 0.20m$
10		
20		
30		
40		
50		
60		
70		

2. For what value(s) does Plan A cost less?

_____

3. For what value(s) does Plan B cost less?

_____

4. For what value(s) do both Plans cost the same?

_____

(handwritten) C | V
$8 + 4d = 5d$
$-4d \mid -4d$
$8 \neq D$

Equations with Variables on Each Side

Some equations, like $8 + 4d = 5d$, have variables on each side of the equals sign. To solve, use the properties of equality to write an equivalent equation with the variables on one side of the equals sign. Then solve the equation.

Examples

 Tutor

1. Solve $8 + 4d = 5d$. Check your solution.

$8 + 4d =$	$5d$	Write the equation.
$-\,4d = -\,4d$		Subtraction Property of Equality
$8 = d$		Simplify by combining like terms.

Subtract 4d from the left side of the equation to isolate the variable.

Subtract 4d from the right side of the equation to keep it balanced.

To check your solution, replace d with 8 in the original equation.

Check $8 + 4d = 5d$	Write the original equation.
$8 + 4(8) \stackrel{?}{=} 5(8)$	Replace d with 8.
$40 = 40$ ✓	The sentence is true.

2. Solve $6n - 1 = 4n - 5$.

$6n - 1 =$	$4n - 5$	Write the equation.
$-\,4n = -\,4n$		Subtraction Property of Equality
$2n - 1 = -5$		Simplify.
$+\,1 = +\,1$		Addition Property of Equality
$2n = -4$		Simplify.
$n = -2$		Mentally divide each side by 2.

Check $6n - 1 = 4n - 5$	Write the original equation.
$6(-2) - 1 \stackrel{?}{=} 4(-2) - 5$	Replace n with -2.
$-13 = -13$ ✓	The sentence is true.

Show your work.

Got It? Do these problems to find out.

Solve each equation. Check your solution.

a. $8a = 5a + 21$

(handwritten)
$-5a \quad -5a$
$\dfrac{3a}{3} = \dfrac{21}{3}$
$a = 7$

b. $3x - 7 = 8x + 23$

(handwritten)
$-3x \quad -3x$
$-7 - 5x + 23$
$-23 \quad 23 - 6 = x$
$-30 = 5x$

(handwritten margin answers)
a. $A = 7$
b. $X = -6$

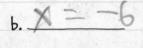

Example

 Tutor

3. Green's Gym charges a one time fee of $50 plus $30 per session for a personal trainer. A new fitness center charges a yearly fee of $250 plus $10 for each session with a trainer. For how many sessions is the cost of the two plans the same?

Words	fee of $50 plus $30 per session is the same as a fee of $250 plus $10 per session.

Variable	Let s represent the number of sessions.

Equation	$50 + 30s = 250 + 10s$

$$50 + 30s = 250 + 10s \quad \text{Write the equation.}$$
$$\underline{-10s = \qquad -10s} \quad \text{Subtraction Property of Equality}$$
$$50 + 20s = 250 \quad \text{Simplify.}$$
$$\underline{-50 \qquad = -50} \quad \text{Addition Property of Equality}$$
$$20s = 200 \quad \text{Simplify.}$$
$$\frac{20s}{20} = \frac{200}{20} \quad \text{Division Property of Equality}$$
$$s = 10 \quad \text{Simplify.}$$

So, the cost is the same for 10 personal trainer sessions.

Check

Green's Gym: $50 plus 10 sessions at $30 per session
$$50 + 10 \cdot 30 = 50 + 300$$
$$= \$350$$

new fitness center: $250 plus 10 sessions at $10 per session
$$250 + 10 \cdot 10 = 250 + 100$$
$$= \$350 \checkmark$$

Got It? Do this problem to find out.

 Show your work.

c. The length of a flag is 0.3 foot less than twice its width. If the perimeter is 14.4 feet longer than the width, find the dimensions of the flag.

c. _____

Equations with Rational Coefficients

In some equations, the coefficients of the variables are rational numbers. Remember when working with fractions, you need to have a common denominator before you add or subtract.

4. Solve $\frac{2}{3}x - 1 = 9 - \frac{1}{6}x$.

$\frac{4}{6}x - 1 = 9 - \frac{1}{6}x$ The common denominator of the coefficients is 6. Rewrite the equation.

$+\frac{1}{6}x \qquad = \quad +\frac{1}{6}x$ Addition Property of Equality

$\frac{5}{6}x - 1 = 9$ Simplify.

$+1 = +1$ Addition Property of Equality

$\frac{5}{6}x = 10$ Simplify.

$\left(\frac{6}{5}\right)\frac{5}{6}x = 10\left(\frac{6}{5}\right)$ Multiplication Property of Equality

$x = 12$ Simplify.

Show your work.

e. _____

f. _____

Got It? Do these problems to find out.

e. $\frac{1}{2}p + 7 = \frac{3}{4}p + 9$

f. $-\frac{5}{4}c - \frac{1}{2} = -\frac{3}{4} + \frac{5}{8}c$

Check

Guided Practice

Solve each equation. Check your solution. (Examples 1, 2, 4)

1. $5n + 9 = 2n$

2. $7y - 8 = 6y + 1$

3. $\frac{3}{5}x - 15 = \frac{6}{5}x + 12$

Show your work.

4. EZ Car Rental charges $40 a day plus $0.25 per mile. Ace Rent-A-Car charges $25 a day plus $0.45 per mile. What number of miles results in the same cost for one day? (Example 3) _____

5. ⓔ **Building on the Essential Question** How is solving an equation with the variable on each side similar to solving a two-step equation? _____

_____

_____

_____

Rate Yourself!

How well do you understand how to solve equations? Circle the figure that applies.

Clear   Somewhat Clear   Not So Clear

For more help, go online to access a Personal Tutor.

Tutor

Extra Practice

Solve each equation. Check your solution.

14. $9g - 14 = 2g$

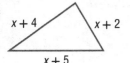

$$9g - 14 = 2g$$
$$\underline{-9g \qquad = -9g}$$
$$\frac{-14}{-7} = \frac{-7g}{-7}$$
$$2 = g$$

15. $-6f + 13 = 2f - 11$

16. $2.5h - 15 = 4h$

17. $2z - 31 = -9z + 24$

18. Will averages 18 points a game and is the all-time scoring leader on his team with 483 points. Tom averages 21 points a game and is currently second on the all-time scorers list with 462 points. If both players continue to play at the same rate, how many more games will it take until Tom and Will have scored the same number of total points?

19. Eighteen less than three times a number is twice the number. Define a variable, write an equation, and solve to find the number.

_____

CCGPS **Reason Abstractly** Write an equation to find the value of *x* so that each pair of polygons has the same perimeter. Then solve.

20.

Triangle with sides $x + 4$, $x + 2$, $x + 5$

Rectangle with sides $x + 1$ and $x + 3$

_____

21.

Pentagon with sides $12x$, $12x$, $12x$, $12x$, $12x$

Triangle with sides $x + 7$, $6x + 9$, $x + 10$

_____

22. Find the value of x so that the polygons have the same perimeter.

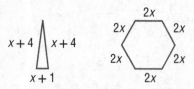

    Ⓐ 4   Ⓒ 2

    Ⓑ 3   Ⓓ 1

23. Which of the following equations has a solution of 5?

  Ⓕ $-12x - 6 = -10x + 4$

  Ⓖ $12x - 6 = 10x + 4$

  Ⓗ $12x + 6 = 10x - 4$

  Ⓘ $12x - 6 = 10x - 4$

24. Carpet cleaner A charges \$28.25 plus \$18 a room. Carpet cleaner B charges \$19.85 plus \$32 a room. Which equation can be used to find the number of rooms for which the total cost of both carpet cleaners is the same?

  Ⓐ $28.25x + 18 = 19.85x + 32$ Ⓒ $28.25 + 18x = 19.85 + 32x$

  Ⓑ $28.25 + 32x = 19.85 + 18x$ Ⓓ $(28.25 + 18)x = (19.85 + 32)x$

(CCGPS) Common Core Review

Write each expression in simplest form. MCC7.EE.2

25. $5x + 6 - x =$ _____

26. $8 - 3n + 3n =$ _____

27. $7a - 7a - 9 =$ _____

28. $3 - 4y + 9y =$ _____

Use the Distributive Property to write each expression as an equivalent expression. MCC7.EE.1

29. $6(x + 5) =$ _____

30. $-8(y - 1) =$ _____

31. $-3(-5z + 12) =$ _____

32. $\frac{1}{3}(6z + 10) =$ _____

Solve Multi-Step Equations

What You'll Learn

Scan the lesson. Write the definitions of null set and identity.

- _____
  _____

- _____
  _____

Essential Question

WHAT is equivalence?

Vocabulary

null set
identity

Math Symbols

∅ null set
{ } empty set

Common Core GPS

Content Standards
MCC8.EE.7, MCC8.EE.7a,
MCC8.EE.7b

Mathematical Practices
1, 2, 3, 4

Real-World Link

Lacrosse Coach Everly wants to order uniform shirts for all the players p on her women's lacrosse team. Each shirt costs $20. There is an additional cost d for a player to put her name on the shirt. Use the steps below to write an equation for the total cost c if every player on the team orders a shirt with her name on it.

1. Circle the variables above and underline what they represent.

2. Write an expression that represents the cost of one shirt with a player's name on it.

$$\boxed{} + \boxed{}$$

cost of shirt + cost of name

3. Use the expression to write an equation that can be used to find the total cost if every player on the team orders a shirt with her name on it.

$$\boxed{} \left(\boxed{} + \boxed{} \right) = c$$

number of players (cost of shirt + cost of name) = total cost

4. Suppose the total cost for 15 players to buy shirts is $420. Write an equation to show the total cost of the shirts if all of the players put their names on the shirts.

_____

_____

where did it go?

Solve Multi-Step Equations

Some equations contain expressions with grouping symbols. To solve these equations, first expand the expression using the Distributive Property. Then collect like terms if needed, and solve the equation using the Properties of Equality.

Example

1. Solve $15(20 + d) = 420$.

$15(20 + d) =$	420	Write the equation.
$300 + 15d =$	420	Distributive Property
$-300 \quad\quad = -300$		Subtraction Property of Equality
$15d =$	120	Simplify.
$\dfrac{15d}{15} = \dfrac{120}{15}$		Division Property of Equality
$d =$	8	Simplify.

Show your work.

Got It? Do these problems to find out.

a. $\underline{\quad X = -20 \quad}$

b. $\underline{\quad A \geq 12 \quad}$

a. $-3(9 + x) = 33$ 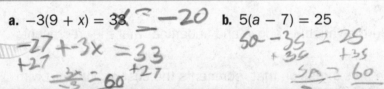   b. $5(a - 7) = 25$

(handwritten work) $-27 + -3x = 33$
$+27 \qquad +27$
$\dfrac{-3x}{-3} = 60$

(handwritten work) $5a - 35 = 25$
$\quad +35 \quad +35$
$\dfrac{5A}{5} = \dfrac{60}{5}$
$a = 12$

Key Concept — Number of Solutions

	Null Set	One Solution	Identity
Words	no solution	one solution	infinitely many solutions
Symbols	$a = b$	$x = a$	$a = a$
Example	$3x + 4 = 3x$ $4 = 0$	$2x = 20$ $x = 10$	$4x + 2 = 4x + 2$ $2 = 2$
	Since $4 \neq 0$, there is no solution.		Since $2 = 2$, the solution is all numbers.

Some equations have no solution. When this occurs, the solution is the **null set** or empty set and is shown by the symbol ∅ or { }. Other equations may have every number as their solution. An equation that is true for every value of the variable is called an **identity**.

Examples

Tutor

2. Solve $6(x - 3) + 10 = 2(3x - 4)$.

$6(x - 3) + 10 = 2(3x - 4)$	Write the equation.
$6x - 18 + 10 = 6x - 8$	Distributive Property
$6x - 8 = 6x - 8$	Collect like terms.
$\underline{+ 8 = \quad + 8}$	Addition Property of Equality
$6x = 6x$	Simplify.
$\dfrac{6x}{6} = \dfrac{6x}{6}$	Division Property of Equality
$x = x$	Simplify.

The statement $x = x$ is *always* true. The equation is an identity and the solution set is all numbers.

Check	$6(x - 3) + 10 = 2(3x - 4)$	Write the original equation.
	$6(5 - 3) + 10 \overset{?}{=} 2[3(5) - 4]$	Substitute any value for x.
	$6(2) + 10 \overset{?}{=} 2(15 - 4)$	Simplify.
	$22 = 22$ ✓	

STOP and Reflect

How do you know if the solution $5 = 0$ indicates no solution, one solution, or infinitely many solutions?

- - - - - - - - - - - - - - - - - - - -

3. Solve $8(4 - 2x) = 4(3 - 5x) + 4x$.

$8(4 - 2x) = 4(3 - 5x) + 4x$	Write the equation.
$32 - 16x = 12 - 20x + 4x$	Distributive Property
$32 - 16x = 12 - 16x$	Collect like terms.
$\underline{+ 16x = \quad + 16x}$	Addition Property of Equality
$32 = 12$	Simplify.

The statement $32 = 12$ is *never* true. The equation has no solution and the solution set is ∅.

Check	$8(4 - 2x) = 4(3 - 5x) + 4x$	Write the equation.
	$8[4 - 2(2)] \overset{?}{=} 4[3 - 5(2)] + 4(2)$	Substitute any value for x.
	$8(0) \overset{?}{=} 4(-7) + 8$	Simplify.
	$0 \neq -20$ ✓	Since $0 \neq -20$, the equation has no solution.

Show your work.

c. _____

Got It? Do these problems to find out.

d. _____

c. $3(6 - 4x) = -2(6x - 9)$ **d.** $2(3x + 5) = 5(2x - 4) - 4x$

$18 - 12x = -12x + 18$ $6x + 10 = 14x - 20$
$-18 + 12x \quad + 12x$ $-6x \qquad -6x$
$\qquad 18 = 18$ $11 = 8x - 20$
$\qquad\qquad\qquad\qquad +10 \qquad\qquad +10$
$\qquad\qquad\qquad\qquad \cancel{0} = 8x$

Example

4. At the fair, Hunter bought 3 snacks and 10 ride tickets. Each ride ticket costs $1.50 less than a snack. If he spent a total of $24.00, what was the cost of each snack?

Write an equation to represent the problem.

$3s + 10(s - 1.5) = 24$	Write the equation.
$3s + 10s - 15 = 24$	Distributive Property
$13s - 15 = 24$	Collect like terms.
$\underline{+ 15 = + 15}$	Addition Property of Equality
$13s = 39$	Simplify.
$\dfrac{13s}{13} = \dfrac{39}{13}$	Division Property of Equality
$s = 3$	Simplify.

So, the cost of each snack was $3.

Guided Practice

Solve each equation. Check your solution. (Examples 1–3)

1. $-8(w - 6) = 32$

Show your work.

2. $8z - 22 = 3(3z + 11) - z$

3. Mr. Richards's class is holding a canned food drive for charity. Juliet collected 10 more cans than Rosana. Santiago collected twice as many cans as Juliet. If they collected 130 cans altogether, how many cans did Juliet collect? (Example 4) _____

4. 🄮 **Building on the Essential Question** How many possible solutions are there to a linear equation in one variable? Describe each one.

_____
_____
_____
_____

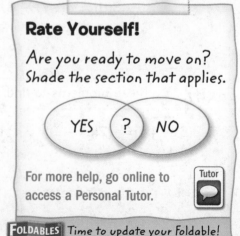

Rate Yourself!

Are you ready to move on? Shade the section that applies.

YES   ?   NO

For more help, go online to access a Personal Tutor.

Tutor 💬

FOLDABLES Time to update your Foldable!

Extra Practice

Solve each equation. Check your solution.

15. $9(j - 4) = 81$

$$9j - 36 = 81$$
$$\underline{+36 = +36}$$
$$9j = 117$$
$$\frac{9j}{9} = \frac{117}{9}$$
$$j = 13$$

Homework Help

16. $8(4q - 5) - 7q = 5(5q - 8)$

$$32q - 40 - 7q = 25q - 40$$
$$25q - 40 = 25q - 40$$
$$\underline{-25q \qquad = -25q}$$
$$-40 = -40$$

The solution set is all numbers.

17. $\frac{1}{2}r + 2\left(\frac{3}{4}r - 1\right) = \frac{1}{4}r + 6$

18. $-5(3m + 6) = -3(4m - 2)$

19. $-7(k + 9) = 9(k - 5) - 14k$

20. $10p - 2(3p - 6) = 4(3p - 6) - 8p$

21. $12(x + 3) = 4(2x + 9) + 4x$

22. $0.2(x + 50) - 6 = 0.4(3x + 20)$

23. CCGPS **Identify Structure** Give an example of a multi-step equation for each of the following solutions.

a. all numbers _____

b. null set _____

24. What is the solution of the equation?

$$-2(3x + 1) - 2x = -4(2x) - 4$$

Ⓐ $x = \dfrac{1}{2}$

Ⓑ $x = -\dfrac{1}{2}$

Ⓒ all numbers

Ⓓ no solution

25. What value of x makes the perimeters of the figures below equal?

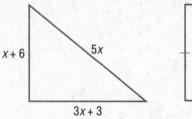 

Ⓕ 2   Ⓗ 4

Ⓖ 3   Ⓘ 5

CCGPS **Common Core Review**

Solve each inequality. Graph the solution set on a number line. MCC7.EE.4b

26. $a - 5 < 2$ _____

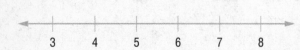

27. $x - 9 \geq -12$ _____

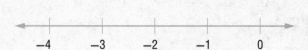

28. $5y \leq -30$ _____

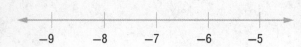

29. $-\dfrac{n}{4} > -2$ _____

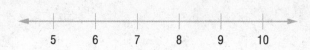

30. $4h - 7 \leq 13$ _____

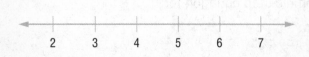

31. $-3m + 5 > 17$ _____

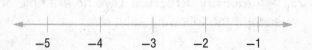

21ST CENTURY CAREER
in Design

Skateboard Designer

If you love the sport of skateboarding, and you are creative and have strong math skills, you should think about a career designing skateboards. A skateboard designer applies engineering principles and artistic ability to design high-performance skateboards that are both strong and safe. To have a career in skateboard design, you should study physics and mathematics and have a good understanding of skateboarding.

College & Career READINESS

Explore college and careers at ccr.mcgraw-hill.com

Is This the Career for You?

Are you interested in becoming a skateboard designer? Take some of the following courses in high school.

◆ Digital Design
◆ Geometry
◆ Physics
◆ Trigonometry

Turn the page to find out how math relates to a career in Design.

It's Great to Skate

Use the information in the table to solve each problem.

1. The total width of two standard shortboards and a technical shortboard is 23.5 inches. Write an equation to represent the situation.

   _____

2. Solve the equation from Exercise 1 to find the width of a standard shortboard.

   _____

3. The total length of two longboards and a standard shortboard is 113.4 inches. Write and solve an equation to find the length of a longboard. _____

   _____

4. The total width of three technical shortboards is 4.5 inches more than the total width of two longboards. Write and solve an equation to find the width of a longboard.

   _____

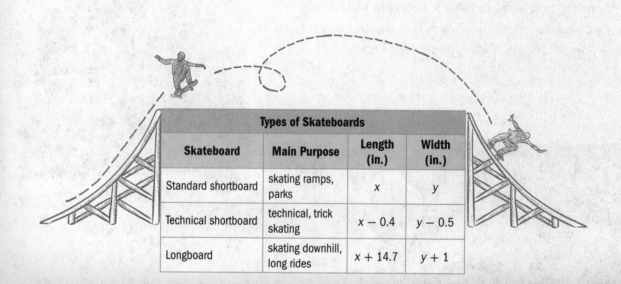

Types of Skateboards			
Skateboard	**Main Purpose**	**Length (in.)**	**Width (in.)**
Standard shortboard	skating ramps, parks	x	y
Technical shortboard	technical, trick skating	$x - 0.4$	$y - 0.5$
Longboard	skating downhill, long rides	$x + 14.7$	$y + 1$

Career Project

It's time to update your career portfolio! Describe the skills that would be necessary for a skateboard designer to possess. Determine whether this type of career would be a good fit for you.

_____

_____

_____

_____

_____

What problem-solving skill might you use as a skateboard designer?

_____

_____

_____

_____

Vocabulary Check

Unscramble each of the clue words. After unscrambling all of the terms, use the numbered letters to find the name of a famous mathematician.

FOCICTIENEF

⬜⬜⬜⬜⬜⬜⬜⬜⬜⬜⬜
　　　　　2　　　　　　11

TECVALMIITUPLI SEVNEIR

⬜⬜⬜⬜⬜⬜⬜⬜⬜⬜⬜⬜⬜⬜⬜
　　　　　　　　　　　　6

⬜⬜⬜⬜⬜⬜
　13　　　3

DEYTINTI

⬜⬜⬜⬜⬜⬜⬜⬜
4　　　9

LLUNETS

⬜⬜⬜⬜　⬜⬜⬜

PERRITPEOS

⬜⬜⬜⬜⬜⬜⬜⬜⬜⬜
　　　　　　　　　1

REABIASVL

⬜⬜⬜⬜⬜⬜⬜⬜⬜
　　　　　　　10　5

PEOCILRACR

⬜⬜⬜⬜⬜⬜⬜⬜⬜⬜
　　　　　　12　8　7

⬜⬜⬜　⬜⬜⬜⬜⬜　⬜⬜**W**⬜⬜⬜
1　2　3　4　5　6　7　8　9　10　11　12　13

Complete each sentence using one of the unscrambled words above.

1. The _____ is the numerical factor of a term that contains a variable.

2. Another name for the reciprocal is the _____.

3. In mathematics, statments that are true for all numbers are _____.

4. When writing an equation from a real-world problem, it is important to define the _____.

Use Your  FOLDABLES

Use your Foldable to help review the chapter.

Tape here

Solving Equations

Tab 1

Write About It

Tab 2

Solve
$6(x-3) + 10 = 2(4x-5)$

Got it?

Number the steps in the order needed to solve each equation. Then solve the equation.

1. $5(x + 3) = 170$

  <u>2</u> Subtract 15 from each side.

  <u>1</u> Multiply x and 3 by 5.

  <u>3</u> Divide each side by 5.

    $x = \underline{\;31\;}$

 The first one is done for you.

2. $2p - 9 = 6p + 7$

  ___ Divide each side by 4.

  ___ Subtract 7 from each side.

  ___ Subtract 2p from each side.

    $p = \underline{\qquad}$

3. $-\dfrac{2}{3}(a + 3) = \dfrac{5}{3}a - 19$

  ___ Add $\dfrac{2}{3}a$ to each side.

  ___ Add 19 to each side.

  ___ Multiply a and 3 by $-\dfrac{2}{3}$.

  ___ Multiply each side by $\dfrac{3}{7}$.

    $a = \underline{\qquad}$

Problem Solving

1. The area of Arizona covered by desert is about 5,880 square miles. If 42% of the total area is desert, about how many square miles is Arizona's total area? (Lesson 1) _____

2. Four adults spend $37 for admission and $3 for parking at the zoo. Solve the equation $4a + 3 = 40$ to find the cost of admission per person.

(Lesson 2) _____

3. **Reason Abstractly** Jerome completes 8 extra credit problems on the first day and then 4 problems each day until the worksheet is complete. There are 28 problems on the worksheet. Write and solve an equation to find how many days it will take Jerome to complete the worksheet after

the first day. (Lesson 3) _____

4. Elin wants to fence in two different garden plots in her back yard with two rolls of fencing that are the same length. Write and solve an equation to find the value of x so that the figures below have the

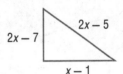

same perimeter. (Lesson 4) _____

5. **Financial Literacy** Mr. and Mrs. Hawkins have budgeted $500 for Marion's graduation party. The cost to rent the room is $150. How much can they spend per person on food if each of the 30 guests receives a

$2.50 group photo? (Lesson 5) _____

Reflect

Use what you learned about equivalence to complete the graphic organizer.
Draw or write an example for each category.

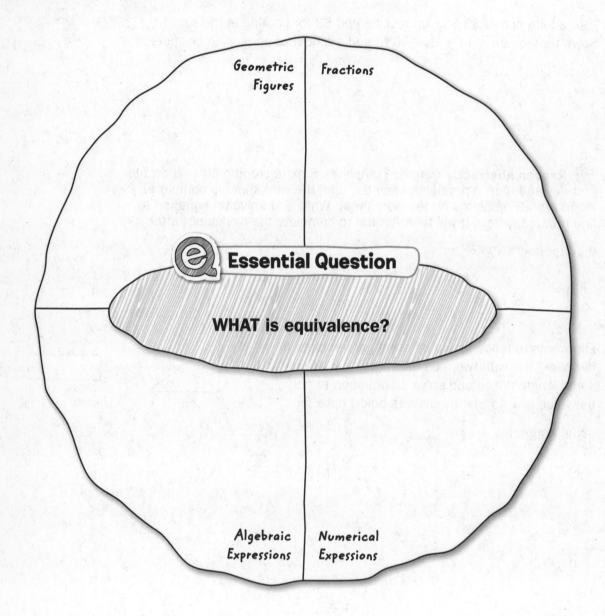

Geometric Figures

Fractions

Essential Question

WHAT is equivalence?

Algebraic Expressions

Numerical Expressions

 Answer the Essential Question. WHAT is equivalence?

_____

_____

COLLABORATIVE PROJECT

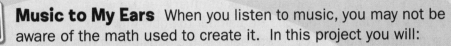 **Music to My Ears** When you listen to music, you may not be aware of the math used to create it. In this project you will:

- **Collaborate** with your classmates as you research the connections between math and music.

- **Share** the results of your research in a creative way.

- **Reflect** on how mathematical ideas can be represented.

By the end of this project, you just might be ready to write a hit song!

 Collaborate

Go Online Work with your group to research and complete each activity. You will use your results in the Share section on the following page.

1. Choose a song on a CD or on your MP3 player. Listen to the song and describe the beats or rhythm using repeating numbers. For example, a song may have a rhythm that can be described by 1-2-3-1-2-3-... .

2. Research and describe the different types of musical notes. Make sure to use rational numbers. Include a drawing of each note on sheet music.

3. Research Pythagoras' findings about music, notes and frequency, and harmony. Write a few paragraphs about what you found and create a list of the types of numbers you find in your research.

4. Describe the Fibonacci Sequence. Then give some examples of how Fibonacci numbers are found in music.

5. Find the digital music sales in a recent year. Write this number in both standard form and scientific notation. Then compare the digital music sales to CD music sales for the same year. Create a display to show what you find.

 **Share**

With your group, decide on a way to share what you have learned about math and music. Some suggestions are listed below, but you can also think of other creative ways to present your information. Remember to show how you used mathematics to complete each of the activities in this project!

connect with Health

Health Literacy Many studies have been done that show a positive connection between music and good health. Research the Internet to find information about one such study.

- Create your own short piece of music based on your knowledge of notes and frequency. Make a recording of the music and explain how it is harmonious.
- Use presentation software to demonstrate some ways math and music are connected.

Check out the note on the right to connect this project with other subjects.

 **Reflect**

6. **ⓔ Answer the Essential Question** HOW can mathematical ideas be represented?

 a. How did you use what you learned about real numbers in this chapter to represent mathematical ideas in this project?

 _____

 _____

 _____

 b. In this project, you discovered how mathematical ideas are represented in music. Explain how mathematical ideas are represented in other parts of culture.

 _____

 _____

 _____

COLLABORATIVE PROJECT

▶ Watch

Web Design 101 When designing a good Web page, there are many details to consider in order to make your Web page stand out. In this project, you will:

- **Collaborate** with your classmates as you research an animal and design a Web page.

- **Share** the results of your research in a creative way

- **ℰ Reflect** on how you communicate mathematical ideas effectively.

By the end of this Project, you will be ready to design a live Web page about your favorite animal!

👥 Collaborate

⏻ Go Online Work with your group to research and complete each activity. You will use your results in the Share section on the following page.

1. Choose your favorite animal. Research information about that animal, such as the population over the past 10 years, the kinds of food it eats, sleeping habits, its average lifespan, average size, and average speed. Present this information using tables and graphs.

2. Use the distance formula, distance = rate × time, to write an equation that represents the distance your animal can travel at its average speed. Find the average speed of two other animals and write equations using the distance formula. Graph all three equations on the same coordinate plane. Then describe the graphs.

3. Research the elements needed to make a good Web page. Then make a sketch of your own Web page about the favorite animal that you selected in Exercise 1. Be sure to include tables, equations, graphs, and photos.

4. Find another animal in the same animal kingdom as your favorite animal. On the sketch of your Web page, include a link to this other animal and an equation that describes one of its characteristics.

5. Research the cost of taking a Web design class. Write an equation that represents the time it will take you to save enough money for the class. Share this equation as you write a few paragraphs that explain your plan on how to save enough money

Share

With your group, decide on a way to share what you have learned about your animal and Web pages. Some suggestions are listed below, but you can also think of other creative ways to present your information. Remember to show how you used mathematics to complete each of the activities in this project!

- If possible, use Web page creation software to turn your design into a live Web page.
- Imagine you are going to be interviewed by a reporter about your work on this project. Write down what will be discussed in the interview. You may wish to actually record an interview.

Check out the note on the right to connect this project with other subjects.

connect with Economics

Business Literacy Research Web design jobs in your area. Find out the following:

- What type of education is required?
- What skills should a Web designer possess?

Reflect

6. @ **Answer the Essential Question** HOW can you communicate mathematical ideas effectively?

   a. How did you use what you learned in the Equations in One Variable chapter to communicate mathematical ideas effectively in this project?

   _____

   _____

   _____

   b. How did you use what you learned in the Equations in Two Variables chapter to communicate mathematical ideas effectively in this project?

   _____

   _____

   _____

COLLABORATIVE PROJECT

Green Thumb If you have a knack for gardening, volunteering in a community garden is a great way to get involved with your community and also earn a little money. In this project you will:

- **Collaborate** with your classmates as you research the costs involved with growing vegetables and predict possible profits.

- **Share** the results of your research in a creative way.

- **Reflect** on how you find and use patterns to model real-world situations.

By the end of this Project, you just might be a young entrepreneur!

Collaborate

Go Online Work with your group to research and complete each activity. You will use your results in the Share section on the following page.

1. Choose a vegetable that is sold individually, and find its cost at a grocery store. Write an equation to represent the total cost as a function of the number of vegetables. Make a function table to find the cost of 1, 2, 3, 4, 5, and 6 vegetables. Then graph the ordered pairs.

2. Research a vegetable you would like to grow in a community garden. Find the costs involved such as buying seeds and gardening tools. Then determine how much you will charge per vegetable (or per pound) based on grocery store or farm market prices.

3. Based on the information you found in Exercise 2, write a linear function to represent your profit. Describe what the variables represent. Then graph and describe the function.

4. Research the following terms: *gross profit, total revenue, and gross profit margin.* Make a diagram explaining these terms. Then find your gross profit margin based on estimated gross profit and total revenue. What does your gross profit tell you?

5. Research the average temperatures in your area for the growing season of the vegetable you chose. Then sketch a qualitative graph that shows the change in temperature over the growing season. Include a brief explanation of your graph.

 **Share**

With your group, decide on a way to share what you have learned about growing and selling vegetables. Some suggestions are listed below, but you can also think of other creative ways to present your information. Remember to show how you used mathematics to complete each of the activities in this project!

- Imagine you sell your vegetables at a farmer's market. Describe your experience in a blog.
- Use a budget spreadsheet to show how your vegetable can generate a profit. Include tables, equations, and graphs.

 **with Science**

Environmental Literacy Research information about Earth's soil and the qualities needed to grow plants. Some questions to consider are:

- What type of soil allows fruits and vegetables to grow well?
- What type of soil is typically found in your area?
- What could you add to the soil to make it better for growing your plants?

Check out the note on the right to connect this project with other subjects.

 Reflect

6. **Ⓠ Answer the Essential Question** How can you find and use patterns to model real-world situations?

   a. How did you use what you learned about constructing functions in this chapter to find and use patterns to model real-world situations in this project?

   _____

   _____

   _____

   b. How did you use what you learned about different representations of functions in this chapter to find and use patterns to model real-world situations in this project?

   _____

   _____

   _____

COLLABORATIVE PROJECT

Watch ▶

Design That Ride Designers apply many geometric concepts to build exciting new rides. In this project you will:

- **Collaborate** with your classmates as you research amusement park rides.
- **Share** the results of your research in a creative way.
- **ⓔ Reflect** on how you use different measurements to solve real-life problems.

By the end of this project, you'll be ready to design a new amusement park ride!

Collaborate

ⓤ Go Online Work with your group to research and complete each activity. You will use your results in the Share section on the following page.

1. Find photos of several different types of amusement park rides. Then describe and label any parallel lines, angles, triangles, congruent figures, similar figures, and three-dimensional shapes you observe.

2. Make a sketch of a current amusement park ride. Research and label its dimensions. Then use what you know about angles, congruence, similarity, the Pythagorean Theorem, surface area, and volume to label as many of its other attributes as you can.

3. Find several examples of amusement park rides that use transformations. Explain the transformation(s) that the ride exhibits.

4. Research different types of trusses. Then explain why trusses are used in the design of some amusement park rides. Include drawings to justify your explanation.

5. Research *potential energy* and *kinetic energy* as they relate to roller coasters. Then create a drawing that explains the concepts.

 **Share**

With your group, decide on a way to share what you have learned about designing an amusement park ride. Some suggestions are listed below, but you can also think of other creative ways to present your information. Remember to show how you used mathematics to complete each of the activities in this project.

 **connect** with **Social Studies**

Global Literacy Research information about amusement parks in other countries. Some questions to consider are:

· How are the rides different from those in the United States?

· When and where was the earliest amusement park constructed?

· Design an amusement park ride using online simulations. Don't forget to give your ride a name.
· Imagine a nearby amusement park is seeking suggestions for a new ride. Write a proposal for your ride. Be sure to include drawings.

Check out the note on the right to connect this project with other subjects.

 **Reflect**

6. Ⓔ **Answer the Essential Question** HOW can you use different measurements to solve real-life problems?

   a. How did you use what you learned about the measurements of triangles to solve real-life problems in this project?

   _____

   _____

   _____

   b. How did you use what you learned about the measurements involved in congruence and similarity to solve real-life problems in this project?

   _____

   _____

   _____

   c. How did you use what you learned about volume and surface area to solve real-life problems in this project?

   _____

   _____

COLLABORATIVE PROJECT

Olympic Games The Olympics consist of many types of sports. Many of these have a unique scoring process that determines the winner. In this project you will:

- **Collaborate** with your classmates as you gather Olympics statistics.

- **Share** the results of your research in a creative way.

- **Reflect** on why learning mathematics is important.

By the end of this project, you will understand how scatter plots and data analysis are involved in presenting Olympic Games statistics.

 Collaborate

Go Online Work with your group to research and complete each activity. You will use your results in the Share section on the following page.

1. Choose a country that has participated in basketball in the Summer Olympics. Use the Internet to research the team. Find their average points per game over the past 10 Summer Olympic Games. Record the information in a table.

2. Make a scatter plot of the data from Exercise 1. Determine if the data can be used to predict the average number of points in the next Summer Olympics. If so, make a prediction.

3. Research the number of Olympic records the U.S. has received in the Olympic sport of your choice. Use a graph of your choice and interpret the graph.

4. Research the winning scores in archery over the past 10 Summer Olympics. Draw a histogram to display the data. Interpret the graph.

5. During the ranking round in archery each player will shoot a total of 72 arrows. Create a score card for one player in the first round. Summarize the data in a box plot and interpret the graph.

Share

With your group, decide on a way to share what you have learned about Olympic scoring. Some suggestions are listed below, but you can also think of other creative ways to present your information. Remember to show how you used mathematics in your project!

- Act as a television reporter for the Olympics and describe the scores and medals won in a few events. Include graphics that would appear on screen.
- Choose an Olympic sport that you do not know much about. Explain the scoring system in your sport. Then create tables and graphs to present real data from your sport in the most recent Olympics.

Check out the note on the right to connect this project with other subjects.

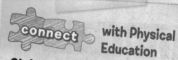

connect **with Physical Education**

Global Awareness Research information on how to play or participate in a sport that is popular in another country. Some questions to consider are:

- What are the basic rules?
- What are the jobs of the offense and the defense?

Reflect

6. **Answer the Essential Question** Why is learning mathematics important.

    a. How did you use what you learned about scatter plots in this chapter to represent mathematical ideas in this project?

    _____

    _____

    _____

    _____

    b. How did you use what you learned about data analysis to communicate mathematical ideas effectively in this project?

    _____

    _____

    _____

    _____

Glossary/Glosario

Go online for the eGlossary.

The eGlossary contains words and definitions in the following 13 languages:

Arabic	Cantonese	Hmong	Spanish	Urdu
Bengali	English	Korean	Tagalog	Vietnamese
Brazilian Portuguese	Haitian Creole	Russian		

English | Español

Aa

accuracy The degree of closeness of a measurement to the true value.

acute angle An angle whose measure is less than 90°.

acute triangle A triangle with all acute angles.

Addition Property of Equality If you add the same number to each side of an equation, the two sides remain equal.

adjacent angles Angles that share a common vertex, a common side, and do not overlap. In the figure, the adjacent angles are ∠5 and ∠6.

algebra A branch of mathematics that involves expressions with variables.

algebraic expression A combination of variables, numbers, and at least one operation.

exactitud Cercanía de una medida a su valor verdadero.

ángulo agudo Ángulo que mide menos de 90°.

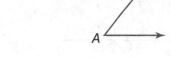

triángulo acutángulo Triángulo con todos los ángulos agudos.

propiedad de adición de la igualdad Si sumas el mismo número a ambos lados de una ecuación, los dos lados permanecen iguales.

ángulos adyacentes Ángulos que comparten un vértice, un lado común y no se traslapan. En la figura, los ángulos adyacentes son ∠5 y ∠6.

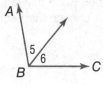

álgebra Rama de las matemáticas que trabaja con expresiones con variables.

expresión algebraica Una combinación de variables, números y por lo menos una operación.

alternate exterior angles Exterior angles that lie on opposite sides of the transversal. In the figure, transversal *t* intersects lines ℓ and *m*. ∠1 and ∠7, and ∠2 and ∠8 are alternate exterior angles. If line ℓ and *m* are parallel, then these pairs of angles are congruent.

ángulos alternos externos Ángulos externos que se encuentran en lados opuestos de la transversal. En la figura, la transversal *t* interseca las rectas ℓ y *m*. ∠1 y ∠7, y ∠2 y ∠8 son ángulos alternos externos. Si las rectas ℓ y *m* son paralelas, entonces estos ángulos son pares de ángulos congruentes.

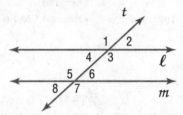

alternate interior angles Interior angles that lie on opposite sides of the transversal. In the figure below, transversal *t* intersects lines ℓ and *m*. ∠3 and ∠5, and ∠4 and ∠6 are alternate interior angles. If lines ℓ and *m* are parallel, then these pairs of angles are congruent.

ángulos alternos internos Ángulos internos que se encuentran en lados opuestos de la transversal. En la figura, la transversal *t* interseca las rectas ℓ y *m*. ∠3 y ∠5, y ∠4 y ∠6 son ángulos alternos internos. Si las rectas ℓ y *m* son paralelas, entonces estos ángulos son pares de ángulos congruentes.

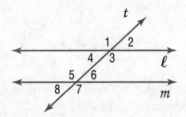

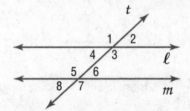

angle of rotation The degree measure of the angle through which a figure is rotated.

ángulo de rotación Medida en grados del ángulo sobre el cual se rota una figura.

arc One of two parts of a circle separated by a central angle.

arco Una de dos partes de un círculo separadas por un ángulo central.

Associative Property The way in which three numbers are grouped when they are added or multiplied does not change their sum or product.

propiedad asociativa La forma en que se agrupan tres números al sumarlos o multiplicarlos no altera su suma o producto.

---

base In a power, the number that is the common factor. In 10^3, the base is 10. That is, $10^3 = 10 \times 10 \times 10$.

base En una potencia, número que es el factor común. En 10^3, la base es 10. Es decir, $10^3 = 10 \times 10 \times 10$.

base One of the two parallel congruent faces of a prism.

base Una de las dos caras paralelas congruentes de un prisma.

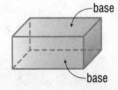

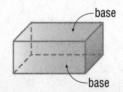

biased sample A sample drawn in such a way that one or more parts of the population are favored over others.

muestra sesgada Muestra en que se favorece una o más partes de una población.

bivariate data Data with two variables, or pairs of numerical observations.

datos bivariantes Datos con dos variables, o pares de observaciones numéricas.

box plot A method of visually displaying a distribution of data values by using the median, quartiles, and extremes of the data set. A box shows the middle 50% of the data.

diagrama de caja Un método de mostrar visualmente una distribución de valores usando la mediana, cuartiles y extremos del conjunto de datos. Una caja muestra el 50% del medio de los datos.

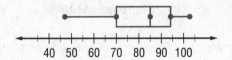

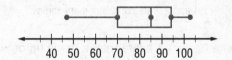

Cc

center The given point from which all points on a circle are the same distance.

centro Un punto dado del cual equidistan todos los puntos de un círculo.

center of dilation The center point from which dilations are performed.

centro de la homotecia Punto fijo en torno al cual se realizan las homotecias.

center of rotation A fixed point around which shapes move in a circular motion to a new position.

centro de rotación Punto fijo alrededor del cual se giran las figuras en movimiento circular alrededor de un punto fijo.

central angle An angle that intersects a circle in two points and has its vertex at the center of the circle.

ángulo central Ángulo que interseca un círculo en dos puntos y cuyo vértice es el centro del círculo.

circle The set of all points in a plane that are the same distance from a given point called the center.

círculo Conjunto de todos los puntos en un plano que equidistan de un punto dado llamado centro.

circumference The distance around a circle.

circunferencia La distancia alrededor de un círculo.

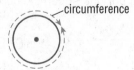

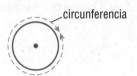

chord A segment with endpoints that are on a circle.

cuerda Segmento cuyos extremos están sobre un círculo.

coefficient The numerical factor of a term that contains a variable.

coeficiente Factor numérico de un término que contiene una variable.

common difference The difference between any two consecutive terms in an arithmetic sequence.

diferencia común La diferencia entre cualquier par de términos consecutivos en una sucesión aritmética.

Commutative Property The order in which two numbers are added or multiplied does not change their sum or product.

propiedad conmutativa La forma en que se suman o multiplican dos números no altera su suma o producto.

complementary angles Two angles are complementary if the sum of their measures is 90°.

ángulos complementarios Dos ángulos son complementarios si la suma de sus medidas es 90°.

∠1 and ∠2 are complementary angles.

∠1 y ∠2 son complementarios.

composite figure A figure that is made up of two or more shapes.

figura compleja Figura compuesta de dos o más formas.

composite solid An object made up of more than one type of solid.

sólido complejo Cuerpo compuesto de más de un tipo de sólido.

composition of transformations The resulting transformation when a transformation is applied to a figure and then another transformation is applied to its image.

composición de transformaciones Transformación que resulta cuando se aplica una transformación a una figura y luego se le aplica otra transformación a su imagen.

compound event An event that consists of two or more simple events.

evento compuesto Evento que consta de dos o más eventos simples.

compound interest Interest paid on the initial principal and on interest earned in the past.

interés compuesto Interés que se paga por el capital inicial y sobre el interés ganado en el pasado.

cone A three-dimensional figure with one circular base connected by a curved surface to a single vertex.

cono Una figura tridimensional con una circular base conectada por una superficie curva para un solo vértice.

vertex

vértice

congruent Having the same measure; if one image can be obtained by another by a sequence of rotations, reflections, or translations.

congruente Que tienen la misma medida; si una imagen puede obtenerse de otra por una secuencia de rotaciones, reflexiones o traslaciones.

constant A term without a variable.

constante Término sin variables.

constant of proportionality The constant ratio in a proportional linear relationship.

constante de proporcionalidad La razón constante en una relación lineal proporcional.

constant of variation A constant ratio in a direct variation.

constante de variación Razón constante en una relación de variación directa.

constant rate of change The rate of change between any two points in a linear relationship is the same or *constant*.

tasa constante de cambio La tasa de cambio entre dos puntos cualesquiera en una relación lineal permanece igual o *constante*.

continuous data Data that can take on any value. There is no space between data values for a given domain. Graphs are represented by solid lines.

datos continuos Datos que pueden tomar cualquier valor. No hay espacio entre los valores de los datos para un dominio dado. Las gráficas se representan con rectas sólidas.

convenience sample A sample which includes members of the population that are easily accessed.

muestra de conveniencia Muestra que incluye miembros de una población fácilmente accesibles.

converse The converse of a theorem is formed when the parts of the theorem are reversed. The converse of the Pythagorean Theorem can be used to test whether a triangle is a right triangle. If the sides of the triangle have lengths a, b, and c, such that $c^2 = a^2 + b^2$, then the triangle is a right triangle.

recíproco El recíproco de un teorema se forma cuando se invierten las partes del teorema. El recíproco del teorema de Pitágoras puede usarse para averiguar si un triángulo es un triángulo rectángulo. Si las longitudes de los lados de un triángulo son a, b y c, tales que $c^2 = a^2 + b^2$, entonces el triángulo es un triángulo rectángulo.

coordinate plane A coordinate system in which a horizontal number line and a vertical number line intersect at their zero points.

plano de coordenadas Sistema de coordenadas en que una recta numérica horizontal y una recta numérica vertical se intersecan en sus puntos cero.

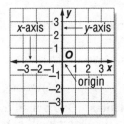

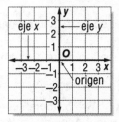

coplanar Lines that lie in the same plane.

coplanario Rectas que yacen en el mismo plano.

corresponding angles Angles that are in the same position on two parallel lines in relation to a transversal.

ángulos correspondientes Ángulos que están en la misma posición sobre dos rectas paralelas en relación con la transversal.

corresponding parts Parts of congruent or similar figures that match.

partes correspondientes Partes de figuras congruentes o semejantes que coinciden.

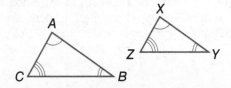

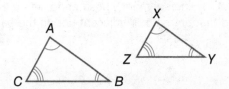

counterexample A statement or example that shows a conjecture is false.

cross section The intersection of a solid and a plane.

cube root One of three equal factors of a number. If $a^3 = b$, then a is the cube root of b. The cube root of 64 is 4 since $4^3 = 64$.

cylinder A three-dimensional figure with two parallel congruent circular bases connected by a curved surface.

contraejemplo Ejemplo o enunciado que demuestra que una conjetura es falsa.

sección transversal Intersección de un sólido y un plano.

raíz cúbica Uno de tres factores iguales de un número. Si $a^3 = b$, entonces a es la raíz cúbica de b. La raíz cúbica de 64 es 4, dado que $4^3 = 64$.

cilindro Una figura tridimensional con dos paralelas congruentes circulares bases conectados por una superficie curva.

deductive reasoning A system of reasoning that uses facts, rules, definitions, or properties to reach logical conclusions.

defining a variable Choosing a variable and a quantity for the variable to represent in an expression or equation.

degree A unit used to measure angles.

degree A unit used to measure temperature.

dependent events Two or more events in which the outcome of one event does affect the outcome of the other event or events.

dependent variable The variable in a relation with a value that depends on the value of the independent variable.

derived unit A unit that is derived from a measurement system base unit, such as length, mass, or time.

diagonal A line segment whose endpoints are vertices that are neither adjacent nor on the same face.

razonamiento deductivo Sistema de razonamiento que emplea hechos, reglas, definiciones o propiedades para obtener conclusions lógicas.

definir una variable El elegir una variable y una cantidad que esté representada por la variable en una expresión o en una ecuación.

grado Unidad que se usa para medir ángulos.

grado Unidad que se usa para medir la temperatura.

eventos dependientes Dos o más eventos en que el resultado de uno de ellos afecta el resultado de los otros eventos.

variable dependiente La variable en una relación cuyo valor depende del valor de la variable independiente.

unidad derivada Unidad derivada de una unidad básica de un sistema de medidas como por ejemplo, la longitud, la masa o el tiempo.

diagonal Segmento de recta cuyos extremos son vértices que no son ni adyacentes ni yacen en la misma cara.

diameter   The distance across a circle through its center.

dilation   A transformation that enlarges or reduces a figure by a scale factor.

dimensional analysis   The process of including units of measurement when you compute.

direct variation   A relationship between two variable quantities with a constant ratio.

discount   The amount by which a regular price is reduced.

discrete data   Data with space between possible data values. Graphs are represented by dots.

disjoint events   Events that cannot happen at the same time.

Distance Formula   The distance d between two points with coordinates (x_1, y_1) and (x_2, y_2) is given by the formula

$$d = \sqrt{(x_1 - x_2)^2 + (y_1 - y_2)^2}.$$

distribution   A way to show the arrangement of data values.

Distributive Property   To multiply a sum by a number, multiply each addend by the number outside the parentheses.

$$5(x + 3) = 5x + 15$$

Division Property of Equality   If you divide each side of an equation by the same nonzero number, the two sides remain equal.

domain   The set of x-coordinates in a relation.

double box plot   Two box plots graphed on the same number line.

diámetro   La distancia a través de un círculo pasando por el centro.

homotecia   Transformación que produce la ampliación o reducción de una imagen por un factor de escala.

análisis dimensional   Proceso que incorpora las unidades de medida al hacer cálculos.

variación directa   Relación entre dos cantidades variables con una razón constante.

descuento   La cantidad de reducción del precio normal.

datos discretos   Datos con espacios entre posibles valores de datos. Las gráficas están representadas por puntos.

eventos disjuntos   Eventos que no pueden ocurrir al mismo tiempo.

fórmula de la distancia   La distancia d entre dos puntos con coordenadas (x_1, y_1) and (x_2, y_2) viene dada por la fórmula

$$d = \sqrt{(x_1 - x_2)^2 + (y_1 - y_2)^2}.$$

distribución   Una manera de mostrar la agrupación de valores.

propiedad distributiva   Para multiplicar una suma por un número, multiplica cada sumando por el número fuera de los paréntesis.

$$5(x + 3) = 5x + 15$$

propiedad de división de la igualdad   Si cada lado de una ecuación se divide entre el mismo número no nulo, los dos lados permanecen iguales.

dominio   Conjunto de coordenadas x en una relación.

doble diagrama de puntos   Dos diagramas de caja sobre la misma recta numérica.

edge The line segment where two faces of a polyhedron intersect.

edge

arista El segmento de línea donde se cruzan dos caras de un poliedro.

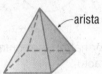
arista

equation A mathematical sentence stating that two quantities are equal.

ecuación Enunciado matemático que establece que dos cantidades son iguales.

equiangular A polygon in which all angles are congruent.

equiangular Polígono en el cual todos los ángulos son congruentes.

equilateral triangle A triangle with three congruent sides.

triángulo equilátero Triángulo con tres lados congruentes.

equivalent expressions Expressions that have the same value regardless of the value(s) of the variable(s).

expresiones equivalentes Expresiones que poseen el mismo valor, sin importar los valores de la(s) variable(s).

event An outcome is a possible result.

evento Un resultado posible.

experimental probability An estimated probability based on the relative frequency of positive outcomes occurring during an experiment.

probabilidad experimental Probabilidad estimada que se basa en la frecuencia relativa de los resultados positivos que ocurren durante un experimento.

exponent In a power, the number of times the base is used as a factor. In 10^3, the exponent is 3.

exponente En una potencia, el número de veces que la base se usa como factor. En 10^3, el exponente es 3.

exponential function A nonlinear function in which the base is a constant and the exponent is an independent variable.

función exponencial Función no lineal en la cual la base es una constante y el exponente es una variable independiente.

exterior angles The four outer angles formed by two lines cut by a transversal.

ángulo externo Los cuatro ángulos exteriores que se forman cuando una transversal corta dos rectas.

face A flat surface of a polyhedron.

face

cara Una superficie plana de un poliedro.

cara

fair game A game where each player has an equally likely chance of winning.

juego justo Juego donde cada jugador tiene igual posibilidad de ganar.

five-number summary A way of characterizing a set of data that includes the minimum, first quartile, median, third quartile, and the maximum.

resumen de los cinco números Una manera de caracterizar un conjunto de datos que incluye el mínimo, el primer cuartil, la mediana, el tercer cuartil y el máximo.

formal proof A two-column proof containing statements and reasons.

demonstración formal Demonstración endos columnas contiene enunciados y razonamientos.

function A relation in which each member of the domain (input value) is paired with exactly one member of the range (output value).

función Relación en la cual a cada elemento del dominio (valor de entrada) le corresponde exactamente un único elemento del rango (valor de salida).

function table A table organizing the domain, rule, and range of a function.

tabla de funciones Tabla que organiza la regla de entrada y de salida de una función.

Fundamental Counting Principle Uses multiplication of the number of ways each event in an experiment can occur to find the number of possible outcomes in a sample space.

principio fundamental de contar Método que usa la multiplicación del número de maneras en que cada evento puede ocurrir en un experimento, para calcular el número de resultados posibles en un espacio muestral.

geometric sequence A sequence in which each term after the first is found by multiplying the previous term by a constant.

sucesión geométrica Sucesión en la cual cada término después del primero se determina multiplicando el término anterior por una constante.

half-plane The part of the coordinate plane on one side of the boundary.

semiplano Parte del plano de coordenadas en un lado de la frontera.

hemisphere One of two congruent halves of a sphere.

hemisferio Una de dos mitades congruentes de una esfera.

hypotenuse The side opposite the right angle in a right triangle.

hipotenusa El lado opuesto al ángulo recto de un triángulo rectángulo.

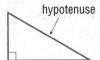

hypotenuse

hipotenusa

identity An equation that is true for every value for the variable.

identidad Ecuación que es verdad para cada valor de la variable.

image The resulting figure after a transformation.

imagen Figura que resulta después de una transformación.

independent events Two or more events in which the outcome of one event does not affect the outcome of the other event(s).

eventos independientes Dos o más eventos en los cuales el resultado de un evento no afecta el resultado de los otros eventos.

independent variable The variable in a function with a value that is subject to choice.

variable independiente Variable en una función cuyo valor está sujeto a elección.

indirect measurement A technique using properties of similar polygons to find distances or lengths that are difficult to measure directly.

medición indirecta Técnica que usa las propiedades de polígonos semejantes para calcular distancias o longitudes difíciles de medir directamente.

inductive reasoning Reasoning that uses a number of specific examples to arrive at a plausible generalization or prediction. Conclusions arrived at by inductive reasoning lack the logical certainty of those arrived at by deductive reasoning.

razonamiento inductivo Razonamiento que usa varios ejemplos especificos para lograr una generalización o una predicción plausible. Las conclusiones obtenidas por razonamiento inductivo carecen de la certeza lógica de aquellas obtenidas por razonamiento deductivo.

inequality A mathematical sentence that contains $<$, $>$, $\neq$, $\leq$, or $\geq$.

desigualdad Enunciado matemático que contiene $<$, $>$, $\neq$, $\leq$, o $\geq$.

inscribed angle An angle that has its vertex on the circle. Its sides contain chords of the circle.

ángulo inscrito Ángulo cuyo vértice está en el círculo y cuyos lados contienen cuerdas del círculo.

informal proof A paragraph proof.

demostración informal Demonstración en forma de párrafo.

interest The amount of money paid or earned for the use of money.

interés Cantidad que se cobra o se paga por el uso del dinero.

interior angle An angle inside a polygon.

ángulo interno Ángulo dentro de un polígono.

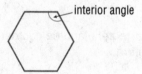

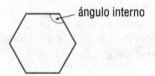

interior angles The four inside angles formed by two lines cut by a transversal.

ángulo interno Los cuatro ángulos internos formados por dos rectas intersecadas por una transversal.

interquartile range A measure of variation in a set of numerical data. It is the difference between the first quartile and the third quartile.

rango intercuartílico Una medida de la variación en un conjunto de datos numéricos. Es la diferencia entre el primer y el tercer cuartil.

inverse operations Pairs of operations that undo each other. Addition and subtraction are inverse operations. Multiplication and division are inverse operations.

peraciones inversas Pares de operaciones que se anulan mutuamente. La adición y la sustracción son operaciones inversas. La multiplicación y la división son operaciones inversas.

irrational number A number that cannot be expressed as the quotient $\frac{a}{b}$, where a and b are integers and $b \neq 0$.

números irracionales Número que no se puede expresar como el cociente $\frac{a}{b}$, donde a y b son enteros y $b \neq 0$.

isosceles triangle A triangle with at least two congruent sides.

triángulo isóceles Triángulo con por lo menos dos lados congruentes.

lateral area The sum of the areas of the lateral faces of a solid.

área lateral La suma de las áreas de las caras laterales de un sólido.

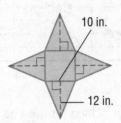

lateral area $= 4\left(\frac{1}{2} \times 10 \times 12\right) = 240$ square inches

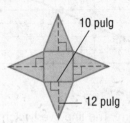

área lateral $= 4\left(\frac{1}{2} \times 10 \times 12\right) = 240$ pulgadas cuadradas

lateral face Any flat surface that is not a base.

cara lateral Cualquier superficie plana que no es la base.

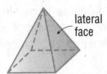

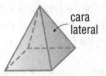

legs The two sides of a right triangle that form the right angle.

catetos Los dos lados de un triángulo rectángulo que forman el ángulo recto.

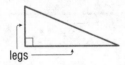

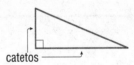

like fractions Fractions that have the same denominators.

fracciones semejantes Fracciones que tienen el mismo denominador.

like terms Terms that contain the same variable(s) to the same powers.

términos semejantes Términos que contienen la misma variable o variables elevadas a la misma potencia.

linear To fall in a straight line.

lineal Que cae en una línea recta.

linear equation An equation with a graph that is a straight line.

ecuación lineal Ecuación cuya gráfica es una recta.

linear function A function in which the graph of the solutions forms a line.

función lineal Función en la cual la gráfica de las soluciones forma un recta.

linear relationship A relationship that has a straight-line graph.

relación lineal Relación cuya gráfica es una recta.

line of best fit A line that is very close to most of the data points in a scatter plot.

recta de mejor ajuste Recta que más se acerca a la mayoría de puntos de los datos en un diagrama de dispersión.

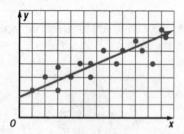

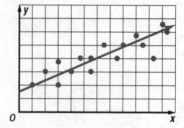

line of reflection The line over which a figure is reflected.

línea de reflexión Línea a través de la cual se refleja una figura.

line of symmetry Each half of a figure is a mirror image of the other half when a line of symmetry is drawn.

eje de simetría Recta que divide una figura en dos mitades especulares.

line symmetry A figure has line symmetry if a line can be drawn so that one half of the figure is a mirror image of the other half.

simetría lineal Una figura tiene simetría lineal si se puede trazar una recta de manera que una mitad de la figura sea una imagen especular de la otra mitad.

literal equation An equation or formula that has more than one variable.

ecuación literal Ecuación o fórmula con más de una variable.

Mm

markup The amount the price of an item is increased above the price the store paid for the item.

margen de utilidad Cantidad de aumento en el precio de un artículo por encima del precio que paga la tienda por dicho artículo.

mean The sum of the data divided by the number of items in the set.

media La suma de datos dividida entre el número total de artículos.

mean absolute deviation The average of the absolute values of differences between the mean and each value in a data set.

desviación media absoluta El promedio de los valores absolutos de diferencias entre el medio y cada valor de un conjunto de datos.

measures of center Numbers that are used to describe the center of a set of data. These measures include the mean, median, and mode.

medidas del centro Números que describen el centro de un conjunto de datos. Estas medidas incluyen la media, la mediana y la moda.

measures of variation Numbers used to describe the distribution or spread of a set of data.

medidas de variación Números que se usan para describir la distribución o separación de un conjunto de datos.

median A measure of center in a set of numerical data. The median of a list of values is the value appearing at the center of a sorted version of the list—or the mean of the two central values, if the list contains an even number of values.

mediana Una medida del centro en un conjunto de datos numéricos. La mediana de una lista de valores es el valor que aparece en el centro de una versión ordenada de la lista, o la media de los dos valores centrales si la lista contiene un número par de valores.

mode The number(s) or item(s) that appear most often in a set of data.

moda El número(s) o artículo(s) que aparece con más frecuencia en un conjunto de datos.

monomial A number, a variable, or a product of a number and one or more variables.

monomio Un número, una variable o el producto de un número por una o más variables.

Multiplication Property of Equality If you multiply each side of an equation by the same number, the two sides remain equal.

propiedad de multiplicación de la igualdad Si cada lado de una ecuación se multiplica por el mismo número, los lados permanecen iguales.

multiplicative inverses Two numbers with a product of 1. The multiplicative inverse of $\frac{2}{3}$ is $\frac{3}{2}$.

inversos multiplicativo Dos números cuyo producto es 1. El inverso multiplicativo de $\frac{2}{3}$ es $\frac{3}{2}$.

Nn

net A two-dimensional pattern of a three-dimensional figure.

red Patrón bidimensional de una figura tridimensional.

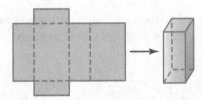

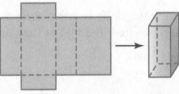

nonlinear function A function whose rate of change is not constant. The graph of a nonlinear function is not a straight line.

función no lineal Función cuya tasa de cambio no es constante. La gráfica de una función no lineal no es una recta.

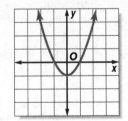

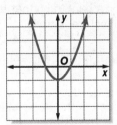

null set The empty set.

conjunto nulo El conjunto vacío.

Oo

obtuse angle An angle whose measure is between 90° and 180°.

ángulo obtuso Ángulo cuya medida está entre 90° y 180°.

obtuse triangle A triangle with one obtuse angle.

triángulo obtusángulo Triángulo con un ángulo obtuso.

ordered pair   A pair of numbers used to locate a point in the coordinate plane. The ordered pair is written in this form: (*x*-coordinate, *y*-coordinate).

par ordenado   Par de números que se utiliza para ubicar un punto en un plano de coordenadas. Se escribe de la siguiente forma: (coordenada *x*, coordenada *y*).

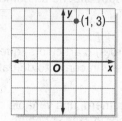

origin   The point of intersection of the *x*-axis and *y*-axis in a coordinate plane.

origen   Punto en que el eje *x* y el eje *y* se intersecan en un plano de coordenadas.

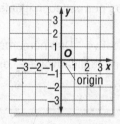

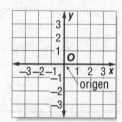

outcome   One possible result of a probability event. For example, 4 is an outcome when a number cube is rolled.

resultado   Una consecuencia posible de un evento de probabilidad. Por ejemplo, 4 es un resultado posible al lanzar un cubo numérico.

outlier   Data that are more than 1.5 times the interquartile range from the first or third quartiles.

valor atípico   Datos que distan de los cuartiles respectivos más de 1.5 veces la amplitud intercuartílica.

paragraph proof   A paragraph that explains why a statement or conjecture is true.

prueba por párrafo   Párrafo que explica por qué es verdadero un enunciado o una conjetura.

parallel   Lines that never intersect no matter how far they extend.

paralelo   Rectas que nunca se intersecan sea cual sea su extensión.

parallel lines   Lines in the same plane that never intersect or cross. The symbol ‖ means parallel.

rectas paralelas   Rectas que yacen en un mismo plano y que no se intersecan. El símbolo ‖ significa paralela a.

parallelogram   A quadrilateral with both pairs of opposite sides parallel and congruent.

paralelogramo   Cuadrilátero con ambos pares de lados opuestos, paralelos y congruentes.

percent equation An equivalent form of a percent proportion in which the percent is written as a decimal.

$$\text{part} = \text{percent} \cdot \text{whole}$$

percent of change A ratio that compares the change in quantity to the original amount.

$$\text{percent of change} = \frac{\text{amount of change}}{\text{original amount}}$$

percent of decrease When the percent of change is negative.

percent of increase When the percent of change is positive.

percent proportion Compares part of a quantity to the whole quantity using a percent.

$$\frac{\text{part}}{\text{whole}} = \frac{\text{percent}}{100}$$

perfect cube A rational number whose cube root is a whole number. 27 is a perfect cube because its cube root is 3.

perfect square A rational number whose square root is a whole number. 25 is a perfect square because its square root is 5.

permutation An arrangement or listing in which order is important.

perpendicular lines Two lines that intersect to form right angles.

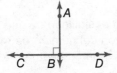

pi The ratio of the circumference of a circle to its diameter. The Greek letter π represents this number. The value of pi is always 3.1415926... .

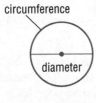

circumference

diameter

$$\pi = \frac{C}{d}$$

point-slope form An equation of the form $y - y_1 = m(x - x_1)$, where m is the slope and $(x_1 - y_1)$ is a given point on a nonvertical line.

ecuación porcentual Forma equivalente de proporción porcentual en la cual el por ciento se escribe como un decimal.

$$\text{parte} = \text{por ciento} \cdot \text{entero}$$

porcentaje de cambio Razón que compara el cambio en una cantidad a la cantidad original.

$$\text{procentaje de cambio} = \frac{\text{cantidad de cambio}}{\text{cantidad original}}$$

porcentaje de disminución Cuando el porcentaje de cambio es negativo.

porcentaje de aumento Cuando el porcentaje de cambio es positivo.

proporción porcentual Compara parte de una cantidad con la cantidad total mediante un por ciento.

$$\frac{\text{parte}}{\text{entero}} = \frac{\text{por ciento}}{100}$$

cubo perfecto Número racional cuya raíz cúbica es un número entero. 27 es un cubo perfecto porque su raíz cúbica es 3.

cuadrados perfectos Número racional cuya raíz cuadrada es un número entero. 25 es un cuadrado perfecto porque su raíz cuadrada es 5.

permutación Arreglo o lista donde el orden es importante.

rectas perpendiculares Dos rectas que se intersecan formando ángulos rectos.

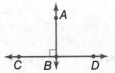

pi Razón de la circunferencia de un círculo al diámetro del mismo. La letra griega π representa este número. El valor de pi es siempre 3.1415926... .

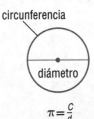

circunferencia

diámetro

$$\pi = \frac{C}{d}$$

forma punto-pendiente Ecuación de la forma $y - y_1 = m(x - x_1)$ donde m es la pendiente y $(x_1 - y_1)$ es un punto dado de una recta no vertical.

polygon A simple, closed figure formed by three or more line segments.

polígono Figura simple y cerrada formada por tres o más segmentos de recta.

polyhedron A three-dimensional figure with faces that are polygons.

poliedro Una figura tridimensional con caras que son polígonos.

power A product of repeated factors using an exponent and a base. The power 7^3 is read *seven to the third power,* or *seven cubed.*

potencia Producto de factores repetidos con un exponente y una base. La potencia 7^3 se lee *siete a la tercera potencia* o *siete al cubo.*

precision The ability of a measurement to be consistently reproduced.

precisión Capacidad de una medida a ser reproducida consistentemente.

preimage The original figure before a transformation.

preimagen Figura original antes de una transformación.

principal The amount of money invested or borrowed.

capital Cantidad de dinero que se invierte o que se toma prestada.

prism A polyhedron with two parallel congruent faces called bases.

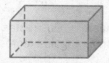

prisma Poliedro con dos caras congruentes y paralelas llamadas bases.

probability The chance that some event will happen. It is the ratio of the number of ways a certain event can occur to the number of possible outcomes.

probabilidad La posibilidad de que suceda un evento. Es la razón del número de maneras en que puede ocurrir un evento al número total de resultados posibles.

proof A logical argument in which each statement that is made is supported by a statement that is accepted as true.

prueba Argumento lógico en el cual cada enunciado hecho se respalda con un enunciado que se acepta como verdadero.

property A statement that is true for any numbers.

propiedad Enunciado que se cumple para cualquier número.

pyramid A polyhedron with one base that is a polygon and three or more triangular faces that meet at a common vertex.

pirámide Un poliedro con una base que es un polígono y tres o más caras triangulares que se encuentran en un vértice común.

Pythagorean Theorem   In a right triangle, the square of the length of the hypotenuse c is equal to the sum of the squares of the lengths of the legs a and b. $a^2 + b^2 = c^2$

Teorema de Pitágoras   En un triángulo rectángulo, el cuadrado de la longitud de la hipotenusa es igual a la suma de los cuadrados de las longitudes de los catetos. $a^2 + b^2 = c^2$

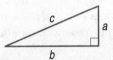

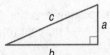

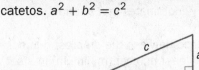

quadrants   The four sections of the coordinate plane.

cuadrantes   Las cuatro secciones del plano de coordenadas.

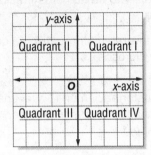

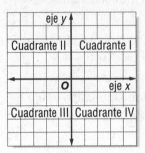

quadratic function   A function in which the greatest power of the variable is 2.

función cuadrática   Función en la cual la potencia mayor de la variable es 2.

quadrilateral   A closed figure with four sides and four angles.

cuadrilátero   Figura cerrada con cuatro lados y cuatro ángulos.

qualitative graph   A graph used to represent situations that do not necessarily have numerical values.

gráfica cualitativa   Gráfica que se usa para representar situaciones que no tienen valores numéricos necesariamente.

quantitative data   Data that can be given a numerical value.

datos cualitativos   Datos que no se pueden dar un valor numérico.

quartiles   Values that divide a set of data into four equal parts.

cuartiles   Valores que dividen un conjunto de datos en cuatro partes iguales.

radical sign   The symbol used to indicate a positive square root, $\sqrt{}$.

signo radical   Símbolo que se usa para indicar una raíz cuadrada no positiva, $\sqrt{}$.

radius   The distance from the center of a circle to any point on the circle.

radio   Distancia desde el centro de un círculo hasta cualquier punto del mismo.

random Outcomes occur at random if each outcome is equally likely to occur.

range The set of y-coordinates in a relation.

range The difference between the greatest number (maximum) and the least number (minimum) in a set of data.

rational number Numbers that can be written as the ratio of two integers in which the denominator is not zero. All integers, fractions, mixed numbers, and percents are rational numbers.

real numbers The set of rational numbers together with the set of irrational numbers.

reciprocals The multiplicative inverse of a number. The product of reciprocals is 1.

reflection A transformation where a figure is flipped over a line. Also called a flip.

regular polygon A polygon that is equilateral and equiangular.

regular pyramid A pyramid whose base is a regular polygon.

relation Any set of ordered pairs.

relative frequency The ratio of the number of experimental successes to the total number of experimental attempts.

remote interior angles The angles of a triangle that are not adjacent to a given exterior angle.

repeating decimal Decimal form of a rational number.

rhombus A parallelogram with four congruent sides.

azar Los resultados ocurren al azar si todos los resultados son equiprobables.

rango Conjunto de coordenadas y en una relación.

rango La diferencia entre el número mayor (máximo) y el número menor (mínimo) en un conjunto de datos.

número racional Números que pueden escribirse como la razón de dos enteros en los que el denominador no es cero. Todos los enteros, fracciones, números mixtos y porcentajes son números racionales.

número real El conjunto de números racionales junto con el conjunto de números irracionales.

recíproco El inverso multiplicativo de un número. El producto de recíprocos es 1.

reflexión Transformación en la cual una figura se voltea sobre una recta. También se conoce como simetría de espejo.

polígono regular Polígono equilátero y equiangular.

pirámide regular Pirámide cuya base es un polígono regular.

relación Cualquier conjunto de pares ordenados.

frecuencia relativa Razón del número de éxitos experimentales al número total de intentos experimentales.

ángulos internos no adyacentes Ángulos de un triángulo que no son adya centes a un ángulo exterior dado.

decimal periódico Forma decimal de un número racional.

rombo Paralelogramo con cuatro lados congruentes.

right angle   An angle whose measure is exactly 90°.

x

right triangle   A triangle with one right angle.

rise   The vertical change between any two points on a line.

rotation   A transformation in which a figure is turned about a fixed point.

rotational symmetry   A type of symmetry a figure has if it can be rotated less than 360° about its center and still look like the original.

run   The horizontal change between any two points on a line.

ángulo recto   Ángulo que mide exactamente 90°.

x

triángulo rectángulo   Triángulo con un ángulo recto.

elevación   El cambio vertical entre cualquier par de puntos en una recta.

rotación   Transformación en la cual una figura se gira alrededor de un punto fijo.

simetría rotacional   Tipo de simetría que tiene una figura si se puede girar menos que 360° en torno al centro y aún sigue viéndose como la figura original.

carrera   El cambio horizontal entre cualquier par de puntos en una recta.

sales tax   An additional amount of money charged on certain goods and services.

sample   A randomly-selected group chosen for the purpose of collecting data.

sample space   The set of all possible outcomes of a probability experiment.

scale factor   The ratio of the lengths of two corresponding sides of two similar polygons.

impuesto sobre las ventas   Cantidad de dinero adicional que se cobra por ciertos artículos y servicios.

muestra   Subconjunto de una población que se usa con el propósito de recoger datos.

espacio muestral   Conjunto de todos los resultados posibles de un experimento de probabilidad.

factor de escala   La razón de las longitudes de dos lados correspondientes de dos polígonos semejantes.

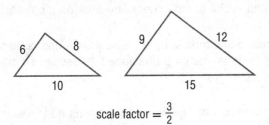

scale factor = $\frac{3}{2}$

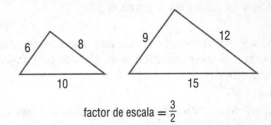

factor de escala = $\frac{3}{2}$

scalene triangle   A triangle with no congruent sides.

triángulo escaleno   Triángulo sin lados congruentes.

scatter plot A graph that shows the relationship between a data set with two variables graphed as ordered pairs on a coordinate plane.

diagrama de dispersión Gráfica que muestra la relación entre un conjunto de datos con dos variables graficadas como pares ordenados en un plano de coordenadas.

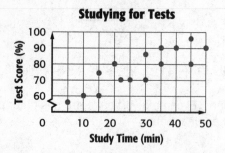

Studying for Tests

Tiempo de estudio para pruebas

scientific notation A compact way of writing numbers with absolute values that are very large or very small. In scientific notation, 5,500 is 5.5×10^3.

notación científica Manera abreviada de escribir números con valores absolutos que son muy grandes o muy pequeños. En notación científica, 5,500 es 5.5×10^3.

selling price The amount the customer pays for an item.

precio de venta Cantidad de dinero que paga un consumidor por un artículo.

semicircle An arc measuring 180°.

semicírculo Arco que mide 180°.

sequence An ordered list of numbers, such as 0, 1, 2, 3 or 2, 4, 6, 8.

sucesión Lista ordenada de números, tales como 0, 1, 2, 3 o 2, 4, 6, 8.

similar If one image can be obtained from another by a sequence of transformations and dilations.

similar Si una imagen puede obtenerse de otra mediante una secuencia de transformaciones y dilataciones.

similar polygons Polygons that have the same shape.

polígonos semejantes Polígonos con la misma forma.

similar solids Solids that have exactly the same shape, but not necessarily the same size.

sólidos semejantes Sólidos que tienen exactamente la misma forma, pero no necesariamente el mismo tamaño.

simple interest Interest paid only on the initial principal of a savings account or loan.

interés simple Interés que se paga sólo sobre el capital inicial de una cuenta de ahorros o préstamo.

simple random sample A sample where each item or person in the population is as likely to be chosen as any other.

muestra aleatoria simple Muestra de una población que tiene la misma probabilidad de escogerse que cualquier otra.

simplest form An algebraic expression that has no like terms and no parentheses.

forma reducida Expresión algebraica que carece de términos semejantes y de paréntesis.

simplify To perform all possible operations in an expression.

simplificar Realizar todas las operaciones posibles en una expresión.

simulation An experiment that is designed to model the action in a given situation.

simulacro Un experimento diseñado para modelar la acción en una situación dada.

slant height   The altitude or height of each lateral face of a pyramid.

altura oblicua   La longitud de la altura de cada cara lateral de una pirámide.

slope   The rate of change between any two points on a line. The ratio of the rise, or vertical change, to the run, or horizontal change.

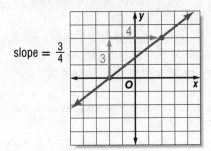

slope = $\frac{3}{4}$

pendiente   Razón de cambio entre cualquier par de puntos en una recta. La razón de la altura, o cambio vertical, a la carrera, o cambio horizontal.

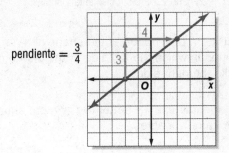

pendiente = $\frac{3}{4}$

slope-intercept form   An equation written in the form $y = mx + b$, where m is the slope and b is the y-intercept.

forma pendiente intersección   Ecuación de la forma $y = mx + b$, donde m es la pendiente y b es la intersección y.

solid   A three-dimensional figure formed by intersecting planes.

sólido   Figura tridimensional formada por planos que se intersecan.

sphere   The set of all points in space that are a given distance from a given point called the center.

esfera   Conjunto de todos los puntos en el espacio que están a una distancia dada de un punto dado llamado centro.

square root   One of the two equal factors of a number. If $a^2 = b$, then a is the square root of b. A square root of 144 is 12 since $12^2 = 144$.

raíz cuadrada   Uno de dos factores iguales de un número. Si $a^2 = b$, la a es la raíz cuadrada de b. Una raíz cuadrada de 144 es 12 porque $12^2 = 144$.

standard deviation   A measure of variation that describes how the data deviates from the mean of the data.

desviación estándar   Una medida de variación que describe cómo los datos se desvía de la media de los datos.

standard form   An equation written in the form $Ax + By = C$.

forma estándar   Ecuación escrita en la forma $Ax + By = C$.

straight angle   An angle whose measure is exactly 180°.

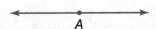

ángulo llano   Ángulo que mide exactamente 180°.

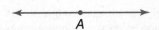

substitution   An algebraic model that can be used to find the exact solution of a system of equations.

sustitución   Modelo algebraico que se puede usar para calcular la solución exacta de un sistema de ecuaciones.

Subtraction Property of Equality   If you subtract the same number from each side of an equation, the two sides remain equal.

propiedad de sustracción de la igualdad   Si sustraes el mismo número de ambos lados de una ecuación, los dos lados permanecen iguales.

supplementary angles   Two angles are supplementary if the sum of their measures is 180°.

ángulos suplementarios   Dos ángulos son suplementarios si la suma de sus medidas es 180°.

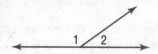

∠1 and ∠2 are supplementary angles.

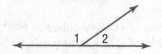

∠1 y ∠2 son ángulos suplementarios.

symmetric   A description of the shape of a distribution in which the left side of the distribution looks like the right side.

simétrico   Una descripción de la forma de una distribución en la que el lado izquierdo de la distribución se parece el lado derecho.

system of equations   A set of two or more equations with the same variables.

sistema de ecuaciones   Sistema de ecuaciones con las mismas variables.

term   A number, a variable, or a product of numbers and variables.

término   Un número, una variable o un producto de números y variables.

term   Each part of an algebraic expression separated by an addition or subtraction sign.

término   Cada parte de un expresión algebraica separada por un signo adición o un signo sustracción.

terminating decimal   A repeating decimal where the repeating digit is zero.

decimal finito   Un decimal periódico donde el dígito que se repite es cero.

theorem   A statement or conjecture that can be proven.

teorema   Un enunciado o conjetura que puede probarse.

theoretical probability   Probability based on known characteristics or facts.

probabilidad teórica   Probabilidad que se basa en características o hechos conocidos.

third quartile   For a data set with median M, the third quartile is the median of the data values greater than M.

tercer cuartil   Para un conjunto de datos con la mediana M, el tercer cuartil es la mediana de los valores mayores que M.

three-dimensional figure   A figure with length, width, and height.

figura tridimensional   Figura que tiene largo, ancho y alto.

total surface area   The sum of the areas of the surfaces of a solid.

área de superficie total   La suma del área de las superficies de un sólido.

transformation   An operation that maps a geometric figure, preimage, onto a new figure, image.

transformación   Operación que convierte una figura geométrica, la pre-imagen, en una figura nueva, la imagen.

translation   A transformation that slides a figure from one position to another without turning.

traslación   Transformación en la cual una figura se desliza de una posición a otra sin hacerla girar.

transversal   A line that intersects two or more other lines.

transversal   Recta que interseca dos o más rectas.

trapezoid   A quadrilateral with exactly one pair of parallel sides.

trapecio   Cuadrilátero con exactamente un par de lados paralelos.

tree diagram   A diagram used to show the total number of possible outcomes in a probability experiment.

diagrama de árbol   Diagrama que se usa para mostrar el número total de resultados posibles en un experimento de probabilidad.

triangle   A figure formed by three line segments that intersect only at their endpoints.

triángulo   Figura formada por tres segmentos de recta que se intersecan sólo en sus extremos.

two-column proof   A formal proof that contains statements and reasons organized in two columns. Each step is called a statement, and the properties that justify each step are called reasons.

demostración de dos columnas   Demonstración formal que contiene enunciados y razones organizadas en dos columnas. Cada paso se llama enunciado y las propiedades que lo justifican son las razones.

two-step equation   An equation that contains two operations.

ecuación de dos pasos   Ecuación que contiene dos operaciones.

two-step inequality   An inequality that contains two operations.

desigualdad de dos pasos   Desigualdad que contiene dos operaciones.

two-way table   A table that shows data that pertain to two different categories.

tabla de doble entrada   Una tabla que muestra datos que pertenecen a dos categorías diferentes.

unbiased sample   A sample that is selected so that it is representative of the entire population.

muestra no sesgada   Muestra que se selecciona de modo que sea representativa de la población entera.

unit rate/ratio   A rate or ratio with a denominator of 1.

tasa/razón unitaria   Una tasa o razón con un denominador de 1.

univariate data   Data with one variable.

datos univariate   Datos con una variable.

unlike fractions   Fractions whose denominators are different.

fracciones con distinto denominador   Fracciones cuyos denominadores son diferentes.

variable   A symbol, usually a letter, used to represent a number in mathematical expressions or sentences.

variable   Un símbolo, por lo general, una letra, que se usa para representar números en expresiones o enunciados matemáticos.

vertex   The point where the sides of an angle meet.

vértice   Punto donde se encuentran los lados.

vertex   The point where three or more faces of a polyhedron intersect.

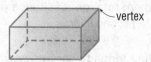

vértice   El punto donde tres o más caras de un poliedro se cruzan.

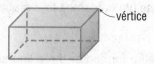

vertex   The point at the tip of a cone.

vértice   El punto en la punta de un cono.

vertical angles   Opposite angles formed by the intersection of two lines. Vertical angles are congruent. In the figure, the vertical angles are ∠1 and ∠3, and ∠2 and ∠4.

ángulos opuestos por el vértice   Ángulos congruentes que se forman de la intersección de dos rectas. En la figura, los ángulos opuestos por el vértice son ∠1 y ∠3, y ∠2 y ∠4.

volume   The measure of the space occupied by a solid. Standard measures are cubic units such as in^3 or ft^3.

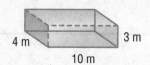

$V = 10 \times 4 \times 3 = 120$ cubic meters

volumen   Medida del espacio que ocupa un sólido. Las medidas estándar son las unidades cúbicas, como $pulg^3$ o $pies^3$.

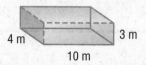

$V = 10 \times 4 \times 3 = 120$ metros cúbicos

voluntary response sample   A sample which involves only those who want to participate in the sampling.

muestra de respuesta voluntaria   Muestra que involucra sólo aquellos que quieren participar en el muestreo.

x-axis   The horizontal number line that helps to form the coordinate plane.

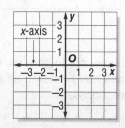

eje x   La recta numérica horizontal que ayuda a formar el plano de coordenadas.

GL24   Glossary

x-coordinate   The first number of an ordered pair.

coordenada x   El primer número de un par ordenado.

x-intercept   The x-coordinate of the point where the line crosses the x-axis.

intersección x   La coordenada x del punto donde cruza la gráfica el eje x.

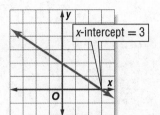

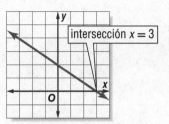

y-axis   The vertical number line that helps to form the coordinate plane.

eje y   La recta numérica vertical que ayuda a formar el plano de coordenadas.

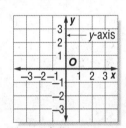

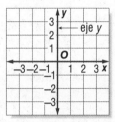

y-coordinate   The second number of an ordered pair.

coordenada y   El segundo número de un par ordenado.

y-intercept   The y-coordinate of the point where the line crosses the y-axis.

intersección y   La coordenada y del punto donde cruza la gráfica el eje y.

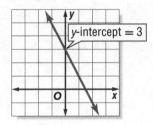

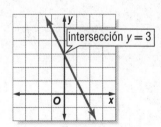

Chapter 1 Transformations

Chapter 1 Are You Ready?

1. Sample answer:

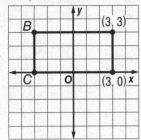

3.

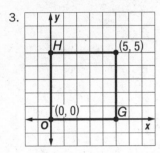

5. −2 **7.** 6 **9.** −6 **11.** 2

Lesson 1-1 Independent Practice

1. corresponding **3** $m\angle 4 = 30°$, $m\angle 7 = 150°$;
Sample answer: $\angle 1$ and $\angle 7$ are corresponding angles
so their measures are equal. $\angle 1$ and $\angle 4$ are
supplementary. So, $m\angle 4 = 180° − 150°$ or 30°.
5. 110°; Sample answer: $\angle 2$ and $\angle 8$ are alternate interior
angles, so they have the same measure. **7a.** 20 **7b.** 40
9. They are supplementary. **11.** A

Lesson 1-1 Extra Practice

13. alternate interior; $\angle 3$ and $\angle 6$ are interior angles that
lie on opposite sides of the transversal. They are alternate
interior angles. 15. alternate interior **17.** 110°; Sample
answer: $\angle 2$ and $\angle 6$ are corresponding angles, so they
have the same measure. **19.** 43°; Sample answer: $\angle 3$
and $\angle 4$ are supplementary. So, $m\angle 4 = 180 − 137$ or 43°.
21. D **23.** $\angle 1$ and $\angle 5$, $\angle 2$ and $\angle 6$, $\angle 3$ and $\angle 7$, $\angle 4$ and
$\angle 8$ **25.** neither **27.** complementary

Lesson 1-2 Independent Practice

1. 65 **3.** 24°, 48°, 108° **5.** 112 **7.** 45 **9** 105°
11 90°, 60°, 30° **13.** Sample answer: Since $\angle 1$ and $\angle 4$
form a linear pair, $m\angle 1 + m\angle 4 = 180°$. By the Subtraction
Property of Equality, $m\angle 1 = 180 − m\angle 4$. Since ABC is a

triangle, $m\angle 2 + m\angle 3 + m\angle 4 = 180$. By the Subtraction
Property of Equality, $m\angle 2 + m\angle 3 = 180 − m\angle 4$. So by
substitution, $m\angle 2 + m\angle 3 = m\angle 1$. **15.** C

Lesson 1-2 Extra Practice

17. 100 **19.** 50 **21.** 120 **23.** 48°, 60°, 72° **25.** 70
27. 25; 50 **29.** G **31.** Yes; the two corners at the
intersection have measures of 108° and 72°. Therefore it
is within the safety limit. **33.** 105

Lesson 1-3 Independent Practice

1. 540° **3** 1,980° **5** 36° **7.** 24° **9.** 60°, 90°,
90°, 120°; 360° **11.** 130

13. 18

$$\frac{(n − 2)180}{n} = 160$$
$(n − 2)180 = 160n$ — Multiplication Property
of Equality
$180n − 360 = 160n$ — Distributive Property
$20n = 360$ — Properties of Equality
$n = 18$ — Division Property of
Equality

15. I

Lesson 1-3 Extra Practice

17. 2,160° **19.** 140° **21.** 161.1° **23.** 40°
25. 20° **27.** Sample answer: The sum of the interior
angles will still be 720° because even though the
figures are not regular, they are still hexagons.
29. complementary **31.** 51 **33.** 27

Lesson 1-4 Independent Practice

1

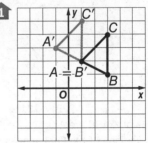

$A'(−1, 3)$, $B'(1, 2)$, $C'(1, 5)$
3. $P'(6, 5)$, $Q'(11, 3)$, $R'(3, 11)$ **5.** $(x − 3, y − 3)$
7 $K''(−3, 1)$, $L''(0, 4)$, $M''(−1, 7)$, $N''(−4, 8)$ **9.** the same
as the original position of the figure; Sample answer:
Since −5 and 5 are opposites, and −7 and 7 are
opposites, the translations cancel each other out. **11.** B

Lesson 1-4 Extra Practice

13.

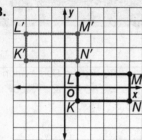

$K'(-3, 2)$, $L'(-3, 4)$, $M'(1, 4)$, $N'(1, 2)$

15. $A'(-3, -3)$, $B'(-1, -2)$, $C'(4, -4)$, $D'(2, -8)$ **17.** 1

19. G **21.** 7 **23.** -78 **25.** -240

Lesson 1-5 Independent Practice

1.

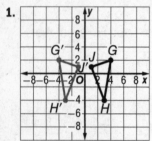

$G'(-4, 2)$, $H'(-3, -4)$, $J'(-1, 1)$

3.

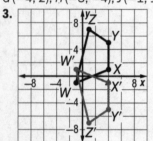

$W'(-1, 1)$, $X'(4, -1)$, $Y'(4, -5)$, $Z'(1, -7)$

5. $A'(-3, -3)$, $B'(3, -3)$

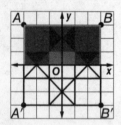

7 x-axis **9.** $J''(7, -4)$, $K''(-7, -1)$, $L''(-2, 2)$ **11.** no;
Sample answer: If the vertices of $\triangle ABC$ are $A(0, 0)$,
$B(2, 2)$, and $C(0, 4)$, then the vertices of the final image are
$A''(0, 0)$, $B''(-2, -2)$, and $C''(0, -4)$.

Lesson 1-5 Extra Practice

13.

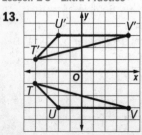

$T'(-4, 1)$, $U'(-2, 3)$, $V'(4, 3)$

15.

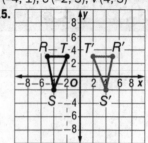

$R'(5, 3)$, $S'(4, -2)$, $T'(2, 3)$

17. $A'(3, 3)$, $B'(1, -2)$

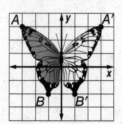

19. y-axis **21.** H

23.

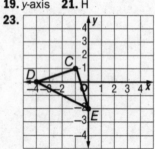

25.

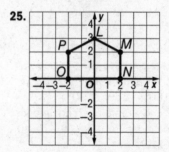

Problem-Solving Investigation Act It Out

Case 3. 6 ways **Case 5.** 6 times

Lesson 1-6 Independent Practice

1

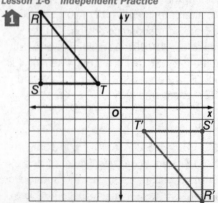

$R'(7, -8)$, $S'(7, -2)$, $T'(2, -2)$

3.

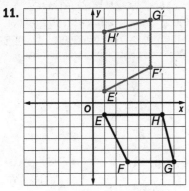

5 I and N   **7.** $A''(0, 4)$, $B''(0, -2)$, $C''(-2, 0)$ **9.** B

11.

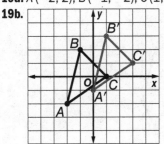

$E'(1, 1)$, $F'(5, 3)$, $G'(5, 7)$, $H'(1, 6)$ **13.** $M'(4, -1)$, $N'(1, -3)$, $P'(3, -5)$ **15.** $M'(-4, 1)$, $N'(-1, 3)$, $P'(-3, 5)$ **17.** H

19a. $A'(-2, 2)$, $B'(-1, -2)$, $C'(1, 0)$

19b.

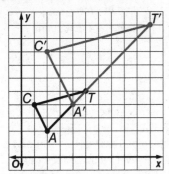

1 $C'(2, 8)$, $A'(4, 4)$, $T'(10, 10)$

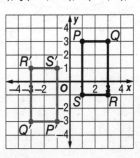

3. $\frac{1}{5}$ **5** **a.** $A''(-6, -9)$, $B''(0, 0)$, $C''(3, -3)$ **b.** $A''(-6, -9)$, $B''(0, 0)$, $C''(3, -3)$ **c.** Yes; Sample answer: since the coordinates of the answers to Exercises a and b are the same, the order in which you perform them does not matter.   **7a.** $(-12, -18)$ **7b.** The final coordinates are three times the original coordinates.   **7c.** Sample answer:

Yes; multiply the scale factors of each dilation to find the scale factor of the final dilation.   **9.** C

11. $V'(-9, 12)$, $X'(-6, 0)$, $W'(3, 6)$

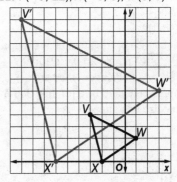

13a. $X'(0, 0)$, $Y'(-6, -2)$, $Z'(-4, -6)$

13b.

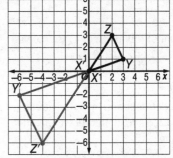

13c. $\triangle X'Y'Z'$ is the image of $\triangle XYZ$ after a dilation of 2 and a rotation of 180° about the origin.   **15.** H   **17.** 1 in. = 5 ft

19. $\frac{16}{1}$ **21.**

Cities	Map	Actual
Wichita to Topeka	$2\frac{3}{4}$ in.	137.5 mi
Salina to Kansas City	3 in.	150 mi

Chapter Review   Vocabulary Check

1. Translation   **3.** transformation; preimage; image

Chapter Review   Key Concept Check

1. correct   **3.** correct

Chapter Review   Problem Solving

1. $P'(0, 6)$

3. $P'(-1, -3)$, $Q'(-3, -3)$, $R'(-3, 1)$, $S'(-1, 1)$

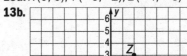

Chapter 2 Congruence and Similarity

Chapter 2 Are You Ready?

1. 3.5 **3.** 14.8 **5.** 2 **7.** −3 **9.** $\frac{5}{3}$

Lesson 2-1 Independent Practice

1 not congruent; No sequence of transformations maps *RSTU* onto *WXYZ* exactly. **3** Sample answer: 90° clockwise rotation followed by a translation; they are congruent because an image produced by a rotation and a translation have the same size and shape.

5.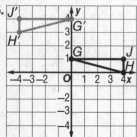

4 units, 1 unit, $\sqrt{17}$ units; 4 units, 1 unit, $\sqrt{17}$ units; yes
7. $A'(−4, 5)$, $B'(−1, 4)$, $C'(−2, 0)$ **9.** D

Lesson 2-1 Extra Practice

11. congruent; A reflection followed by a translation maps △*FGH* onto △*MNP*. **13.** Sample answer: a reflection followed by a translation **15.** B

17. 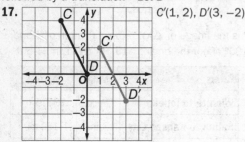 $C'(1, 2)$, $D'(3, −2)$

Lesson 2-2 Independent Practice

1 $\angle N \cong \angle S$, $\angle M \cong \angle T$, $\angle O \cong \angle V$; $\overline{ON} \cong \overline{VS}$, $\overline{NM} \cong \overline{ST}$, $\overline{MO} \cong \overline{TV}$ **3** $\angle U \cong \angle H$, $\angle V \cong \angle J$, $\angle W \cong \angle I$, $\angle X \cong \angle K$; $\overline{UV} \cong \overline{HJ}$, $\overline{VW} \cong \overline{JI}$, $\overline{WX} \cong \overline{IK}$, $\overline{XU} \cong \overline{KH}$ Sample answer: If you reflect parallelogram *UVWX* over the *x*-axis, then translate it 4 units to the right, it coincides with parallelogram *HJIK*.

5a.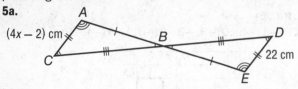

5b. 6
7a.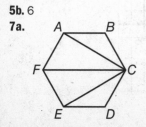

7b. 4 **7c.** △*ABC* $\cong$ △*CDE* and △*CAF* $\cong$ △*CEF*. **9a.** true; Sample answer: If the figures are congruent, the corresponding sides have equal length. Therefore, the sum of the lengths of the sides will be equal. **9b.** false; Sample answer: Triangle *ABC* has a perimeter of 24 inches. Square *MNOP* has a perimeter of 24 inches. They have the same perimeter but because they are different shapes, they are not congruent.

Lesson 2-2 Extra Practice

11. Corresponding angles: $\angle S \cong \angle Y$, $\angle STZ \cong \angle YTW$, $\angle Z \cong \angle W$; Corresponding sides: $\overline{SZ} \cong \overline{YW}$, $\overline{ZT} \cong \overline{WT}$, $\overline{TS} \cong \overline{TY}$
13. $\angle K \cong \angle F$, $\angle L \cong \angle G$, $\angle M \cong \angle H$, $\angle N \cong \angle J$; $\overline{KL} \cong \overline{FG}$, $\overline{LM} \cong \overline{GH}$, $\overline{MN} \cong \overline{HJ}$, $\overline{NK} \cong \overline{JF}$ Sample answer: If you reflect quadrilateral *KLMN* over the *y*-axis, then translate it 5 units up and 2 units to the left, it coincides with quadrilateral *FGHJ*.
15a.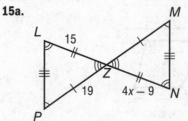

15b. 6 **17.** $\angle A \cong \angle D$, $\angle B \cong \angle E$, $\angle C \cong \angle F$; $\overline{AB} \cong \overline{DE}$, $\overline{BC} \cong \overline{EF}$, $\overline{CA} \cong \overline{FD}$
19.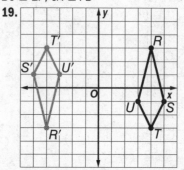

$R'(−4, −3)$, $S'(−5, 1)$, $T'(−4, 3)$, $U'(−3, 1)$

Problem-Solving Investigation Draw a Diagram

Case 3. The diagonals of a rectangle are congruent.
Case 5. 3

Lesson 2-3 Independent Practice

1 yes; Sample answer: A rotation, a translation of 4 units down, and a dilation with a scale factor of $\frac{3}{2}$ maps △*XYW* onto △*VUW*. **3** 6.75 in. by 11.25 in.; yes
5. Sample answer: translation of 1 unit to the right and 1 unit down followed by a dilation with a scale factor of 4
7. Product of dilation(s) should equal 1. **9.** false; Sample answer: If you perform the dilation after a translation, the translation is multiplied by the same scale factor.

Lesson 2-3 Extra Practice

11. no; $\frac{CD}{GH} = \frac{6}{4}$ and $\frac{DE}{JG} = \frac{2}{1}$; $\frac{6}{4} \neq \frac{2}{1}$, so the two figures are not similar. **13.** 7.5 ft by 6 ft; yes **15.** B **17.** $\frac{4}{3}$

19. $A'(-2, 2)$, $B'(2, 2)$, $C'(2, -2)$

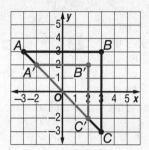

Lesson 2-4   Independent Practice

1 No; The corresponding angles are congruent, but $\frac{3}{7} \neq \frac{4}{8}$.   **3** translation and dilation; 4.5   **5a.** Figure 1: 96 cm^2; Figure 2: 294 cm^2 **5b.** Sample answer: The scale factor of the side lengths is $\frac{14}{8}$ or $\frac{7}{4}$. The ratio of the areas is $\frac{49}{16}$. The ratio of the areas is the scale factor of the side lengths squared.   **7.** 400 ft

9. false; Sample answer: In rectangles, all corresponding angles are congruent but not all sides are proportional. Rectangle A is not similar to Rectangle B, since $\frac{4}{4} \neq \frac{1}{2}$.

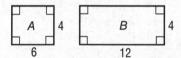

11. D

Lesson 2-4   Extra Practice

13. No; the corresponding angles are congruent, but $\frac{5}{4} \neq \frac{8}{6}$.   **15.** 70 ft   **17.** A   **19.** D   **21.** $\frac{1}{24}$ **23.** $\frac{1}{2}$ **25.** $\frac{1}{7,920}$

Lesson 2-5   Independent Practice

1. The triangles are not similar.   **3.** 200 ft   **5** 37.5 m   **7** $\frac{136}{34} = \frac{h}{1.5}$; 6 feet tall   **11.** Sample answer: The length of the tall object's shadow, the length of the shadow of a nearby object with a height that is directly measurable, and the height of the nearby object.

Lesson 2-5   Extra Practice

13. 90 ft   **15.** 6 m   **17a.** $\frac{h}{ED} = \frac{BC}{DC}$ **17b.** The distance from the mirror to the person, the distance from the mirror to the base of the flag, the height of the person's eyes.   **19.** B   **21.** Yes; the corresponding angles are congruent and $\frac{5}{10} = \frac{4}{8}$.

23.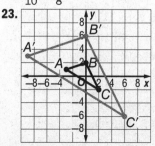

$A'(-9, 3)$, $B'(0, 6)$, $C'(6, -6)$

Lesson 2-6   Independent Practice

1 57 mm   **3.** 160 ft   **5** 126 ft^2

7.

If the scale factor is...	Multiply the ...			
	Length by	Width by	Perimeter by	Area by
2	2	2	2	4
4	4	4	4	16
0.5	0.5	0.5	0.5	0.25
$\frac{2}{3}$	$\frac{2}{3}$	$\frac{2}{3}$	$\frac{2}{3}$	$\frac{4}{9}$
k	k	k	k	k^2

9. Robert is thinking of size in terms of area and Denise is thinking of size in terms of perimeter.

Lesson 2-6   Extra Practice

11. 30 cm   **13.** 25.6 in.; 38.4 in^2 **15.** 300 in^2 **17.** C   **19.** 36 times

21.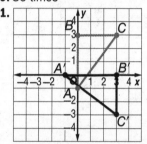

Chapter Review   Vocabulary Check

1. congruent   **3.** corresponding parts   **5.** composition of transformations

Chapter Review   Key Concept Check

1. congruent; a reflection over the x-axis   **3.** congruent; a 90° clockwise rotation about the origin

Chapter Review   Problem Solving

1. yes; Sample answer: A reflection and a translation will map figure A onto figure B.   **3.** 60 ft   **5.** 15 in.; 13.5 in^2

Chapter 3 Real Numbers

Chapter 3   Are You Ready?

1. 256   **3.** \$2,048   **5.** $2 \times 2 \times 2 \times 3$ **7.** $2 \times 2 \times 5 \times 5$ **9.** $-1 \times 2 \times 3 \times 7$

Lesson 3-1   Independent Practice

1. 0.4   **3.** 0.825   **5** $-0.\overline{54}$ **7a.** $0.0\overline{6}$ **7b.** $0.1\overline{6}$ **7c.** 0.333   **7d.** 0.417   **9** $-7\frac{8}{25}$ **11.** $-\frac{5}{11}$ **13.** $5\frac{11}{20}$ **15.** $1\frac{1}{16}$ in.; 1.0625 in.   **17.** Sample answer: When dividing, there are two possibilities for the remainder. If the remainder is 0, the decimal terminates. If the remainder is not 0, then at the point where the remainder repeats or equals the original dividend the decimal begins to repeat. **19.** D

Lesson 3-1 *Extra Practice*

21. $7\frac{5}{33}$ **23.** 5.3125 **25.** $-1\frac{11}{20}$ **27.** $-\frac{1}{11}$ **29.** $2\frac{2}{5}$ in.
31. 0.45 **33.** Felisa: 0.9; Morgan: 0.542; Yasmine: 0.682; Gail: 0.714 **35.** I **37.** > **39.** =

Lesson 3-2 *Independent Practice*

1. $(-5)^4$ **3.** m^5 **5.** $\frac{1}{81}$ **7.** 8,000,000,000 or 8 billion
9. -311 **11.** 16 **13a.** 10^6 **13b.** 10^9 **13c.** 10^{15}
15. Sample answer: As the exponent decreases by 1, the simplified answer is divided by 3; $\frac{1}{2}$

Lesson 3-2 *Extra Practice*

17. $3^3 \cdot p^3$ **19.** $\left(-\frac{5}{6}\right)^3$ **21.** $4^2 \cdot b^2$ **23.** 224 **25.** =
27a.

Side Length (in.)	Perimeter (in.)	Area (in²)
1	4	1
2	8	4
3	12	9
4	16	16
5	20	25
6	24	36
7	28	49
8	32	64
9	36	81
10	40	100

27b.

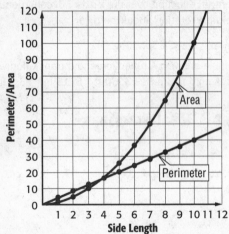

Perimeter and Area of a Square

27c. Sample answer: The graph representing perimeter of a square is linear because each side length is multiplied by 4. The graph representing area of a square is nonlinear because each side length is squared and does not increase at a constant rate. **29.** 1,331 **31a.** 10

31b. 5,120 **33.** -31 **35.** 1

Lesson 3-3 *Independent Practice*

1. $(-6)^7$ or $-279,936$ **3.** $-35a^5b^5c^5$ **5.** $2t^3$
7. 3^3x^2 or $27x^2$ **9.** 6^5 or 7,776
11. 10^{14} instructions **13a.** 10^9 times greater **13b.** 10^6
or one million **15.** 9 **17.** 6 **19.** 7
21. Equal; sample answer: Using the quotient of powers,
$\frac{3^{100}}{3^{99}} = 3^{100-99}$ or 3^1, which is 3. **23.** A

Lesson 3-3 *Extra Practice*

25. h^1 or h **27.** $-8w^{11}$ **29.** 2^8 or 256 **31.** $5^2 \cdot 7^0 \cdot 10$
or 250 **33a.** $2r$ **33b.** $\frac{\pi}{4}$
33c.

Radius (units)	2	3	4	2r
Area of Circle (units²)	π(2)² or 4π	9π	16π	4πr²
Length of 1 Side of the Square	4	6	8	4r
Area of Square (units²)	4² or 16	36	64	16r²
Ratio (Area of circle / Area of square)	$\frac{\pi}{4}$	$\frac{\pi}{4}$	$\frac{\pi}{4}$	$\frac{\pi}{4}$

33d. The ratio is $\frac{\pi}{4}$. **35.** G **37.** -28 **39.** -35 **41.** -9
43. $\frac{1}{8}$

Lesson 3-4 *Independent Practice*

1. 4^6 **3.** d^{42} **5.** 3^8 **7.** $625j^{24}$ **9.** $216a^6b^{18}$
11. $-243w^{15}z^{40}$ **13.** $27c^{18}d^6$ cubic units
15. $729x^{12}y^{18}$ **17.** $-2,048v^{29}$
19a.

Side Length (units)	x	2x	3x
Area of Square (units²)	x²	(2x)² or 4x²	(3x)² or 9x²
Volume of Cube (units³)	x³	(2x)³ or 8x³	(3x)³ or 27x³

19b. If the side length is doubled, the area is quadrupled and the volume is multiplied by 8. If the side length is tripled, the area is multiplied by 9 and the volume is multiplied by 27.
21. 3

Lesson 3-4 *Extra Practice*

23. 2^{14} **25.** 3^8 **27.** z^{55} **29.** 2^{18} **31.** $64g^6h^2$ units²
33. $125r^6s^9$ units³ **35.** $0.25k^{10}$ **37.** $\frac{1}{16}w^{10}z^6$ **39.** D
41. D **43.** 6^{11} **45.** $18x^{14}$ **47.** Bridalveil: 620 ft; Fall Creek: 256 ft; Shoshone: 212 ft

Problem-Solving Investigation *The Four-Step Plan*

Case 3. 18 tour guides **Case 5.** 21 toothpicks

Lesson 3-5 Independent Practice

1. $\frac{1}{7^{10}}$ 3. $\frac{1}{g^7}$ 5. 12^{-4} 7. 5^{-3} 9. $10^{-1}, 10^{-2}, 10^{-3}$, 10^{-6} 11. $\frac{1}{128}$ **13** y^3 15. 81 17. y^4

19 10^5 or 100,000 times 21. $11^{-3}, 11^0, 11^2$; Sample answer: The exponents in order from least to greatest are $-3, 0, 2$. 23. Sample answer: $\left(\frac{1}{2}\right)^{-1} = 2, \left(\frac{34}{43}\right)^{-1} = \frac{43}{34}$, $\left(\frac{56}{65}\right)^{-1} = \left(\frac{65}{56}\right)$; When you raise a fraction to the -1 power, it is the same as finding the reciprocal of the fraction.

Lesson 3-5 Extra Practice

25. $\frac{1}{3^5}$ 27. $\frac{1}{6^8}$ 29. $\frac{1}{s^9}$ 31. z^{-1} or $\frac{1}{z}$ 33. b^{-12} or $\frac{1}{b^{12}}$ 35. $\frac{1}{16}$ 37. $\frac{1}{10,000}$ 39. 12 41. -11 43. D 45. 3^4; $\frac{1}{81}$ 47. 1,000 49. 100,000 51. 100 53. 100 55. 10

Lesson 3-6 Independent Practice

1. 3,160 3. 0.0000252 5. 7.2×10^{-3}

7 Arctic, Southern, Indian, Atlantic, Pacific 9. 17.32 millimeters; the number is small so choosing a smaller unit of measure is more meaningful. **11** < 13. 1.2×10^6; 1.2×10^5 is only 120,000, but 1.2×10^6 is just over one million. 15. D

Lesson 3-6 Extra Practice

17. 7.07×10^{-6} 19. 0.0078 21. 6.7×10^3 23. 3.7×10^{-2} 25. 2.2×10^3, 310,000, 3.1×10^7, 216,000,000 27. 10 29. I 31. 4.355 33. 4.44 35. 1.6 37. $50x^7$

Lesson 3-7 Independent Practice

1. 8.97×10^8 3. 8.19×10^{-2} **5** 2.375×10^{11} 7. 8,000 times **9** 9.83×10^8 11. 8.70366×10^4

13. $\frac{6.63 \times 10^{-6}}{5.1 \times 10^{-2}} = \left(\frac{6.63}{5.1}\right)\left(\frac{10^{-6}}{10^{-2}}\right)$
$= 1.3 \times 10^{-6 - (-2)}$
$= 1.3 \times 10^{-4}$

15. 10^{109} times

Lesson 3-7 Extra Practice

17. 4.44×10^1 19. 4×10^2 21. 1.334864×10^{10} 23. $13\frac{5}{9}$ h 25. B 27. C

29.

x	x^2	x^3	x	x^2	x^3
1	1	1	7	49	343
2	4	8	8	64	512
3	9	27	9	81	729
4	16	64	10	100	1,000
5	25	125	11	121	1,331
6	36	216	12	144	1,728

Lesson 3-8 Independent Practice

1. 4 3. no real solution **5** -1.6 7. ± 9 9. ± 0.13 11. -0.5 **13** 13 students 15. 44 in. 17. 24 m 19. $\frac{25}{81}$ 21. x 23. D

Lesson 3-8 Extra Practice

25. $-\frac{8}{15}$ 27. ± 1.2 29. -8 31. -7 33. $\pm \frac{3}{8}$ 35. $\frac{1}{2}$ 37. 20 39. 400 41. 60 chairs 43. I 45. 2,197 47. 3,375 49. 55 51. 20 53. $64r^9s^3$ units^3

Lesson 3-9 Independent Practice

1. 5 3. 4 5. 3 **7** 10 9. Sample answer: 54 ft and 57 ft; 55.5 ft and 55.8 feet; 55.71 ft and 55.74 feet; 56 feet **11** about 2.75 seconds 13. $\sqrt[3]{105}, 5, \sqrt{38}, 7$ 15. 10; Since 94 is less than 100, $\sqrt{94}$ is less than 10. 17. She incorrectly estimated. She found half of 200, not the square root. Since $196 < 200 < 225$, the square root of 200 is between 14 and 15. Since 200 is closer to 196, the square root of 200 is about 14. 19. B

Lesson 3-9 Extra Practice

21. 6 23. 5 25. 8 27. 10 or -10 29. 6 in. 31. 70 feet on each side 33. I 35. $\frac{-36}{1}$ 37. $\frac{-6}{125}$ 39. $5^2, 3^3, 4(8)$ 41. $12^2 + 4, 10^3, 25^2 \cdot 3$

Lesson 3-10 Independent Practice

1. rational 3. rational 5. < **7** < **9** $\sqrt{5}, \frac{7}{3}, \sqrt{6}, 2.5, 2.55$

11. about 1.9 m^2 13. > 15. < 17. always 19. always

Lesson 3-10 Extra Practice

21. irrational 23. natural, whole, integer, rational 25. irrational 27. > 29. 18.52 m 31. < 33. > 35. F 37. $\sqrt{32}, 6, 7, \sqrt{53}$ 39. $\frac{1}{7}$ or $-\frac{1}{7}$ 41. 7.92×10^{-2} 43. China, India, United States, Indonesia

Chapter Review Vocabulary Check

Across
5. perfect cube 9. rational number
Down
1. radical sign 3. exponent 7. cube root

Chapter Review Key Concept Check

1. real 3. Power of a Product rule 5. 9^{28} 7. less than

Chapter Review Problem Solving

1. 216 calls 3. 0.004375 lb 5. $2\frac{1}{5}, 2.\overline{2}, \sqrt{5}, 2.25$

Chapter 4 Equations in One Variable

Chapter 4 Are You Ready?

1. -17 **3.** 19 **5.** 7 **7.** $18 + h = 92$; 74 marbles

Lesson 4-1 Independent Practice

1. 72 **3** 24 **5.** -12 **7.** 2 **9.** $\frac{4}{5}$
11 q = total questions; $0.8q = 16$; 20 questions
13. Multiplicative Inverse: $1\frac{1}{3}$, $-\frac{1}{2}$; Division: 0.2, -5
15. true; Sample answer: The product of $\frac{3}{4}$ and $\frac{4}{3}$ is $\frac{12}{12}$, which simplifies to 1. **17.** 53; Since $10 = \frac{1}{5}x$, then $x = 50$ and $x + 3 = 53$.

Lesson 4-1 Extra Practice

19. $1\frac{1}{4}$ **21.** $3\frac{1}{2}$ **23.** -10.5 **25.** $6\frac{3}{10}$ **27.** $\frac{8}{9}$
29.

$$-\frac{7}{8}x = 24$$
$$\left(-\frac{8}{7}\right)\left(-\frac{7}{8}x\right) = 24\left(-\frac{8}{7}\right)$$
$$x = -27\frac{3}{7}$$

31. H **33.** -25 **35.** -5.55 **37.** 2
39. Simone: $s + 37.50 = 127.75$; $90.25; Dan: $s - 65.35 = d$; $24.90

Lesson 4-2 Independent Practice

1. 3 **3.** -4 **5** -52 **7** 5 bracelets **9.** 64
11. -26 **13a.** 146 messages **13b.** 135 messages
15. Sample answer: Andrea saved x dollars each week for 3 weeks. She spent $25 and had $125 left. How much did she save each week?; $50

Lesson 4-2 Extra Practice

17. 6 **19.** -3 **21.** -8 **23.** 7 **25.** -10 **27.** $1.50; Sample answer: Subtraction Property of Equality, Division Property of Equality **29.** 40 **31.** -22 **33.** -4
35. $j + 45 = 79.50$; $34.50

Lesson 4-3 Independent Practice

1. $5n - 4 = 11$ **3** $7n - 6 = -20$
5 s = the number of songs; $0.25s + 9.99 = 113.74$; 415 songs **7.** s = height of the Statue of Liberty; $s + (s + 0.89) = 92.99$; 46.05 m **9a.** $175 = 3c - 20$; 65 mph **9b.** $s = \frac{1}{5} \cdot 175 - 1$; 34 mph
9c. $175 = 6h + 13$; 27 mph **11.** $n + 2n + (n + 3) = 27$; 6, 9, 12 **13.** D

Lesson 4-3 Extra Practice

15. $4n + 16 = -2$ **17.** $6 + 9n = 456$
19. x = the number of groups of pitches; $4 + 0.75x = 7$; 4 groups **21.** D **23.** $3m + 6 = 120$; 38 cards
25. -648 **27.** 6

Problem-Solving Investigation Work Backward

Case 3. $92 **Case 5.** $1,238.50

Lesson 4-4 Independent Practice

1. -2 **3** 10 **5.** 48 **7** Let n = the number; $0.5n - 9 = 4n + 5$; -4 **9a.** Sample answer: Set the side lengths equal to each other and solve for x.
9b. $4x - 2 = 2x + 8$ **9c.** 18 units **11.** Sample answer: You have 20 crafts made and continue to make crafts at the rate of 3 per hour. How many hours will it take you and your friend to make the same amount of crafts, if she makes crafts at a rate of 5 per hour. **13.** A

Lesson 4-4 Extra Practice

15. 3 **17.** 5 **19** Let n = the number; $3n - 18 = 2n$; 18
21. $60x = 8x + 26$; 0.5 **23.** G **25.** $4x + 6$ **27.** -9
29. $6x + 30$ **31.** $15z - 36$

Lesson 4-5 Independent Practice

1. -9 **3** 6 **5.** null set or no solution **7.** -6
9 $4.72 **11a.** $20 + 0.15m = 30 + 0.1m$
11b. $m = 200$; 200 messages **13.** 13 in. and 15 in.

Lesson 4-5 Extra Practice

15. 13 **17.** $4\frac{4}{7}$ **19** -9 **21.** identity or all numbers
23a. Sample answer: $3x + 5 = 3x - 2 + 7$ **23b.** Sample answer: $2(x - 1) = 2x + 2$ **23.** D **25.** G
27. $x \geq -3$

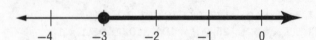

29. $n < 8$

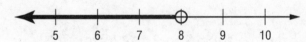

31. $m < -4$

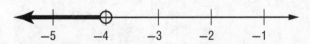

Chapter Review Vocabulary Check

1. coefficient **3.** properties

Chapter Review Key Concept Check

1. 31 **3.** Sample steps: 2; 3; 1; 4; $7\frac{2}{7}$

Chapter Review Problem Solving

1. $14{,}000$ mi^2 **3.** $8 + 4d = 28$; 5 more days **5.** $9.17

Chapter 5 Triangles and the Pythagorean Theorem

Chapter 5 Are You Ready?

1. 86 **3.** 98

4–9.

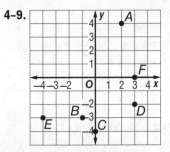

Lesson 5-1 Independent Practice

1 Proof: ∠7 and ∠8 form a <u>straight</u> angle so they are supplementary angles. So, $m\angle 7 + m\angle 8 = \underline{180°}$, by the definition of supplementary angles. By substitution, $\underline{9}x + 11x = 180°$. So, $x = \underline{9}$ by the Division Property of Equality.

3.

	Statements	Reasons
a.	∠1 and ∠2 are supplementary; $m\angle 1 = m\angle 2$	Given
b.	$m\angle 1 + m\angle 2 = 180°$	Definition of supplementary angles
c.	$m\angle 1 + m\angle 1 = 180°$	Substitution
d.	$2(m\angle 1) = 180°$	Simplify.
e.	$m\angle 1 = 90°$	Division Property of Equality
f.	$m\angle 2 = 90°$	$m\angle 1 = m\angle 2$ (Given)
g.	∠1 and ∠2 are right angles.	Definition of right angles

5. Sample answer: Vertical angles have the same measure.
7. B

Lesson 5-1 Extra Practice

9.

	Statements	Reasons
a.	$j \parallel k$, transversal ℓ; $m\angle 3 = 2x - 15$, $m\angle 6 = x + 55$	Given
b.	$m\angle 3 = m\angle 6$	Alternate interior angles have the same measure.
c.	$2x - 15 = x + 55$	Substitution
d.	$x - 15 = 55$	Subtraction Property of Equality
e.	$x = 70$	Addition Property of Equality

11. D   **13.** 28°

Lesson 5-2 Independent Practice

1. $5^2 + 12^2 = c^2$; 13 in.   **3.** $8^2 + b^2 = 18^2$; 16.1 m

5 no; $30^2 + 122^2 \neq 125^2$ **7** $48^2 + 55^2 = c^2$; 73 yd   **9.** $a^2 + 5.1^2 = 12.3^2$; 11.2 m   **11.** 7.8 cm   **13.** C

Lesson 5-2 Extra Practice

15. $a^2 + 10^2 = 15^2$; 11.2 cm   **17.** yes; $24^2 + 143^2 = 145^2$ **19.** no; $56^2 + 16^2 \neq 65^2$ **21.** no; $12^2 + 24^2 \neq 29^2$ **23.** B   **25.** D

Problem-solving Investigation Look for a Pattern

Case 3. 1800°   **Case 5.** 1,234,567,654,321

Lesson 5-3 Independent Practice

1 $5^2 + h^2 = 12^2$; 10.9 ft   **3** 11.7 cm   **5a.** 40 yd   **5b.** 24.7 yd   **9.** 3–5–7; $3^2 + 5^2 \neq 7^2$ **11.** C

Lesson 5-3 Extra Practice

13. 9.0 in.   **15.** about 105 mi   **17.** 20.6 in.   **19.** 168 in.   **21.** B   **23.** 6; $6^2 = 36$ and $7^2 = 49$, since 39 is closer to 36 than 49, $\sqrt{39} \approx 6$.   **25.** 3; $3^3 = 27$ and $4^3 = 64$. Since 30 is closer to 27 than 64, $\sqrt[3]{30} \approx 3$.

Lesson 5-4 Independent Practice

1.

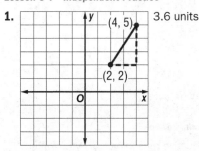

3.6 units

3

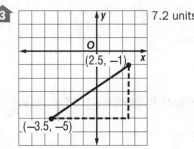

7.2 units

5 1.4 units   **7.** 15.9 units

9a.

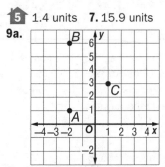

9b. Sample answer: Use the Distance Formula and the points (−2, 6) and (1, 3).   **9c.** 3.6 units; 5 units; 4.2 units
9d. 12.8 units   **11.** Sample answer: (1, 2) and (4, 6)

Lesson 5-4 Extra Practice

13. 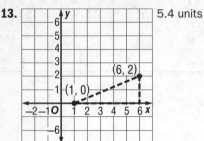 5.4 units

15. 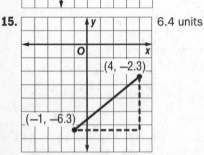 6.4 units

17. 11.4 units **19.** 13.6 units **21.** (−5, −5)

23. 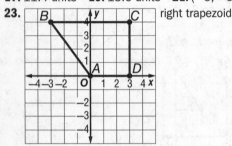 right trapezoid

Chapter Review Vocabulary Check

1. transversal **3.** Deductive reasoning **5.** Pythagorean Theorem **7.** parallel lines **9.** hypotenuse

Chapter Review Problem Solving

1. 15 in. **3.** $25^2 + x^2 = 47^2$; 79.6 cm

Chapter 6 Volume and Surface Area

Chapter 6 Are You Ready?

1. 68 cm^2 **3.** 71.5 m^2 **5.** 72 in^2 **7.** 47.1 **9.** 283.4

Lesson 6-1 Independent Practice

1. 141.4 in^3 **3.** 831.9 lb **5a.** bag: 132 in^3; candle: 29.5 in^3 **5b.** 102.5 in^3 **5c.** 13 packages **7.** Sample answer: The shorter cylinder, because the radius is larger and that is the squared value in the formula. **9.** C

Lesson 6-1 Extra Practice

11. 2,770.9 yd^3 **13.** 81.7 ounces **15.** 8 in.
17a. $V = \pi(1)^2(1)$; $V = \pi(1)^2(2)$; $V = \pi(2)^2(1)$; $V = \pi(2)^2(2)$; **17b.** The height of Cylinder B is twice the height of Cylinder A. The radius of Cylinder C is twice the radius of Cylinder A. The radius and height of Cylinder D are twice the radius and height of Cylinder A. **17d.** When the radius

is doubled, the volume is four times the original volume. When the height is doubled, the volume is twice the original volume. When the radius and height are doubled, the volume is eight times the original volume. **19.** G
21. 201.1 cm^2 **23.** 28.3 in^2 **25.** 50.3 m^2 **27.** 539 m^3

Lesson 6-2 Independent Practice

1. 4,720.8 mm^3 **3** 26.9 ft^3 **5.** 102.6 in^3
7. 1,608.5 cm^3 **9** 36 cm **11.** 10 mm
13. Sample answer:

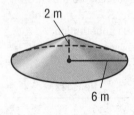 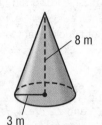

Lesson 6-2 Extra Practice

15 2,989.8 mm^3 **17.** 398.2 m^3 **19.** 402.1 cm^3
21. 32.7 in^3 **23.** 15 in. **25.** 4.5 m **27.** 3.0 yd **29.** A
31. 110 ft^3 **33.** 90 cm^3 **35.** 1,025.4 cm^3

Lesson 6-3 Independent Practice

1 1,563.5 in^3 **3.** 2,144.7 mm^3 **5** 434.9 in^3
7. 107.2 s **9.** 1.5 mm^3 **11.** 10.9 in. **13.** 91.8 cm^3
15. A

Lesson 6-3 Extra Practice

17 3,053.6 in^3 **19.** 883.6 km^3 **21.** 5,747.0 cm^3
23. 5,575.3 cm^3 **25.** 0.0011 grams/mm^3
27. 1,038.2 cm^3 **29.** C **31.** 25.1 mm; 50.3 mm^2
33. 19.5 m; 30.2 m^2 **35.** 134.8 cm^2 **37.** 2,948.9 in^3

Problem-Solving Investigation Solve a Simpler Problem

Case 3. 389.6 ft^3 **Case 5.** 55 squares

Lesson 6-4 Independent Practice

1 88.0 mm^2 **3.** 272.0 mm^2 **5.** 113.1 in^2
7. 1,068.1 yd^2 **9** 241.3 in^2 **11.** No, the surface area of the side of the cylinder will double, but the area of the bases will not. **13.** C

Lesson 6-4 Extra Practice

15 1,105.8 cm^2; 1,508.0 cm^2 **17.** 763.4 in^2
19. Sample answer: $2 \cdot 3 \cdot 4^2 + 2 \cdot 3 \cdot 4 \cdot 4$ or 192 m^2
21. about 85.7% **23.** D **25.** 23.08 ft^2 **27.** 3.5 in^3
31. 158.4 m^3

Lesson 6-5 Independent Practice

1 269.2 in^2 **3.** 785.4 m^2 **5.** 279.5 cm^2
7 13.4 in^2 **9a.** 510.2 mm^2 **9b.** 14.2 mm
11. Enrique did not use the right radius. He did not divide the diameter by 2 to get the radius; 267.04 in^2 **13.** C

Lesson 6-5 Extra Practice

15 461.8 m² **17.** 113.1 in² **19.** 62.8 m²
21. 452.4 in² **23.** 188.5 yd² **25.** 354.1 ft² **27.** D
29. 150.8 ft² **31.** 829.4 cm² **33.** 1,583.4 ft²
35. 1,742.5 ft³ **37.** 5.7 m³

Lesson 6-6 Independent Practice

1. 1,520 cm² **3** 548.8 in² **5.** 19 mm³
7. 8,709,120 ft³; 277,632 ft² **9** 300.8 m³
11. The volume of the first cone is 615.75, so the first cone's volume multiplied by one-sixth cubed is the second cone's volume. The volume of the second cone is about 2.9 cubic inches.

Lesson 6-6 Extra Practice

13 2,700 ft³ **15.** 10 cm³ **17.** 0.65 m² **19.** sometimes
21. always **23a.** 3:1 **23b.** surface area, 9:1; volume, 27:1 **23c.** 602.88 cm² **23d.** 30,520.8 cm³
25. 13.6 in² **27a.** 54,000 ft² **27b.** 13,050 ft²
27c. about 5.6 acres **29.** 100.7 cm² **31.** 318.1 in²

Chapter Review Vocabulary Check

1. sphere **3.** cylinder **5.** cone: a three-dimensional figure with one circular base

Chapter Review Key Concept Check

1. correct

Chapter Review Problem Solving

1. 1,767.1 in³; 824.7 in² **3.** 28,730.9 cm³ **5.** 28.1 in³

Chapter 7 Functions

Chapter 7 Are You Ready?

1. (1.5, 2.5) **3.** (0, 1.5) **5.** (1, 1) **7.** −18 **9.** −3
11. $901

Lesson 7-1 Independent Practice

1 D: {−6, 0, 2, 8}; R: {−9, −8, 5}

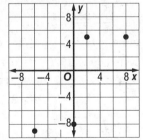

3.

x	825x	y
1	825(1)	825
2	825(2)	1,650
3	825(3)	2,475
4	825(4)	3,300
5	825(5)	4,125

5 a. To get the *y*-value, the *x*-value was multiplied by itself.
b. (1, 1), (2, 4), (3, 9), (4, 16), (5, 25)

c.

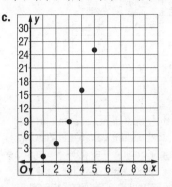

d. Sample answer: This graph curves upward. The points in all of the other graphs in the lesson lie in a straight line.

7a, 7c.

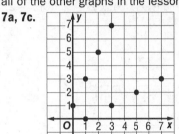

b. (1, 0), (3, 1), (5, 2), (7, 3) **d.** Sample answer: The distance between each point in the original table and the *x*-axis is the same as the distance betweeen the points with the reversed ordered pairs and the *y*-axis. **9.** C

Lesson 7-1 Extra Practice

11. D: {−1.5, 2.5, 3}; R: {−3.5, −1.5, −1, 3.5}

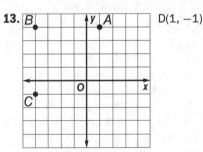

x	y
−1.5	3.5
2.5	−1.5
3	−1
−1.5	−3.5

13. D(1, −1)

15. A **17.** $\left(\frac{3}{4}, \frac{1}{2}\right)$ **19.** $\left(1, -\frac{3}{4}\right)$ **21.** $\left(-\frac{1}{2}, -\frac{1}{2}\right)$
23. $\left(-1, \frac{1}{4}\right)$

Lesson 7-2 Independent Practice

1. 35 **3** 11

5 Sample answer:

x	5 − 2x	f(x)
−2	5 − 2(−2)	9
0	5 − 2(0)	5
3	5 − 2(3)	−1
5	5 − 2(5)	−5

D: {−2, 0, 3, 5}
R: {9, 5, −1, −5}
7a. The total points p(g) is the dependent variable and the number of games g is the independent variable.   **7b.** Only whole numbers between and including 0 and 82 make sense for the domain because you do not want data for a partial game and there are only 82 games in a season. The range will be multiplies of 20.7.   **7c.** p(g) = 20.7g; 186.3 points   **9.** 2   **11.** Sample answer: f(x) = 2x − 2; f(0) = −2, f(−4) = −10, f(3) = 4   **13.** C

Lesson 7-2   Extra Practice

15. −41
17. Sample answer:

x	x − 9	f(x)
−2	−2 − 9	−11
−1	−1 − 9	−10
7	7 − 9	−2
12	12 − 9	3

D: {−2, −1, 7, 12}
R: {−11, −10, −2, 3}
19. Sample answer:

x	4x + 3	f(x)
−4	4(−4) + 3	−13
−2	4(−2) + 3	−5
3	4(3) + 3	15
5	4(5) + 3	23

D: {−4, −2, 3, 5}
R: {−13, −5, 15, 23}
21. m(s) = 5 + 0.50s; $20   **23.** H   **25.** 3   **27.** 8

Lesson 7-3   Independent Practice

1 First part: 68 miles per hour; Second part: 55 miles per hour. The speed for the first leg is greater by 13 miles per hour.   **3** Seth; Seth will have 4(20) or 80 cards and Matt will have 2(20) + 20 or 60 cards.   **5a.** z = 8c; z = 16p; z = 32q   **5b.** the quart equation; Sample answer: The greater the rate of change, the steeper the slope of the graph.   **5c.** The first function has the least rate of change because 8 is less than 16 and 32.   **7.** Sample answer: Both functions have the same rate of change but because they have different y-intercepts, they are parallel lines and parallel lines will never intersect.

Lesson 7-3   Extra Practice

9. Cotton fabric: $7.00 per yard. Special occasion fabric: $\frac{18 − 9}{2 − 1} = \frac{9}{1}$; or $9.00 per yard. Special occasion fabric has the greater rate of change.   **11.** Juan; Sample answer:

In 8 weeks Juan will have 5(8) or $40. Jesse will have saved $37.   **13.** $\frac{3}{11}$ h   **15.** greater than; Her race rate was 22.2 ÷ 2.15 or about 10.3 mph. Her average speed biking was 13.8 mph; 13.8 > 10.3.   **17.** 0   **19.** 52

Problem-Solving Investigation   Make a Table

Case 3. 3 ft   **Case 5.** 2.3 mi

Lesson 7-4   Independent Practice

1 Yes; the rate of change between cost and time for each hour is a constant 3¢ per hour.   **3.** Yes; the rate of change between vinegar and oil for each cup of oil is a constant $\frac{3}{8}$ cup vinegar per cup of oil.   **5** Yes; the rate of change between the actual distance and the map distance for each inch on the map is a constant 7.5 mi/in.   **7.** Yes; the ratio of the cost to time is a constant 3¢ per hour, so the relationship is proportional.   **9.** Yes; the ratio of actual distance to map distance is a constant $\frac{15}{2}$ miles per inch, so the relationship is proportional.

11. Sample answer:

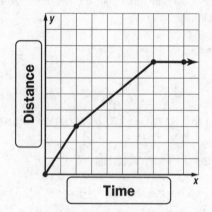

13. D

Lesson 7-4   Extra Practice

15. No; the rate of change from 1 to 2 hours, $\frac{24 − 12}{2 − 1}$ or 12 per hour, is not the same as the rate of change from 3 to 4 hours, $\frac{60 − 36}{4 − 3}$ or 24 per hour, so the rate of change is not constant.   **17.** −50 mph; the distance decreased by 50 miles every hour.   **19.** 0.5; $\frac{1}{2}$ of retail price.   **21.** $15 per week   **23.** 24 mi/gal   **25.** $0.55/red pepper

Lesson 7-5   Independent Practice

1 −$\frac{5}{8}$ **3.** −$\frac{3}{4}$ **5.** 2   **7** −4   **9.** yes; $\frac{1}{15} < \frac{1}{12}$
11. Jacob did not use the x-coordinates in the same order as the y-coordinates.
$$m = \frac{3 − 2}{4 − 0}$$
$$m = \frac{1}{4}$$
13. D

Lesson 7-5 Extra Practice

15. 3   **17.** −3   **19.** 2   **21.** $\frac{1}{5}$ **23.** B   **25.** $\frac{30}{180} = \frac{x}{240}$; 40 minutes   **27.** 15   **29.** 7.5   **31.** −60

Lesson 7-6 Independent Practice

1. $0.50 per paper   **3** Computers R Us; Sample answer: The unit cost for Computer Access is $25 per hour. The unit cost for Computers R Us is $23.50. 23.5 < 25   **5.** yes; 4
7 127 cm   **9.** $y = \frac{2}{5}x$; 4   **11.** Sample answer: (4, 3), (8, 6), (0, 0)   **13.** B

Lesson 7-6 Extra Practice

15. $y = 4.2x$; $4.20 per pound

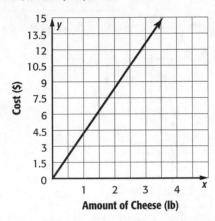

17. tickets to the play; Sample answer: The unit rate per raffle ticket is $5 and the unit rate per play ticket is $6.25. 6.25 > 5   **19.** 36 pages   **21.** $\frac{2}{1}$ or 2   **23.** $-\frac{7}{3}$
25. undefined

Lesson 7-7 Independent Practice

1. 3; 4   **3.** −3; −4   **5** $y = \frac{5}{6}x + 8$ **7.** $y = \frac{5}{4}x - 12$
9.

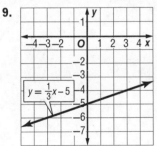

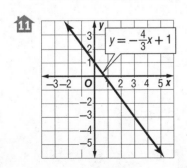

13. 0; Sample answer: A line that has a *y*-intercept but no *x*-intercept is a horizontal line.   **15.** C

Lesson 7-7 Extra Practice

17. $\frac{1}{2}$; −6   **19.** $y = \frac{1}{2}x + 6$ **21.** $y = -\frac{3}{5}x - \frac{1}{5}$
23.

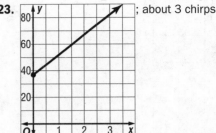

; about 3 chirps

25. A   **27.** 10   **29.** −4   **31.** −5   **33.** yes; $\frac{4}{1}$ or 4

Lesson 7-8 Independent Practice

1

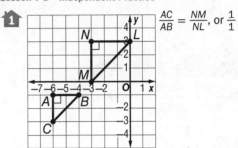

$\frac{AC}{AB} = \frac{NM}{NL}$, or $\frac{1}{1}$

3 $m = -\frac{2}{5}$; The other slope should equal $-\frac{2}{5}$.
5. $P(5, 3)$ **9.** B

Lesson 7-8 Extra Practice

11.

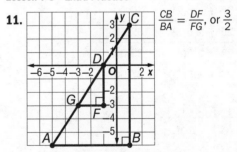

$\frac{CB}{BA} = \frac{DF}{FG}$, or $\frac{3}{2}$

13.

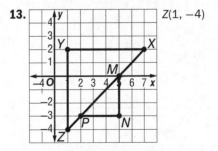

$Z(1, -4)$

15. $D(1, 11)$ **17.** F   **19.** 1   **21.** $-\frac{3}{5}$ **23.** −2   **25.** $\frac{1}{6}$

Lesson 7-9 Independent Practice

1

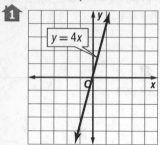

3.

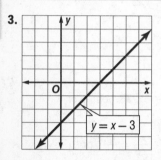

5a. bike: $c = 15 + 4.25h$; scooter: $c = 25 + 2.5h$

5b.

Mountain Bike Rental		
h	$15 + 4.25h$	c
2	$15 + 4.25(2)$	23.50
3	$15 + 4.25(3)$	27.75
4	$15 + 4.25(4)$	32.00
5	$15 + 4.25(5)$	36.25

Scooter Rental		
h	$25 + 4.25h$	c
2	$25 + 2.5(2)$	30.00
3	$25 + 2.5(3)$	32.50
4	$25 + 2.5(4)$	35.00
5	$25 + 2.5(5)$	37.50

5c.

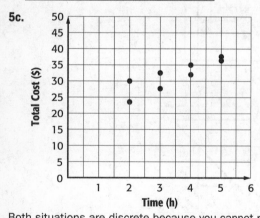

Both situations are discrete because you cannot rent either piece of equipment for a partial hour. **5d.** mountain bike **5e.** $49

7 25 weeks

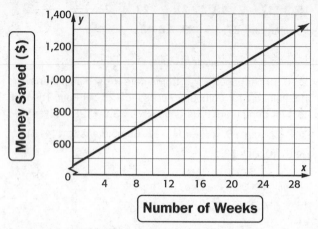

9. Sample answer: $(-2, -4)$, $(0, -2)$, $(2, 0)$, $(4, 2)$; $y = x - 2$

Lesson 7-9 Extra Practice

11.

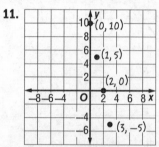

She cannot buy negative amounts. So, she can buy 0 T-shirt packs and 10 shirts individually, 1 T-shirt pack and 5 shirts individually, or 2 T-shirt packs and 0 shirts individually.

13.

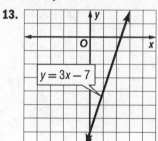

15.

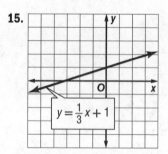

17. D **19.** I **21.** $15n$; 75, 90, 105

Lesson 7-10 Independent Practice

1 Linear; rate of change is constant; as x increases by 2, y increases by 1. **3.** Linear; rate of change is constant; as x increases by 5, y increases by 15. **5** Yes; the rate of change is constant; as the time increases by 1 hour, the distance increases by 65 miles.   **7.** Linear; sample answer: If you graph the function, the ordered pairs (hours, seconds) lie on a straight line.

9.

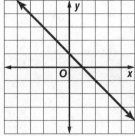

Linear; sample answer: The points lie on a straight line.

11.

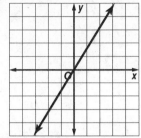

Linear; sample answer: The points lie on a straight line.
13. No; sample answer: the graphs of vertical lines are not functions because there is more than one value of y that corresponds to $x = 2$.   **15.** D

Lesson 7-10   Extra Practice

17. Linear; rate of change is constant; as x increases by 4, y decreases by 3.

19a.

Radius r	Circumference $2 \cdot \pi \cdot r$	Area πr^2
1	$2 \cdot \pi \cdot 1 \approx 6.28$	$\pi \cdot 1^2 \approx 3.14$
2	$2 \cdot \pi \cdot 2 \approx 12.57$	$\pi \cdot 2^2 \approx 12.57$
3	$2 \cdot \pi \cdot 3 \approx 18.85$	$\pi \cdot 3^2 \approx 28.27$
4	$2 \cdot \pi \cdot 4 \approx 25.13$	$\pi \cdot 4^2 \approx 50.27$
5	$2 \cdot \pi \cdot 5 \approx 31.42$	$\pi \cdot 5^2 \approx 78.54$

19b.

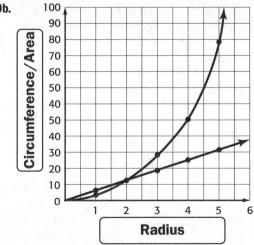

19c. Circumference: linear; sample answer: When the ordered pairs are graphed, the points fall in a line. Area: nonlinear; sample answer: When the ordered pairs are graphed, the points do not fall in a line.   **21.** Jung's savings represent a linear function because the rate of change is constant. As the months increase by 1, the savings increase by 10. Miguel's savings represent a nonlinear function because as the month's increase by 1, the total savings increases at a different rate.   **23.** -14
25a. $c = 5d$; Riley makes an average of 5 phone calls per day.   **25b.** 35 phone calls

Lesson 7-11   Independent Practice

1.

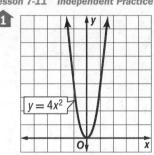

$y = 4x^2$

3.

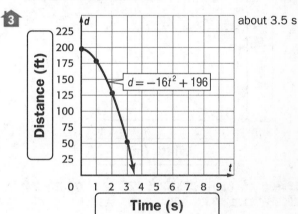

about 3.5 s

$d = -16t^2 + 196$

5a. $A = 12x - x^2$ **5b.** 6 in. by 6 in.   **7.** nonlinear; Sample answer: The function is quadratic.   **9.** linear; Sample answer: The equation is written in slope-intercept form so it is a straight line.   **11.** nonlinear; Sample answer: The function is quadratic.   **13.** Sample answer: $y = x^2 - 3.5$

Lesson 7-11   Extra Practice

15. $y = -x^2 + 2$

x	$-x^2 + 2$	y	(x, y)
-2	$-(-2)^2 + 2$	2	$(-2, 2)$
-1	$-(-1)^2 + 2$	1	$(-1, 1)$
0	$-(0)^2 + 2$	2	$(0, 2)$
1	$-(1) + 2$	1	$(1, 1)$
2	$-(2)^2 + 2$	-2	$(2, -2)$

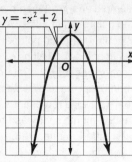

$y = -x^2 + 2$

3.

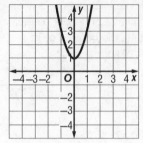

17.

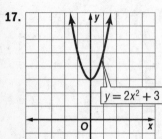

$y = 2x^2 + 3$

Chapter Review   Problem Solving

1. $f(s) = \dfrac{S}{5}$; 3 mi

3.

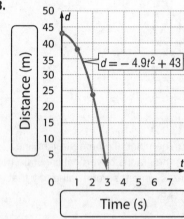

$d = -4.9t^2 + 43$

19a. $A = x^2 + 4x$

19b.

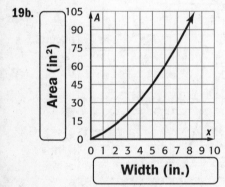

19c. 96 in^2 **21.** H **23.** 1,296 **25.** 243 **27.** 16
29. 36 **31.** 1 **33.** 3 **35.** −2 **37.** −36

Chapter Review   Vocabulary Check

1. relation **3.** independent variable **5.** quadratic function

Chapter Review   Key Concept Check

1.

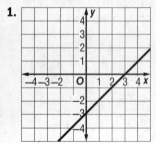

Chapter 8 Scatter Plots and Data Analysis

Chapter 8   Are You Ready?

1. Sample answer: There are 8 different kinds of mammals shown. Most of them have a life span between 10 and 29 years; 4 **3.** 31.6

Lesson 8-1   Independent Practice

1 **a.** $b = 45d$; Forty-five baskets are produced every day.
b. 16,425 baskets **3** **a.** $f = 3.5 + 0.15d$

b.

d	$3.5 + 0.15d$	f
10	3.5 + 0.15(10)	5.00
15	3.5 + 0.15(15)	5.75
20	3.5 + 0.15(20)	6.50
25	3.5 + 0.15(25)	7.25

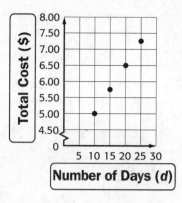

Number of Days (d)

5. Sample answer: $d = 60t$; A car is traveling at a rate of 60 miles per hour. **7.** B

Lesson 8-1   Extra Practice

9a. $d = 15w + 5$ **9b.** $365   **11.** C   **13a.** $28.4z$
13b. 4,260 g   **15.** $8w + 9$

13.

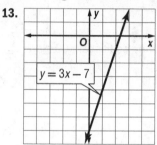

$y = 3x - 7$

15.

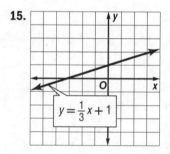

$y = \frac{1}{3}x + 1$

17. D   **19.** I   **21.** $15n$; 75, 90, 105

Lesson 8-2   Independent Practice

1 The teacher read 100 pages per day. The teacher initially read 150 pages.   **3** The class brings in 10 cans per day. The teacher initially had 105 cans.   **5.** Each month Jonas adds 3 DVDs. He started with 9 DVDs.
7. Sample answer: The rate of change is rerepsented by the ratio $\frac{\text{change in } y}{\text{change in } x}$. For a horizontal line, x can increase or decrease, but y does not change. The numerator is 0 so, the rate of change is 0.   **9.** C

Lesson 8-2   Extra Practice

11. The family drove 200 miles per day. They drove 280 miles to their grandmother's house.   **13.** B   **15.** −17   **17.** 14

19-24.

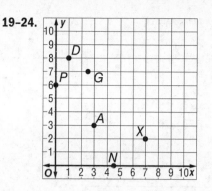

Lesson 8-3   Independent Practice

1 Sample answer: Luis starts out from his home. He walks away from his home, stops to let the dog run around, and walks further away from home. Then he walks towards home.

3 Sample answer:

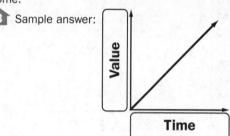

5a. Sample answer: Hector hikes at a steady rate.
5b. Sample answer: Hector suddenly stops hiking.
5c. increase; Sample answer: The graph rises from left to right at the beginning.   **7.** Graph A; Sample answer: Graph A increases from left to right at a constant rate then levels off. This represents a tree growing steadily before it stops growing.

Lesson 8-3   Extra Practice

9. Justine rode her bike at a constant rate in the beginning. She then stopped riding for a period of time. Then she continued riding at a constant rate.   **11.** Sample answer: Mrs. Fraser's electric bill starts out high in January, increases until about March, and then decreases throughout the spring and summer. In the fall, the electric bill increases again.

13. Sample answer:

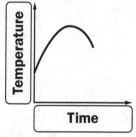

15. A   **17a.** $3p + 5$ **17b.** $65   **19.** $-3t - 45$
21 $-5n - 87$

Lesson 8-4 Independent Practice

1

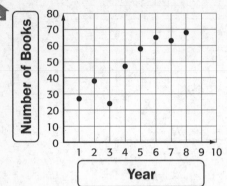

3a.

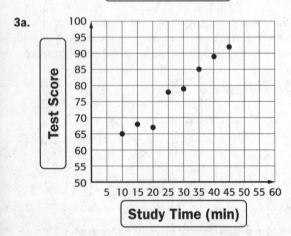

3b. Sample answer: The scatter plot shows a positive linear association. There are no clusters or outliers.
3c. about 98 **5.** positive **7.** A

Lesson 8-4 Extra Practice

9 a.

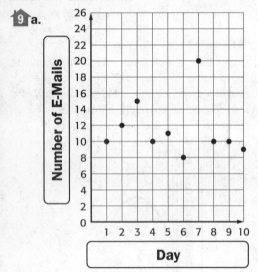

9b. There does not appear to be any relationship between the variables. Linearity cannot be determined and there are no clusters. There appears to be an outlier at 20 E-mails.
9c. Since the scatter plot shows no association between the data, it is not possible to predict how many E-mails will be received on Day 15. **11.** The time does not depend on shoe size. Therefore, the scatter plot shows no association. **13.** D **15.** Sample answer: There are more

than $2\frac{1}{2}$ times more people that speak Mandarin than English.

Lesson 8-5 Independent Practice

1 a. Sample answer: The data points are either on the line of best fit or very close to the line, so the line of best fit is a good model of the data.

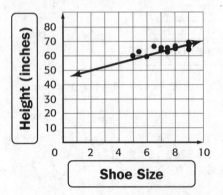

b. Sample answer: 57.5 in. **3 a.** Sample answer:
$y = 500x + 2,250$; Every year an additional 500 girls play ice hockey. In 1996, 2,250 girls played ice hockey.
b. Sample answer: 14,250 girls **7.** C

Lesson 8-5 Extra Practice

9 a. Sample answer:

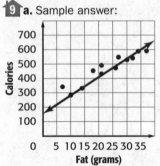

Since the data points are all close to the line, the line of best fit drawn is a good model of the data. **9b.** Sample answer: $y = 12.5x + 155$; A 1 gram increase in fat increases the Calories by 12.5. A sandwich with 0 grams of fat would be 155 Calories. **9c.** Sample answer: 15.6 g

11.

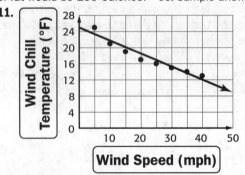

13. I **15.** no association

Lesson 8-6 · Independent Practice

	Chicken	Beef	Total
Rice	20	10	30
Pasta	40	30	70
Total	60	40	100

	Text Message	Instant Message	Total
7th graders	59; 0.70	25; 0.30	84; 1.00
8th graders	59; 0.59	41; 0.41	100; 1.00
Total	118	66	184

Sample answer: Many more 7th grade students text message than instant message. The eighth grade is split more evenly.   **5.** Sample answer: Jasmine should have said, "More than half of the students that do not have an after-school job are on the honor roll."   **7.** the percentage of red-haired students with brown eyes

Lesson 8-6 · Extra Practice

	Popcorn	No Popcorn	Total
Drink	74	15	89
No Drink	10	6	16
Total	84	21	105

11. males; 26 out of 48, or 54%, males volunteer at the animal shelter while only 21 out of 52, or 40%, females volunteer at the animal shelter

13. Sample answer:

	Cat	No Cat	Total
Dog	45; $\frac{45}{123}$ = 0.37	125; $\frac{125}{177}$ = 0.71	170
No Dog	78; $\frac{78}{123}$ = 0.63	52; $\frac{52}{177}$ = 0.29	130
Total	123	177	300

Most people that visited the store and have a cat do not have a dog. Most people that visited the store and did not have a cat, have a dog.   **15.** H   **17.** 36.4; 33; 28 and 33

Problem-Solving Investigation   Use a Graph

Case 3. No, the most glamorous job has the lowest median salary.   **Case 5.** Sample answer: 65 members

Lesson 8-7   Independent Practice

1 mean: 103.1; median: 100; mode: 100; range: 46

3 minimum: 20; Q_1: 21; median: 23.5; Q_3: 29; maximum: 30;

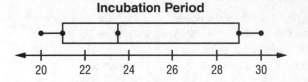

Incubation Period

5a. mean: 11.6; median: 12; mode: 14; range: 16
5b. minimum: 3; Q_1: 9.5; median: 12; Q_3: 14; maximum: 19

5c.

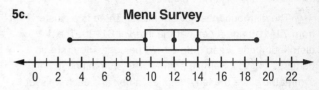

Menu Survey

7. Sample answer: {1, 2, 5, 7, 9, 10, 12, 14, 15, 17, 22} and {0, 2, 5, 7, 9, 10, 12, 14, 15, 17, 27}

Lesson 8-7   Extra Practice

9 mean: 72; median: 60; no mode; range: 108
11a. mean: 149.1; median: 154.5; mode: 162; range: 36
11b. minimum: 128; Q_1: 134; median: 154.5; Q_3: 162; maximum: 164

11c.

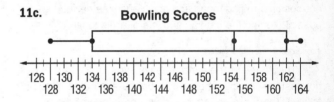

Bowling Scores

13.

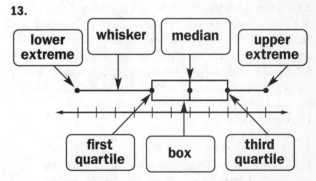

15. H   **17a.** 2 outliers   **17b.** Sample answer: The top half of the data is more spread out than the bottom half of the data. Most major zoos are smaller in area than the few zoos that have very large areas.

Lesson 8-8   Independent Practice

1 8.2; Sample answer: The average distance each data value is from the mean is 8.2 miles per hour.   **3** Speeds that are between 34.2 and 56.8 miles per hour are within one standard deviation of the mean.   **5.** Sample answer: Brian should have said more than half of his data values are within one standard deviation of the mean.   **7.** Lengths that are between 20.6 and 49.4 inches are within two standard deviations of the mean. The mean is 35, so the range is 35 − 2(7.2) or 20.6 to 35 + 2(7.2) or 49.4.   **9.** D

Lesson 8-8   Extra Practice

11a. 11.41; Sample answer: The average distance each data value is from the mean is 11.41 miles per hour. **11b.** Speeds that are between 89.23 and 117.03 miles per hour are within one standard deviation of the mean. **13.** C **15.** G **17.** mean: 42.1; median: 40; mode: 50; range: 45

Lesson 8-9   Independent Practice

1 The distribution is not symmetric. There is a cluster from 71–100 and a peak at the interval 81–90. The distribution has a gap from 61–70 percent. There are no outliers. **3 a.** Sample answer: The distribution is not symmetric since the lengths of each box and each whisker are not the same. There is an outlier at 7.5. **b.** Sample answer: The distribution is not symmetric. So, the median and interquartile range are appropriate measures to use. The data are centered around the median of $4. The spread of the data around the center is $1.25.
5a. The distribution in the top box plot is symmetric, so you would use the mean and the mean absolute deviation. The distribution in the bottom box plot is not symmetric, so you would use the median and the interquartile range. **5b.** It is not possible to find mean and mean absolute deviation. It is possible to find the median and interquartile range.

Lesson 8-9   Extra Practice

7 The shape of the distribution is symmetric. There are no clusters or gaps. The peak of the data is in the interval 31–40. There are no outliers. **9a.** The shape of the distribution is not symmetric since the lengths of each box and each whisker are not the same. There are no outliers. **9b.** The distribution is not symmetric. So, the median and interquartile range are appropriate measures to use. The data are centered around the median of 19 visitors. The spread of the data around the center is about 22. **11.** B **13.** line graph **15.** circle graph **17.** histogram **19.** scatter plot

Chapter Review   Vocabulary Check

1. univariate data **3.** bivariate data **5.** five-number summary **7.** line of best **9.** symmetric **11.** two-way table **13.** mean absolute deviation

Chapter Review   Key Concept Check

Sample answers are given.
Step 1 Draw the line.

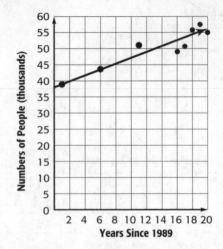

Step 2 Choose two points. (1, 39); (6, 44)
Step 3 Find the slope. $m = 1$
Step 4 Find the y-intercept. $b = 38$
Step 5 Write the equation of the line. $y = x + 38$

Chapter Review   Problem Solving

1a.

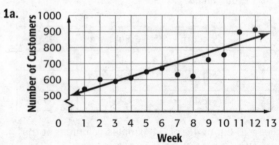

1a. Sample answer: The scatter plot shows a positive linear relationship. There are no clusters or outliers; about 1,100 customers. **1c.** Sample answer: $y = 30x + 500$; 30 additional customers visited the store each week; there were 500 customers in week 0. **3.** minimum: 542; Q_1: 605.5; median: 639.5; Q_3: 738.5; maximum: 910

Chapter 9 Equations in Two Variables

Chapter 9   Are You Ready?

1. 9 **3.** −7 **5.** 6 **7.** $\frac{2}{5}$ **9.** $\frac{1}{5}$ **11.** $-\frac{2}{5}$

Lesson 9-1   Independent Practice

1. x-intercept: 3.5; y-intercept: 7

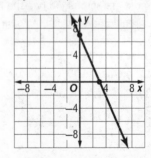

3 x-intercept: $1\frac{1}{4}$; y-intercept: $1\frac{2}{3}$

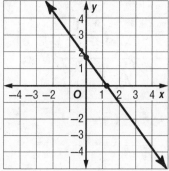

5

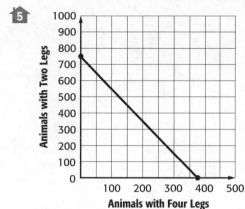

Animals with Four Legs

The x-intercept of 375 means that if the zoo had only four-legged animals, there would be 375 of them. The y-intercept of 750 means that if the zoo had only two-legged animals, there would be 750 of them.   **7.** After $3x = 12$, Carmen didn't divide both sides by 3 to get the x-intercept of 4.
9. D

Lesson 9-1   Extra Practice

11. (12, 0), (0, 8)

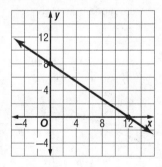

13. (6, 0), (0, 10)

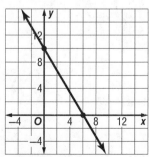

15.

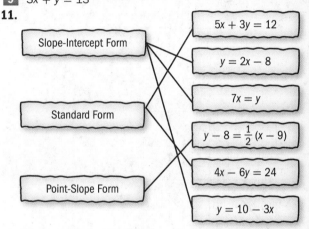

The x-intercept represents the number of hours the painter worked to finish the basement. The y-intercept represents the total amount of money she has to pay the painter.
17. G

Lesson 9-2   Independent Practice

1. $y - 9 = 2(x - 1)$; $y = 2x + 7$ **3.** $y + 5 = \frac{3}{4}(x + 4)$; $y = \frac{3}{4}x - 2$ **5** Sample answer: $y + 4 = -\frac{3}{2}(x - 4)$; $y = -\frac{3}{2}x + 2$ **7.** Sample answer: $y - 14 = \frac{1}{5}(x - 10)$
9 $3x + y = 13$
11.

Slope-Intercept Form

Standard Form

Point-Slope Form

$5x + 3y = 12$

$y = 2x - 8$

$7x = y$

$y - 8 = \frac{1}{2}(x - 9)$

$4x - 6y = 24$

$y = 10 - 3x$

13. Sample answer: $y - 5 = -\frac{1}{2}(x - 2)$; First, use the equation to find the slope and the coordinates of any point on the line. Then use the slope and coordinates to write an equation in point-slope form.

Lesson 9-2   Extra Practice

15. $y - 10 = -4(x + 7)$; $y = -4x - 18$
17. $y - 2 = \frac{2}{3}(x - 6)$; $y = \frac{2}{3}x - 2$ **19.** $4x - 5y = 17$
21. Sample answer: $y - 3 = -\frac{5}{2}(x + 2)$ **23.** C   **25.** $9 per hour   **27.** $120\,t$; 600 mi

Problem-Solving Investigation   Guess, Check, and Revise

Case 3. Sample answer: 3 packages of 8 cards and 4 packages of 12 cards   **Case 5.** 3 rings, 5 toys

Lesson 9-3   Independent Practice

1. (4, 4)

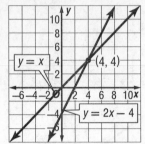

3. no solution

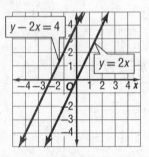

5. (0, 3)

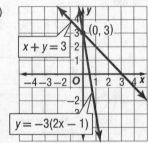

7.

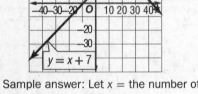

Sample answer: Let x = the number of dogs and y = the number of cats; $x + y = 45$, $y = x + 7$; There are 19 dogs and 26 cats.   **9.** one solution

11a. 70

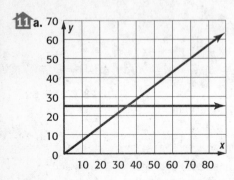

11b. 18 rides   **13.** B

Lesson 9-3   Extra Practice

15. (1, 2)

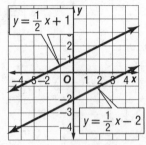

17. no solution

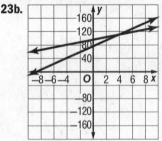

19. (−2, 0); one solution   **21.** A   **23.** $y = 5$ **25.** $x = -28$
27. $y = \frac{1}{4}$

Lesson 9-4   Independent Practice

1. (1, 6)   **3.** (−2, −12)   **5.** (7, 11)   **7.** $\left(\frac{1}{2}, 12\frac{1}{2}\right)$ or
(0.5, 12.5)   **9.** Sample answer: $s + p = 15$; $p + 7 = s$;
(4, 11); She bought 11 shirts and 4 pairs of pants.
11. Sample answer: $8x + 2y = 18$; $3x + y = 7.50$; (1.5, 3);
A muffin costs $1.50 and 1 quart of milk costs $3.   **13.** Ø;
Sample answer: Adding $5x$ to each side of $y = -5x + 8$
results in the equation $5x + y = 8$. Since $5x + y$ cannot
equal both 8 and 2, there are no values for x and y that make
this system of equations true.   **15.** C

Lesson 9-4   Extra Practice

17. (−12, −3)   **19.** (−3, 0)   **21.** (5, −1)
23a. $y = 4x + 95$ and $y = 9x + 75$
23b.

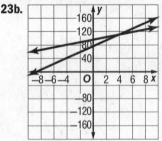

(4, 111); the costs, $111, are the same if 4 students
attend either.   **23c.** nature center   **25.** 12   **27.** 67
29. 22.9   **31.** 97   **33.** 78

Chapter Review   Vocabulary Check

Across
5. direct variation   **7.** x intercept
Down
1. substitution   **3.** y intercept

Chapter Review   Key Concept Check

1. $y = -0.5x + 1$ **3.** $y = 0.5x$ **5.** $x = 5$

Chapter Review   Problem Solving

1. Sample answer: Let $x =$ the number that preferred steak and $y =$ the number that preferred pizza; $x + y = 25$, $y = x + 5$; (10, 15); 10 students preferred steak and 15 students preferred pizza.

3. Sample answer: $y = x + 6$; $y + x = 20$; (7, 13); Lena bought 7 small postcards and 13 large postcards.

Index

Dd

Ee

Ff

Index

Ss

Index

Index

$$=$$

Equation Mat   WM1

Name _____

WM2 **Quarter-Inch Grid**

Name _____

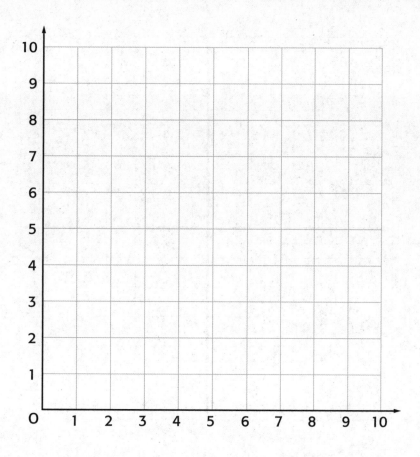

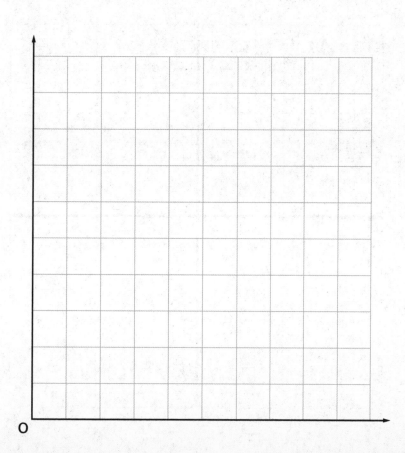

First Quadrant Grids   WM3

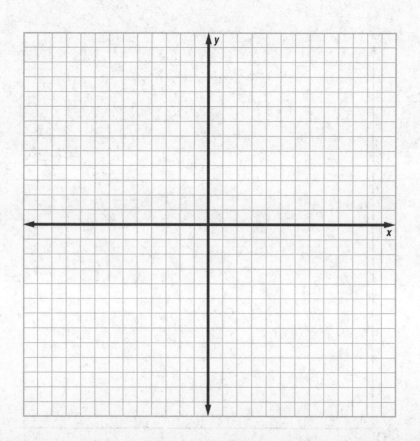

Name _____

Name _____

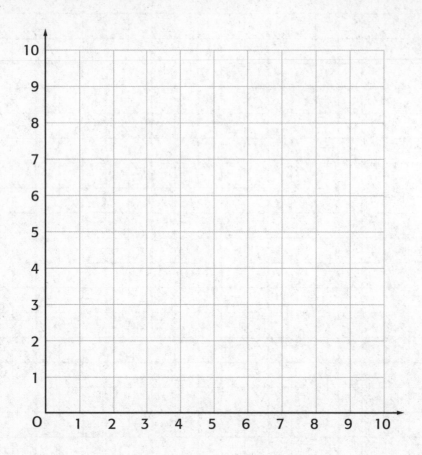

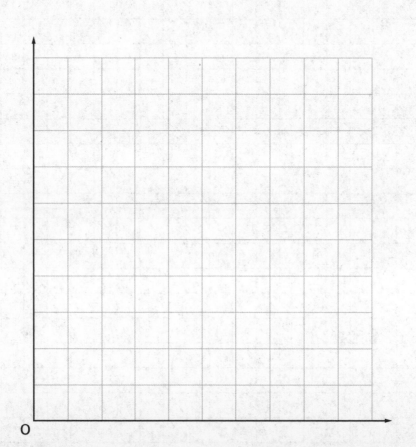

WM6 **First Quadrant Grids**

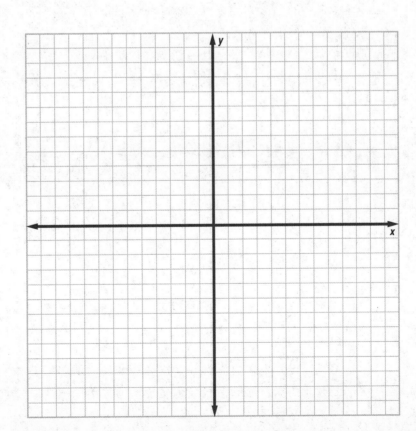

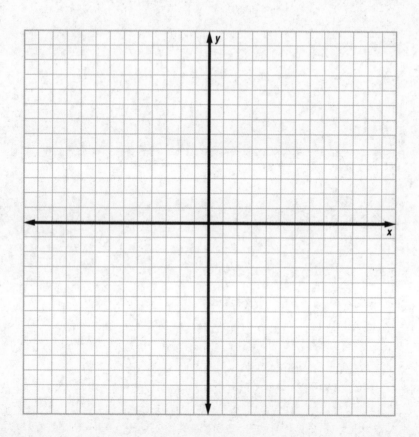

WM8   **Coordinate Planes**

What Are Foldables and How Do I Create Them?

Foldables are three-dimensional graphic organizers that help you create study guides for each chapter in your book.

Step 1 Go to the back of your book to find the Foldable for the chapter you are currently studying. Follow the cutting and assembly instructions at the top of the page.

Step 2 Go to the Key Concept Check at the end of the chapter you are currently studying. Match up the tabs and attach your Foldable to this page. Dotted tabs show where to place your Foldable. Striped tabs indicate where to tape the Foldable.

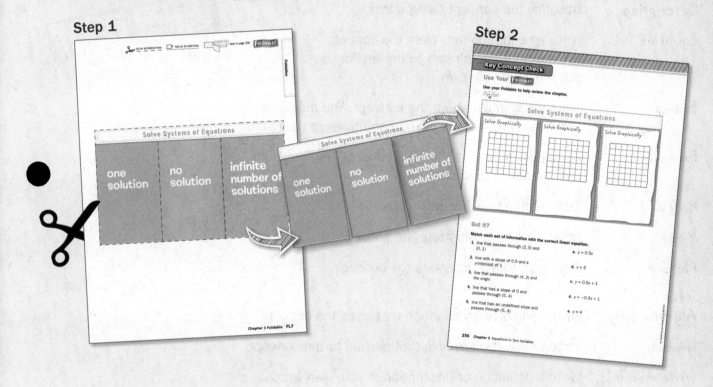

How Will I Know When to Use My Foldable?

When it's time to work on your Foldable, you will see a Foldables logo at the bottom of the **Rate Yourself!** box on the Guided Practice pages. This lets you know that it is time to update it with concepts from that lesson. Once you've completed your Foldable, use it to study for the chapter test.

How Do I Complete My Foldable?

No two Foldables in your book will look alike. However, some will ask you to fill in similar information. Below are some of the instructions you'll see as you complete your Foldable. **HAVE FUN** learning math using Foldables!

Instructions and what they mean

Best Used to...	Complete the sentence explaining when the concept should be used.
Definition	Write a definition in your own words.
Description	Describe the concept using words.
Equation	Write an equation that uses the concept. You may use one already in the text or you can make up your own.
Example	Write an example about the concept. You may use one already in the text or you can make up your own.
Formulas	Write a formula that uses the concept. You may use one already in the text.
How do I ...?	Explain the steps involved in the concept.
Models	Draw a model to illustrate the concept.
Picture	Draw a picture to illustrate the concept.
Solve Algebraically	Write and solve an equation that uses the concept.
Symbols	Write or use the symbols that pertain to the concept.
Write About It	Write a definition or description in your own words.
Words	Write the words that pertain to the concept.

Meet Foldables Author Dinah Zike

Dinah Zike is known for designing hands-on manipulatives that are used nationally and internationally by teachers and parents. Dinah is an explosion of energy and ideas. Her excitement and joy for learning inspires everyone she touches.

Foldables

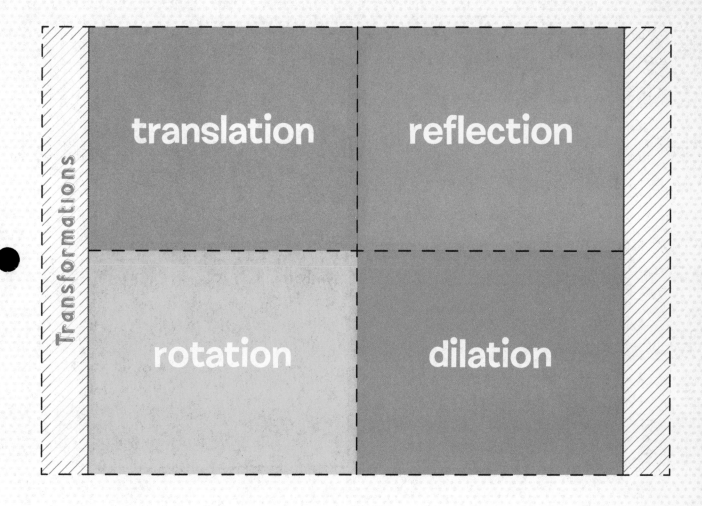

Transformations

translation

reflection

rotation

dilation

✂ cut on all dashed lines   ▭ fold on all solid lines   tape to page 84   **FOLDABLES**

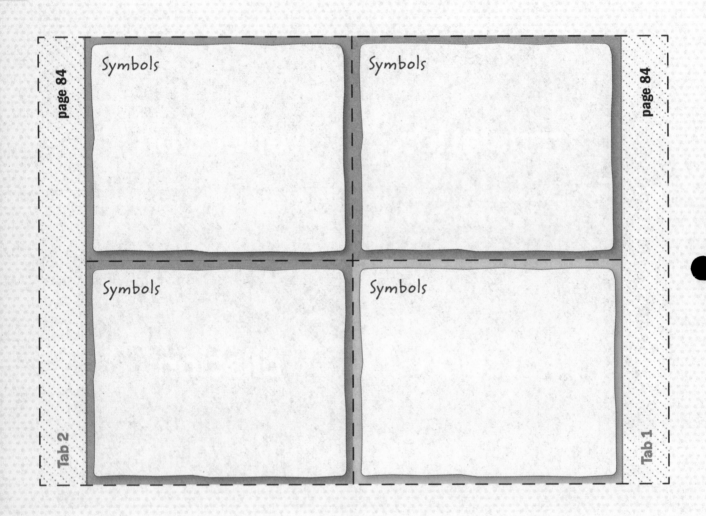

page 84

Symbols

Symbols

page 84

Symbols

Symbols

Tab 2

Tab 1

Congruent Figures

attributes	transformations
attributes	transformations

Similar Figures

Foldables

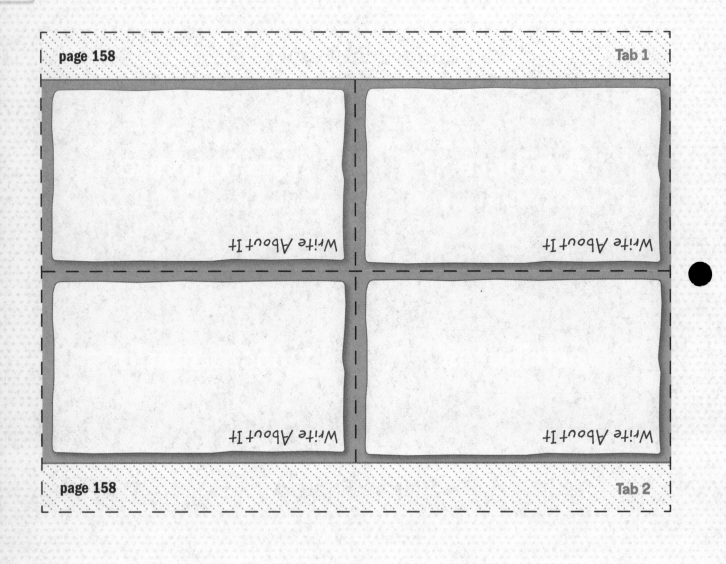

page 158   Tab 1

Write About It   Write About It

Write About It   Write About It

page 158   Tab 2

Laws of Exponents

Product of Powers

Quotient of Powers

Power of Powers

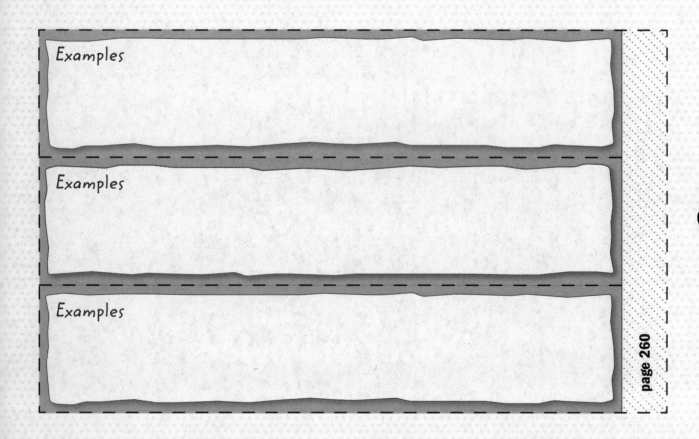

Examples

Examples

Examples

page 260

Solving Equations

property

solution

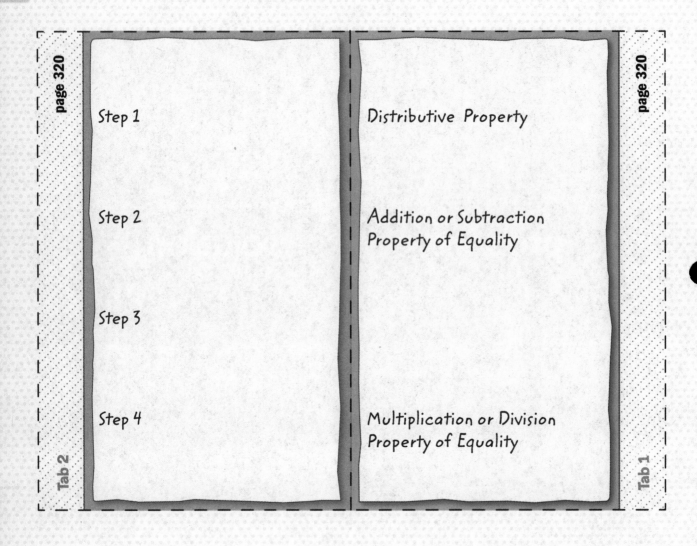

page 320

Step 1

Step 2

Step 3

Step 4

Tab 2

Distributive Property

Addition or Subtraction
Property of Equality

Multiplication or Division
Property of Equality

page 320

Tab 1

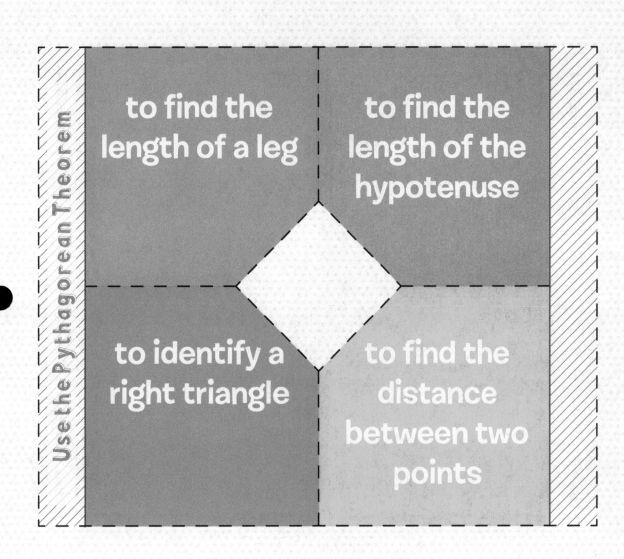

Use the Pythagorean Theorem

to find the length of a leg

to find the length of the hypotenuse

to identify a right triangle

to find the distance between two points

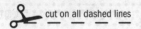 cut on all dashed lines 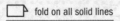 fold on all solid lines  tape to page 374  **FOLDABLES**®

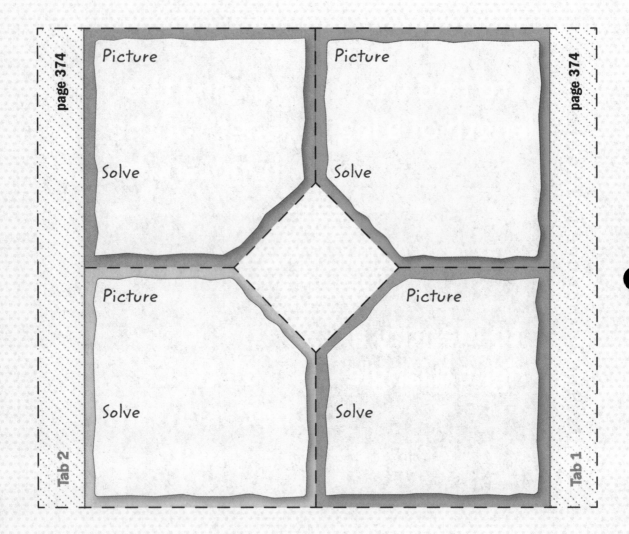

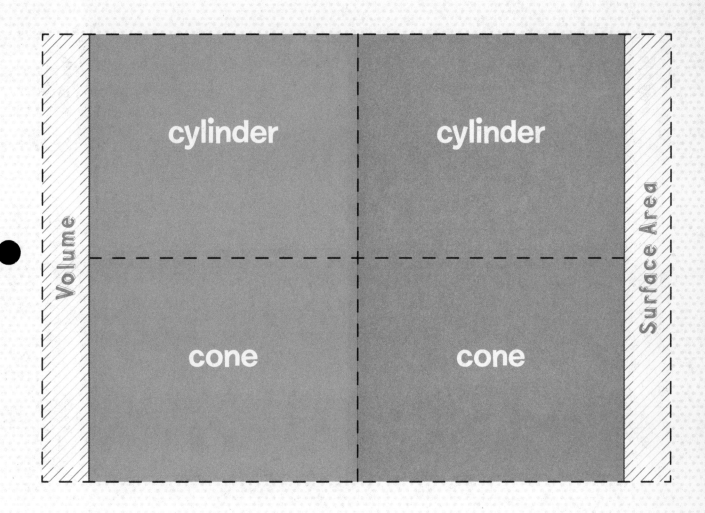

Volume

cylinder

cylinder

Surface Area

cone

cone

✂ cut on all dashed lines   ⬚ fold on all solid lines   ▨ tape to page 446   **FOLDABLES**

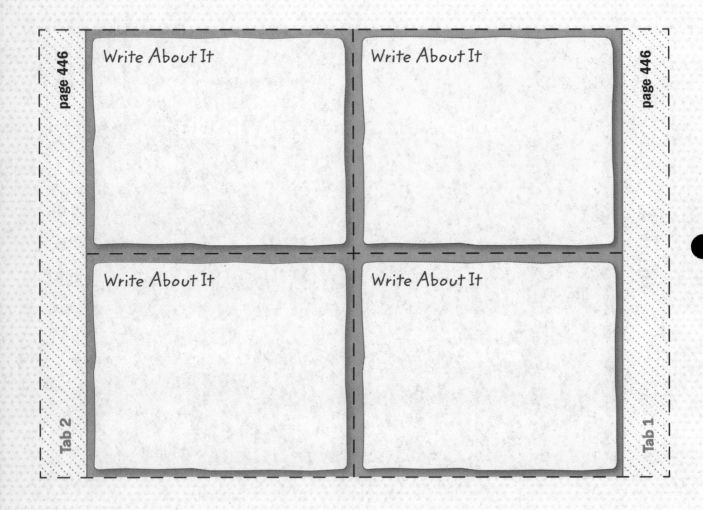

page 446

Write About It

Write About It

Write About It

Write About It

Tab 2

page 446

Tab 1

✂ cut on all dashed lines   ⬚ fold on all solid lines   tape to page 446   **FOLDABLES**

Relations and Functions

relations

functions

linear   nonlinear

cut on all dashed lines   fold on all solid lines   tape to page 566   **FOLDABLES**

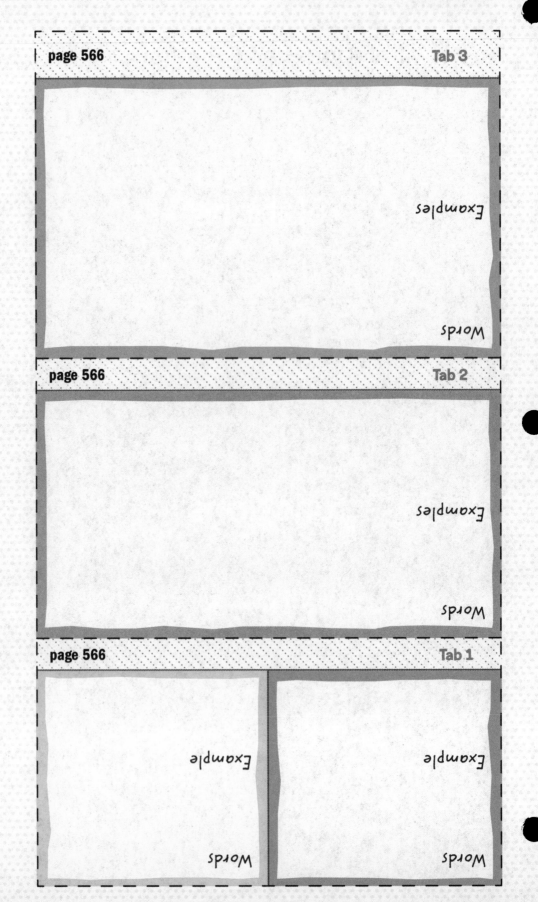

page 566   Tab 3

Examples

Words

page 566   Tab 2

Examples

Words

page 566   Tab 1

Example

Words

Example

Words

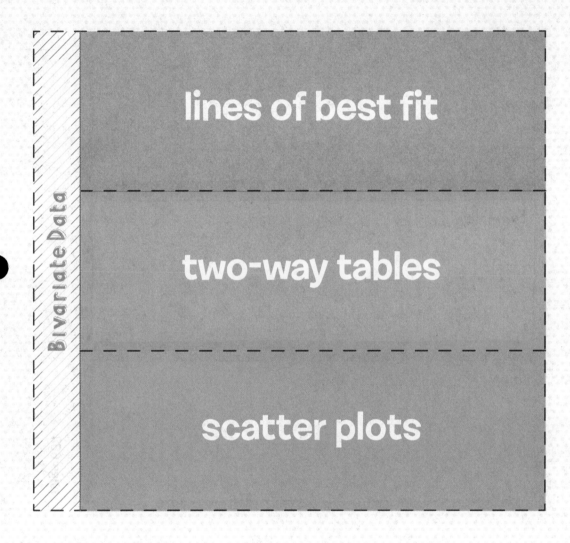

Bivariate Data

lines of best fit

two-way tables

scatter plots

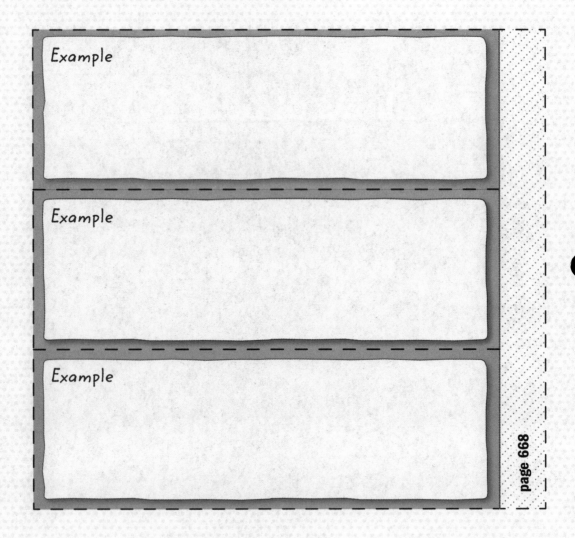

cut on all dashed lines ✂ ┆ ┄ ┄ ┄ | fold on all solid lines | tape to page 668 | **FOLDABLES**

Example

Example

Example

page 668

Solve Systems of Equations

one solution	no solution	infinite number of solutions

✂ cut on all dashed lines   fold on all solid lines   tape to page 722   **FOLDABLES**

page 722

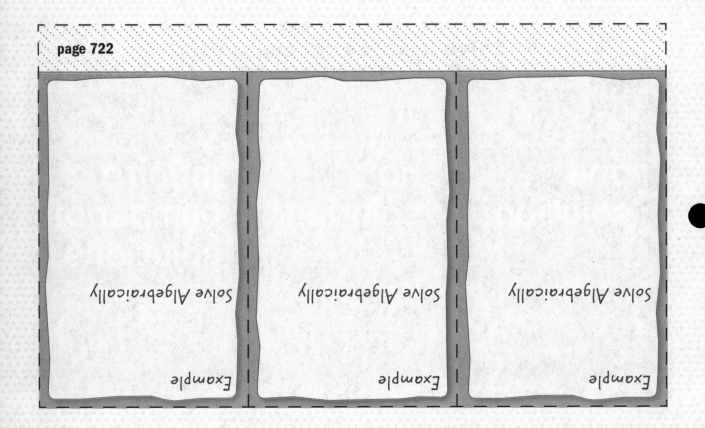

Solve Algebraically

Example

Solve Algebraically

Example

Solve Algebraically

Example